General Class

FCC License Preparation for Element 3 General Class Theory

by
Gordon West
WB6NOA

with Technical Editor
Eric P. Nichols
KL7AJ

Eleventh Edition

Master Publishing, Inc.

Also by Gordon West, WB6NOA
with
Eric P. Nichols, KL7AJ

Technician Class
FCC License Preparation for
Element 2 Technician Class Theory
Also available as an audio book on CD

Extra Class
FCC License Preparation for
Element 4 Extra Class Theory
Also available as an audio book on CD

GROL + RADAR
General Radiotelephone Operator License
Plus Ship Radar Endorsement
with Pete Trotter, KB9SMG and Eric P. Nichols, KL7AJ
FCC Commercial Radio License Preparation for
Element 1, Element 3, and Element 8 Question Pools
Also available with
W5YI Comm Study Software

For more information visit
www.W5YI.org
or call 800-669-9594

About the Authors

Gordon West, WB6NOA

Gordon West has been a ham radio operator for more than 60 years, holding the top Extra Class license, call sign WB6NOA. He also holds the highest FCC commercial operator license, the First Class General Radiotelephone Certificate with Radar Endorsement.

Gordon teaches evening ham radio classes and offers weekend ham radio licensing seminars on a monthly schedule. These seminars cover entry-level and upgrade licenses in ham radio. He has served on the faculty of Coastline College and Orange Coast College.

Gordon is a regular contributor to amateur radio, marine, and general two-way radio magazines. He is a fellow of the Radio Club of America, and a life member of the American Radio Relay League. The ARRL presented Gordon with its "Instructor of the Year" award. The Dayton Amateur Radio Association named Gordon their "2006 Amateur of the Year" for his efforts in recruiting and training new amateurs, in addition to his lifelong involvement in ham radio. Through his Gordon West Radio School, he has trained eight out of ten newly-licensed hams with his classes, books and audio courses over the past 40 years.

Eric P. Nichols, KL7AJ
Technical Editor

Joining author Gordon West for this new Tenth Edition of his ***General Class*** study manual as Technical Editor is Eric P. Nichols, KL7AJ. Eric has been a licensed amateur operator since 1972, holding the top Extra Class license, as well as the FCC GROL commercial license. He has spent his adult career in various aspects of radio research, broadcast communications, and teaching.

A prolific author, he has written many articles for ***QST, QEX,*** and a number of other ham radio magazines, as well as professional journals. In 2010 and again in 2014 he was the recipient of the William Orr, W6SAI, Technical Writing Award conferred by the American Radio Relay League for articles he authored for ***QST*** magazine. He is the author of ***Radio Science for the Radio Amateur***, and ***Propagation and Radio Science***. Along with Gordon West, WB6NOA he is Technical Editor of the ***GROL+RADAR*** study manual for the FCC commercial radio licenses.

Eric lives in North Pole, AK. He has operated just about every mode available to the radio amateur, but always returns to CW on the lower HF bands as his "default" mode. He enjoys restoring vintage "boat anchor" radio equipment as well as designing cutting edge radio instrumentation with Arduino, his latest obsession. Being in interior Alaska, he gets a lot of requests from new hams (and some older ones) for a first-time Alaskan radio contact, and is always willing to try a "sked" on any HF band or mode!

This book was developed and published by:
Master Publishing, Inc.
Glencoe, Il

Editing by:
Pete Trotter, KB9SMG and Julie Scheife, Mayfly Design
Book typesetting by Mayfly Design

Photograph Credit:
All photographs that do not have a source identification are either from the author, or Master Publishing, Inc. originals.

Cartoons by:
Jim Massara, N2EST, based on the original Elmer by Carson Haring, AC0BU

Thanks to the following for their assistance with this book: Suzy West, N6GLF; Don Arnold, W6GPS; Chip Margelli, K7JA; Dennis Gonya, K6LIG; Tracy Lenocker, WM6T; Marilynn Jordan, W7MCJ; Larry Wilson, K6SCH; Jim Ford, N6JF; Dave Forbes, W5FUZ; Dave Mitchell, AJ5F; Jim Colwell, KG5GIF; Dave Stites, W6TUX; Jodi Lenocker, WA6JL; and California Rescue Net members.

Visit Master Publishing
on the Internet at:
www.masterpublishing.com

Eleventh Edition
5 4 3 2 1

Table of Contents

QUESTION POOL NOMENCLATURE

The latest nomenclature changes and question pool numbering system recommended by the Volunteer Examiner Coordinator's Question Pool Committee (QPC) have been incorporated in this book. The General Class (Element 3) question pool has been rewritten at the high-school reading level. This question pool is valid from July 1, 2023 through June 30, 2027.

FCC RULES, REGULATIONS AND POLICIES

The NCVEC QPC releases revised question pools on a regular cycle, and issues deletions as necessary. The FCC releases changes to FCC rules, regulations and policies as they are implemented. This book includes the most recent information released by the FCC at the time this copy was printed.

Preface

Welcome to General Class amateur radio!

The General Class license gives you privileges on all of the worldwide amateur radio bands for long-range skywave communications. These new bands will add to your Technician Class HF, VHF and UHF privileges. With a General Class license, you will receive operating privileges on every VHF/UHF Microwave ham radio band for voice, data, video, and CW.

As a General Class operator, you'll be able to travel the world and always stay in touch using skywave communications. Whether you sail the international waters of the South Seas, or cruise the highways of North America or Europe, you can stay in touch. More good news – recent international agreements allow you to operate in many foreign ports and countries without having to officially sign-up for a reciprocal license.

You'll be able to help our hobby grow with your General Class license! We encourage you to join an all-General Volunteer Examination team to conduct Element 2 Technician Class written exams. As you gain experience with your new license, you can actively recruit new ham radio operators to our hobby and service.

This new Eleventh Edition of our book covers everything you need to know to pass the General Class Element 3 written examination. There is no longer a Morse code test required for any class of ham license! The Federal Communications Commission eliminated the Morse code test requirement effective February 23, 2007.

The question pool in this book is effective July 1, 2023 through June 30, 2027. The only prerequisite to take the exam for your new General Class license is a valid Technician Class license or a recently-earned CSCE for Technician Element 2.

This new edition of ***General Class*** will make your test preparation a breeze. We've reorganized the entire, new Element 3 General Class question pool to improve your learning experience and cut down on the study time required to pass the exam.

We are on the air daily and hope to talk to you soon on the General Class bands!

Gordon West, WB6NOA

Eric P. Nichols, KL7AJ

About This Book

Our book provides you with all of the study material you need to prepare yourself to pass the Element 3 General Class examination. The test questions and 4 distracters are presented in this book exactly as you'll see them on the exam. We have reorganized the questions and answers into common subject groups for more logical learning. This will cut down on your study time and improve your knowledge of how to operate as a General Class ham!

The Federal Communications Commission completely eliminated Morse code testing as a requirement for any amateur radio license effective February 23, 2007. We always encourage our students to know the code, so this book has a complete chapter on fun ways to begin learning Morse code once you are on the air as a new General Class operator. Chapter 5 gives you sound advice on how to learn the Morse code. Even though there is no more code test, knowing the dots and dashes will help you become a better General Class operator.

Our book also provides you with valuable information you need to be an active ham on the HF worldwide bands. To help you get the most out of ***General Class***, here's a look at how the book is organized:

- *Chapter 1* explains in detail the new HF operating privileges you'll earn by passing your Element 3 General Class written examination.
- *Chapter 2* provides a look at the history of amateur radio licensing in the U.S., and the current status of all license classes.
- *Chapter 3* contains all 430 Element 3 General Class questions, 35 of which will be on your upcoming exam. You'll notice that the questions and answers have been reorganized to follow the syllabus Gordo uses to teach General Class at his Radio School weekend sessions. It makes your learning experience easier and more meaningful.
- *Chapter 4* tells you how to find an exam site, what to do before you get to the site, what required papers to bring with you, and what to check for when you pass your exam.
- *Chapter 5* gives solid advice on how to learn Morse code at 5 wpm.
- *The Appendix* contains a list of VECs, a Glossary of important ham radio terms, and other useful information.

If you need additional study materials, we've recorded an audio course that follows this book, and W5YI also has interactive software to allow you to study for upcoming exams on your PC. In addition, Gordo also has recorded audio courses for learning Morse code.

1

General Class Privileges

The General Class amateur license permits you to use segments of every amateur band for worldwide, long-distance voice, data, and video communications. These new privileges add to those you now enjoy with your current amateur license.

The General Class license has always been considered "the big one" because of the almost unlimited skywave privileges this license provides on each of the worldwide ham bands. Although the older, grandfathered Novice and Technician licenses offer slivers of worldwide band privileges, it is the General Class license that gives you major operating "elbow room" on segments of all the worldwide bands. Whether it's day or night, summer or winter, these worldwide bands will offer skywave communications for thousands of miles of range.

Gordo at the controls of the United Nations Station, 4U1UN, in New York.

Never in the history of amateur radio has it been easier than now to obtain the General Class license. There is no more Morse code test. The Federal Communications Commission concluded "...this change (eliminating the code test) eliminates an unnecessary burden that may discourage current amateur radio operators from advancing their skills and participating more fully in the benefits of amateur radio." Most other countries have dropped their Morse code test requirements, too.

The Element 3 theory exam has been dramatically improved in content, better reflecting General Class worldwide radio equipment and antennas. Simple math questions deal with modern, high frequency equipment. No longer will you need to memorize "far out" formulas that you would rarely use as a licensed ham radio operator. There is more emphasis on General Class operating, band plans, data modes, and high frequency simple antennas to build. Although this new question pool is more comprehensive in entire content, your upcoming exam remains at 35 multiple choice questions, 74% passing grade.

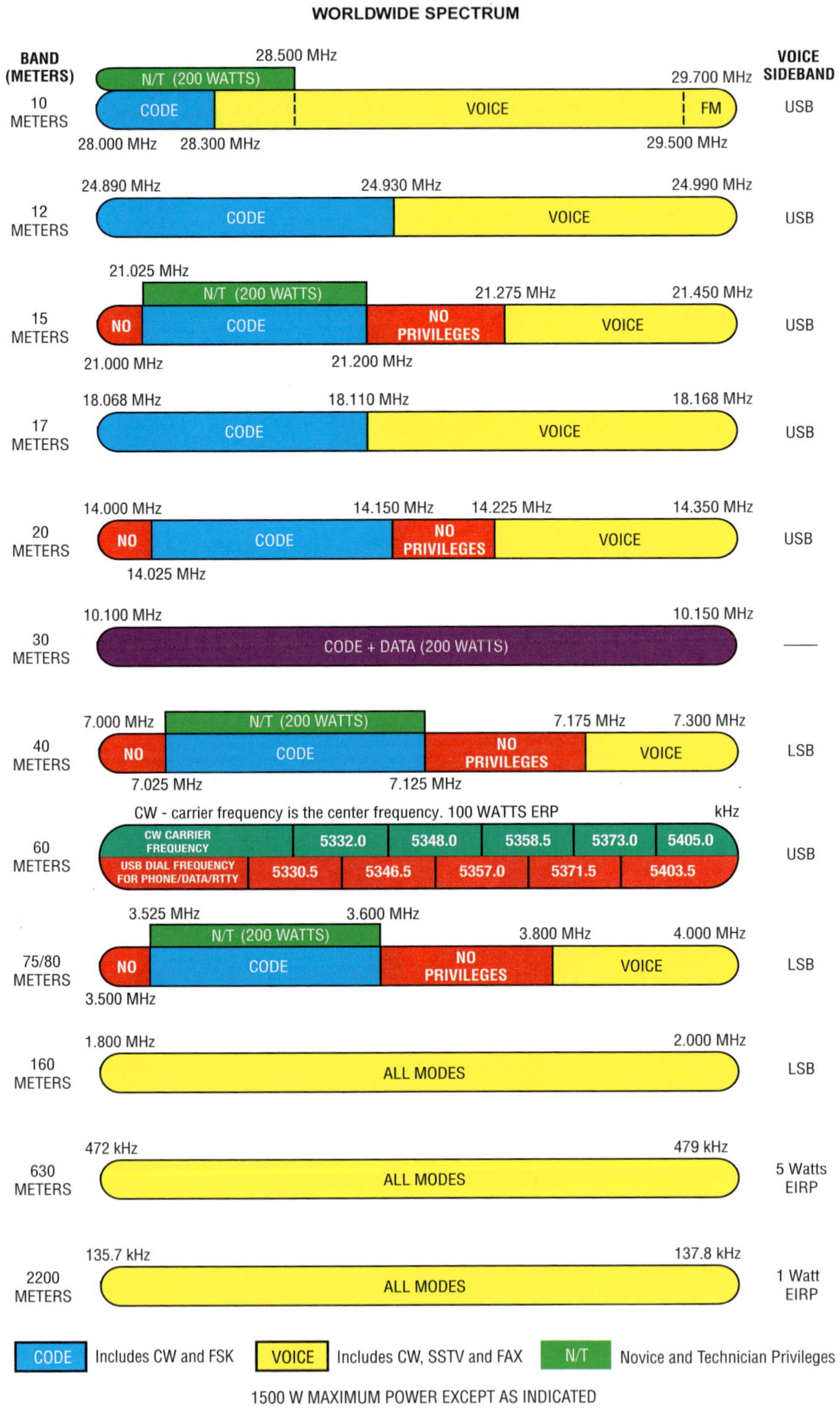

Figure 1-1. General Class HF License Privileges

GENERAL CLASS LICENSE PRIVILEGES

Figure 1-1 graphically illustrates your new General Class code, data, and voice privileges on low frequency (LF) (30 kHz – 300 kHz), medium frequency (MF) (300 kHz-3 MHz) and high frequency (HF) (3 MHz-30 MHz) bands. Code and data privileges are in the designated areas on the left side of each band. Voice privileges are on the right side of each band. Designated areas between the code and voice privileges have "no privileges" for the General Class operator. These are reserved for grandfathered Advanced Class and current Extra Class operators.

As you can see, grandfathered Advanced and Extra Class operators have the same band privileges that you will enjoy as a General Class operator, they just have a little bit more elbow room. But don't worry – there is plenty of room throughout the General Class voice spectrum for working the world!

2200 AND 630 METERS

For home brew experimenters, we now have two new bands below the AM broadcast band! You will need to build your own gear!

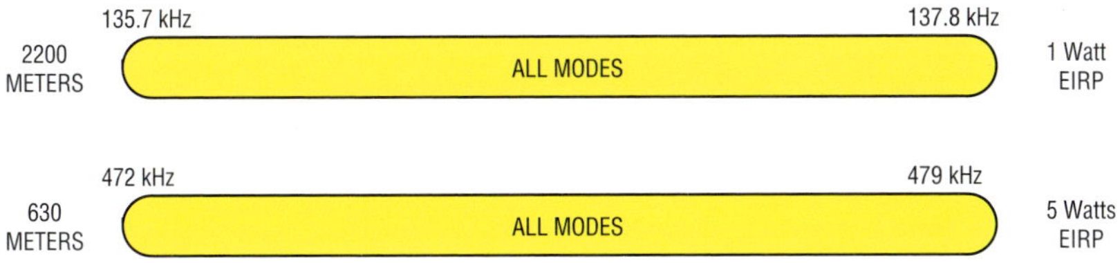

160 METERS, 1.8 MHZ - 2.0 MHZ

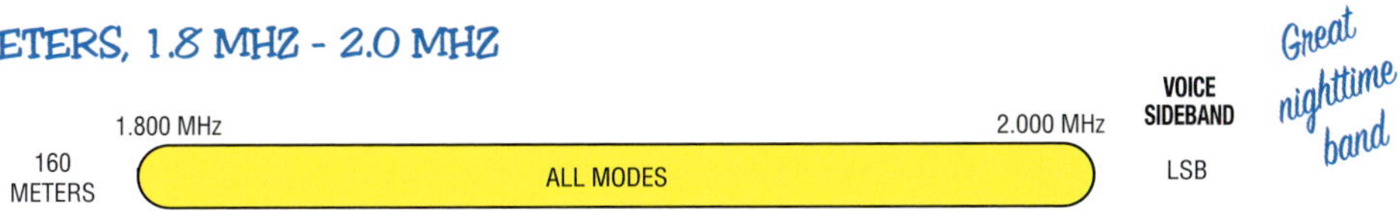

General Class privileges let you operate voice and code from one end to the other of the 160-meter band. These are the same privileges enjoyed by Advanced and Extra Class operators. The 160-meter band is great for long-distance, nighttime communications. At night, 160 meters lets you work the world!

75/80 METERS, 3.500 MHZ - 4.000 MHZ

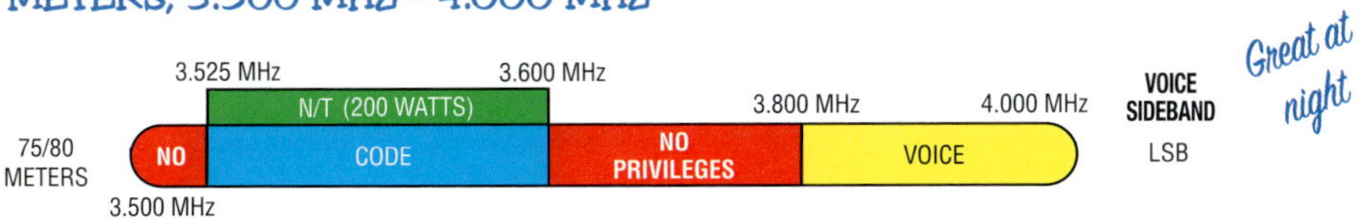

On 75/80 meters, General Class code, data, and radioteletype (RTTY) privileges are from 3.525 to 3.600 MHz. Single sideband voice privileges were recently expanded to 3.800 to 4.000 MHz.

60 METERS – 5 CHANNELS

Good nightowl band

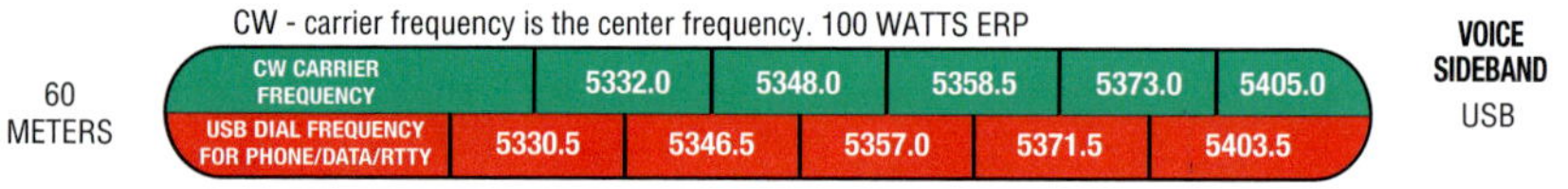

In 2003, the FCC allocated 5 discrete 60 meter channels for ham radio use on a non-interference basis with Government and Military stations, which are primary on this band. We are permitted 100 watts effective radiated power, referenced to a unity gain half-wave dipole. On upper side band (USB), tune your radio dial to read the carrier frequency shown on the lower bar. Voice emissions may not occupy more than 2.8 kHz, common for most ham transceivers. In the data modes, tune to this same carrier frequency and your data signal occupies up 1.5 kHz, in channel center. For CW, select the CW mode and tune to the channel CENTER frequency shown in the upper bar. On newer rigs, these 5 channels are pre-memorized for different modes of operation so no VFO tuning is required! More details for operating on 60 meters are on page 30.

40 METERS, 7.000 MHZ - 7.300 MHZ

Good day & night

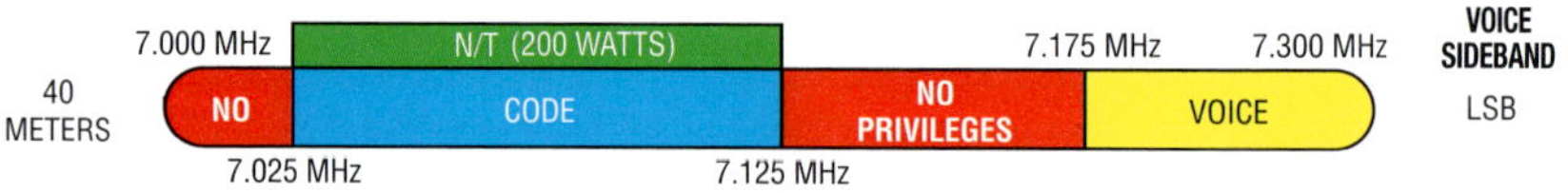

On 40 meters, General Class code, data, and RTTY privileges are enjoyed from 7.025 to 7.125 MHz. Single sideband voice privileges recently were expanded to 7.175 to 7.300 MHz. During daylight hours, 40 meters is a great band for base station and mobile contacts up to 500 miles away. At night, 40 meters skips all over the country, and many times all over the world!

30 METERS, 10.100 MHZ - 10.150 MHZ

Hot band for CW & data

Only code, data, and RTTY are permitted on this band. Thirty meters is located just above the 10-MHz WWV time broadcasts on shortwave radio. Voice is not allowed on this band by any class of amateur operator. Power is limited to 200 watts PEP.

20 METERS, 14.000 MHZ - 14.350 MHZ

Long-range day & evening contacts

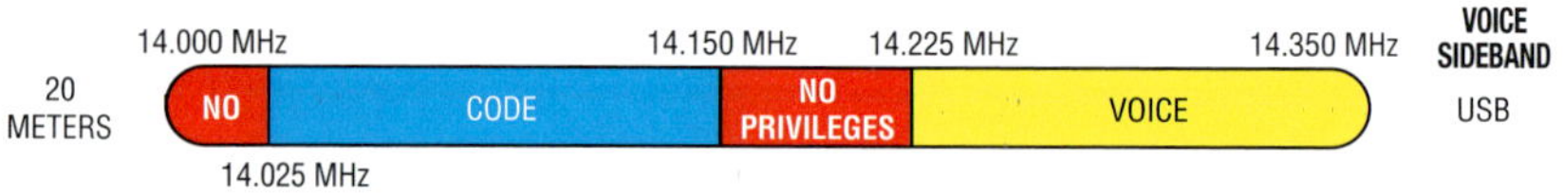

This is the best DX worldwide band there is, day or night! Morse code, data, and radioteletype (RTTY) privileges extend from 14.025 to 14.150 MHz. General Class voice privileges extend from 14.225 to 14.350 MHz. This is where the real DX activity takes place. Almost 24 hours a day, you should be able to work stations in excess of 5000 miles away on the 20-meter band with only a modest antenna setup. If you are a mariner, most of the long range maritime mobile bands are within your privileges as a General Class operator. If you are into recreational vehicles (RVs), there are nets on the 20 meter band all over the country especially for you. The "where it's at" band is 20 meters when you want to work the world from your car, boat, RV, or home shack!

17 METERS, 18.068 MHZ - 18.168 MHZ

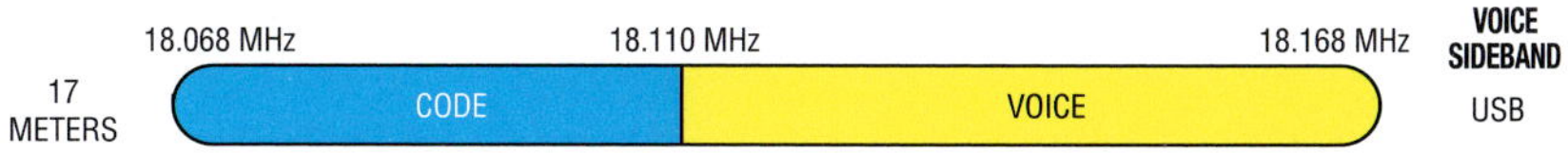

Best during the day

All emission types are authorized on this newer Amateur Radio band. There is plenty of elbow room here with lots of foreign DX coming in day and night. Most new base antennas have 17 meters included.

15 METERS, 21.000 MHZ - 21.450 MHZ

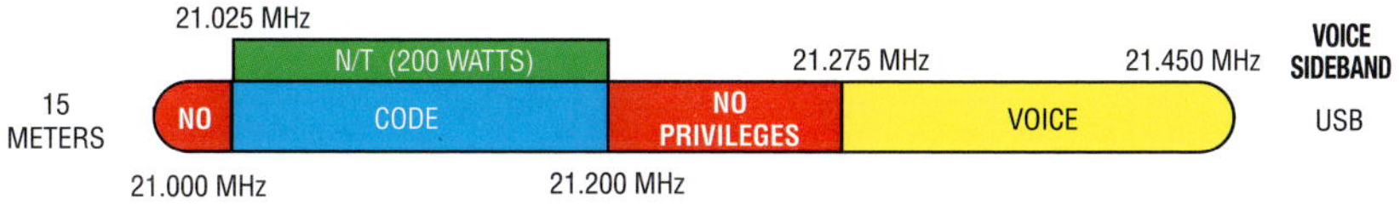

Daytime band

15 meter General Class CW, data and RTTY privileges extend from 21.025 to 21.200 MHz. Single sideband voice privileges recently were expanded on 15 meters to 21.275 to 21.450 MHz. The 15 meter band is great for daytime skywave contacts. This is a popular band for mobile operators because antenna requirements are relatively small. We've worked all over the world on the 15 meter band with mobile equipment.

12 METERS, 24.890 MHZ - 24.990 MHZ

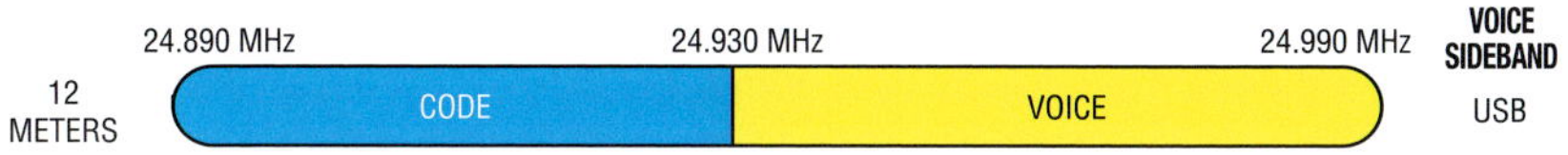

Best in daytime

Code, data, and RTTY privileges on the 12-meter band extend from 24.890 to 24.930 MHz. Voice privileges are from 24.930 to 24.990 MHz. Although this is a very narrow band, expect excellent daytime range throughout the world. At night, range is limited to groundwave coverage because the ionosphere is not receiving sunlight to produce skywave coverage on this band.

10 METERS, 28.000 MHZ - 29.700 MHZ

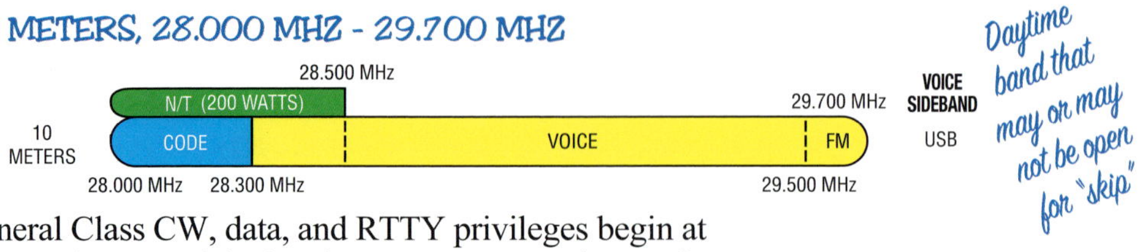

General Class CW, data, and RTTY privileges begin at the very bottom of the band, 28.000 MHz, and extend up to 28.300 MHz. Voice privileges begin at 28.300 MHz and extend up to 29.700 MHz. This expands your voice privileges on this band from those you enjoy as a Technician Class operator. And wait until you try the full fidelity of frequency modulation (FM) on 29.600 MHz! There are even FM repeaters at the top of 10 meters, too.

6 METERS AND UP

Your General Class license allows you unlimited band privileges and unlimited emission privileges on several higher-frequency bands, as shown in *Table 1-1*.

Table 1-1. 6 Meter and Higher Band Privileges

Frequency	Meters
50-54 MHz	6 meters
144-148 MHz	2 meters
222-225 MHz	1.25 meters
420-450 MHz	0.70 meters (70 cm)
902-928 MHz	0.35 meters (35 cm)
1240-1300 MHz	0.23 meters (23 cm)

MICROWAVE BANDS

Your General Class license allows you unlimited band privileges and unlimited emission privileges in the microwave bands, as indicated in *Table 1-2*. These VHF, UHF, and SHF frequencies are the same ones for which you received privileges when you passed your Technician or Technician-Plus Class examinations.

Table 1-2. Microwave Band Frequency Privileges

Frequency	Frequency
2300-2310 MHz	47.0-47.2 GHz
2390-2450 MHz	75.5-1.0 GHz
3.3-3.45 GHz	119.98-20.02 GHz
5.65-5.925 GHz	142-49 GHz
10.0-10.5 GHz	241-50 GHz
24.0-24.25 GHz	All above 300 GHz

Our first book, ***Technician Class***, for Element 2, provides a detailed explanation of the VHF, UHF, and SHF bands and presents the specific ARRL-recommended band plans for these frequencies. ***Technician Class*** is available from your local amateur radio dealer, at hamfests, or by calling The W5YI Group at 800/669-9594, or visit **www.w5yi.org**.

THE CONSIDERATE OPERATOR'S FREQUENCY GUIDE

Nothing in the FCC rules recognizes special privileges on any specific frequency for a net, group, or individual. No one "owns" a frequency. Rather, amateur operators rely on "gentlemen's agreements," good amateur practice, and common sense for all ham operators to check to see if the frequency is in use prior to transmitting – regardless of mode.

That said, here's a handy listing of frequencies that are generally recognized for certain modes or activities. Our thanks to our friends at *ARRL*, who gave us permission to reprint it here.

160 Meters (1.8 – 2.0 MHz)

1.800-2.000	CW
1.800-1.810	Digital Modes
1.810	CW QRP calling frequency
1.843-2.000	SSB, SSTV and other wideband modes
1.910	SSB QRP
1.995-2.000	Experimental
1.999-2.000	Beacons

80 Meters (3.5 – 4.0 MHz)

3.500-3.510	CW DX window
3.560	QRP CW calling frequency
3.570-3.600	RTTY/Data
3.585-3.600	Automatically controlled data stations
3.590	RTTY/Data DX
3.790-3.800	DX window
3.845	SSTV
3.885	AM calling frequency
3.985	QRP SSB calling frequency

40 Meters (7.0 – 7.3 MHz)

7.030	QRP CW calling frequency
7.040	RTTY/Data DX
7.070-7.125	RTTY/Data
7.100-7.105	Automatically controlled data stations
7.171	SSTV
7.173	D-SSTV
7.285	QRP SSB calling frequency
7.290	AM calling frequency

30 Meters (10.1 – 10.15 MHz)

10.130-10.140	RTTY/Data
10.140-10.150	Automatically controlled data stations

20 Meters (14.0 – 14.35 MHz)

14.060	QRP CW calling frequency
14.070-14.095	RTTY/Data
14.095-14.0995	Automatically controlled data stations
14.100	IBP/NCDXF beacons
14.1005-14.112	Automatically controlled data stations
14.230	SSTV
14.233	D-SSTV
14.236	Digital Voice
14.285	QRP SSB calling frequency
14.286	AM calling frequency

17 Meters (18.068 – 18.168 MHz)

18.100-18.105	RTTY/Data
18.105-18.110	Automatically controlled data stations
18.110	IBP/NCDXF beacons
18.162.5	Digital Voice

15 Meters (21.0 – 21.45 MHz)

21.060	QRP CW calling frequency
21.070-21.110	RTTY/Data
21.090-21.100	Automatically controlled data stations
21.150	IBP/NCDXF beacons
21.340	SSTV
21.385	QRP SSB calling frequency

12 Meters (24.89 – 24.99 MHz)

24.920-24.925	RTTY/Data
24.925-24.930	Automatically controlled data stations
24.930	IBP/NCDXF beacons

10 Meters (28.0 – 29.7 MHz)

28.060	QRP CW calling frequency
28.070-28.120	RTTY/Data
28.120-28.189	Automatically controlled data stations
28.190-28.225	Beacons
28.200 – 28.300	Beacons
28.385	QRP SSB calling frequency
28.680	SSTV
29.000-29.200	AM
29.300-29.510	Satellite downlinks
29.520-29.580	Repeater inputs
29.600	FM simplex
29.620-29.680	Repeater outputs

TECHNICIAN EXAM ADMINISTRATION

There is one more very important privilege you gain when you achieve General Class status. As a General Class licensee, you may take part in the administration of Element 2 Technician Class written examinations once you become accredited as a volunteer examiner at the General Class level by a VEC.

So, if you wish to see the amateur service grow in your local area, find 2 other General Class operators, then contact your local or national VEC for accreditation, and start your own testing team for newcomers to our hobby.

Several National VECs now offer REMOTE EXAMS via Zoom or other internet platforms. You could test for your General Class license upgrade right at home! When you pass General, you could also become a Volunteer Examiner and you could join a VE team to proctor Technician Class exams with an accredited team of fellow VEs, fom your home, office, or sitting on a park bench! Ham Exams have now gone paperless! See Chapter 4, TAKING THE GENERAL CLASS EXAMINATION.

To become an accredited Volunteer Examiner as a General Class licensee call the W5YI VEC at 800-669-9594.

SUMMARY

In late 2006, the FCC "refarmed" code, data, and voice privileges for General, Advanced, and Extra Class operators. All of the band charts in this new book have been updated to reflect the added privileges for high frequency voice operation. The FCC tightened up the code spectrum, and added more elbow room to the voice spectrum. General Class operators gained:

- 50 kHz of voice spectrum on 75 meters
- 50 kHz of voice spectrum on 40 meters
- 25 kHz of voice spectrum on 15 meters

With the elimination of the Morse code test on February 23, 2007, and the addition of all of this voice spectrum, General Class is the place to be!

Are you ready to prepare for the General Class Element 3 written examination? We sure hope so. Welcome – in advance – to the worldwide bands! We hope to hear you on the high frequency bands very soon.

2

A Little Ham History!

Ham radio has changed a lot in the 120 years since radio's inception. In the past 25 years, we have seen some monumental changes! So, before we get started preparing for the exam, we're going to give you a little refresher lesson about our hobby, its history, and an overview of how you'll progress through the amateur ranks to the top amateur ticket – the Extra Class license.

In this chapter you'll learn all of the licensing requirements under the FCC rules that became effective April 15, 2000. And you'll learn about the six classes of license that were in effect *prior* to those rules changes. That way, when you run into a Novice, Technician Plus or Advanced Class operator on the air, you'll have some understanding of their skill level, experience, and frequency privileges.

WHAT IS THE AMATEUR SERVICE?

There are more than 766,000 Americans who are licensed amateur radio operators in the U.S. today. The Federal Communications Commission, the Federal agency responsible for licensing amateur operators, defines our radio service this way:

"The amateur service is for qualified persons of all ages who are interested in radio technique solely with a personal aim and without pecuniary interest."

Ham radio is first and foremost a fun hobby! In addition, it is a service. And note the word "qualified" in the FCC's definition – that's the reason why you're studying for an exam; so when you pass the exam, you prove that you are qualified to get on the air.

Millions of operators around the world exchange ham radio greetings and messages by voice, radioteletype, telegraphy, facsimile, and television worldwide. Japan, alone, has more than a million hams! It is very commonplace for U.S. amateurs to communicate with Russian amateurs. China is just getting started with its amateur service. Being a ham operator is a great way to promote international good will.

The benefits of ham radio are countless! Ham operators are probably known best for their contributions during times of disaster. In recent years, many recreational sailors in the Caribbean who have been attacked by modern-day pirates have had their lives saved by hams directing rescue efforts. Following the 9/11 terrorist attacks on the World Trade Center and the Pentagon, literally thousands of local hams assisted with emergency communications. After Katrina blew through New Orleans, ham radio operators were the first to report the levee breach and to warn that flood waters were rushing into the city.

The ham community knows no geographic, political or social barrier. If you study hard and make the effort, you are going to earn your upgrade to General Class and get on the HF worldwide bands. Follow the suggestions in our book and your chances of passing the written exam are excellent, and learning will be easy and fun!

A BRIEF HISTORY OF AMATEUR RADIO LICENSING

Before government licensing of radio stations and amateur operators was instituted in 1912, hams could operate on any wavelength they chose and could even select their own call letters. The Radio Act of 1912 mandated the first Federal licensing of all radio stations and assigned amateurs to the short wavelengths of less than 200 meters. These "new" requirements didn't deter them, and within a few years there were thousands of licensed ham operators in the United States.

Since electromagnetic signals do not respect national boundaries, radio is international in scope. National governments enact and enforce radio laws within a framework of international agreements that are overseen by the International Telecommunications Union. The ITU is a worldwide United Nations agency headquartered in Geneva, Switzerland. The ITU divides the radio spectrum into a number of frequency bands, with each band reserved for a particular use. Amateur radio is fortunate to have many bands allocated to it all across the radio spectrum.

In the U.S., the Federal Communications Commission is the government agency responsible for the regulation of wire and radio communications. The FCC allocates frequency bands in accordance with the ITU plan to the various services – including the amateur service – and regulates stations and operators.

By international agreement, in 1927 the alphabet was apportioned among various nations for basic call sign use. The prefix letters K, N and W were assigned solely to the United States. The letter A is shared by the United States and other countries.

In the early years of amateur radio licensing in the U.S., the classes of licenses were designated by the letters "A," "B," and "C." The highest license class with the most privileges was "A." In 1951, the FCC dropped the letter designations and gave the license classes names – names that are familiar to us today. Class A became Advanced; Class B became General; and Class C became Conditional. At the same time, the FCC also created the Extra Class, and Technician Class licenses. They also added a new Novice Class – a one-year, non-renewable license for beginners that required a 5-wpm Morse code speed proficiency test and a 20-question written examination on elementary theory and regulations, with both tests taken before one licensed ham.

The General exam required 13-wpm code speed, and Extra required 20-wpm. Each of the five written exams was progressively more comprehensive and formed what came to be known as the *Incentive Licensing System.*

In the '70s, the Technician Class license became very popular because of the number of repeater stations appearing on the air that extended the range of VHF and UHF mobile and handheld radios. It also was very fashionable to be able to patch your mobile radio into the telephone system, which allowed hams to make telephone calls from their automobiles long before the advent of cell phones.

In 1979, the international amateur service regulations were changed to permit all countries to waive the manual Morse code proficiency requirement for "...stations making use exclusively of frequencies above 30 MHz." This set the stage for creation of the Technician "no-code" license in 1991, when the 5-wpm Morse code requirement was eliminated. New "no-code" Technician licensees were permitted to operate on all amateur bands above 30 MHz. Applicants for the no-code Technician license had to pass the 35-question Novice and 30-question Technician Class written examinations but no Morse code test.

"No-code" Technician Class amateurs who passed a 5-wpm code test were awarded a Technician-Plus license. Besides their 30 MHz and higher no-code frequency privileges, Tech-Plus licensees gained the Novice CW privileges and a sliver of the 10 meter voice spectrum.

With these changes in 1991, there were six amateur service license classes – Novice, Technician, Technician-Plus, General, Advanced, and Extra – along with five written exams and three Morse code tests used to qualify hams for their various licenses.

The Amateur Service is Restructured

As you can see, through the years the ham radio licensing and privileges underwent a myriad of changes. In 1998, the FCC began working with the ham radio community to restructure our amateur radio service to make it more effective. The objective of this restructuring was to streamline the license process, eliminate unnecessary and duplicated rules, and reduce the emphasis on the Morse code test. The result of this review was a complete restructuring of the U.S. amateur service, which became effective April 15, 2000. The restructuring included a change in the Morse code requirement for General and Extra classes to 5-wpm and the reduction from six to three amateur radio license classes. Since 2000 there have been only 3 amateur radio license classes:

- Technician Class, the HF/VHF/UHF entry level license.
- General Class, the HF entry level license, which required a 5-wpm code test.
- Amateur Extra Class, a technically oriented senior license, based on-5wpm code credit.

The next major change to FCC Amateur Radio rules occurred on February 23, 2007, when the FCC completely eliminated the Morse code examination for all amateur radio licenses! The FCC action was based on 6,200 written comments, with most supporting the elimination of all code tests. At the same time, the FCC also "upgraded" No-code Technician Class operators, awarding them use of the Novice and Technician-Plus high frequency privileges on 80, 40, 15, and 10 meters.

In its public notice announcing elimination of the Morse code test requirement, the FCC Commissioners wrote: "We believe that because the international requirement for telegraphy proficiency has been eliminated, we should treat Morse code telegraphy no differently than other amateur service communication techniques. This change eliminates an unnecessary regulatory burden that may discourage current amateur radio operators from advancing their skills and participating more fully in the benefits of amateur radio."

Eliminating the Morse code test in no way diminishes the enthusiasm many ham operators have for the technique of sending dits and dahs over the air. In fact, we believe we will have more General Class hams learning the code than ever before, now that they can do it on high frequency where practicing code with other hams is fun!

Self-Testing in the Amateur Service

Prior to 1984, all amateur radio exams were administered by FCC personnel at FCC Field Offices around the country. In 1984, the FCC adopted a two-tier system beneath it called the Volunteer Examiner Coordinator (VEC) system to handle amateur radio license exams. The VEC System was formed after Congress passed laws that allowed the FCC to accept the services of Volunteer Examiners (VEs) to prepare and administer amateur service license examinations. The testing activity of VEs is managed by Volunteer Examiner Coordinators (or VECs). A VEC acts as the administrative liaison between the VEs, who administer the various ham examinations, and the FCC, which grants the license.

Also in 1984, the length of term for amateur radio licenses was increased from five to ten years.

A team of three VEs, who must be accredited by a VEC, is required to conduct amateur radio examinations. General Class amateurs may serve as examiners for the Technician class. Advanced Class amateurs may administer exams for Technician and General class. The Extra Class exam may only be administered by VEs who hold an Extra Class license.

In 1986, the FCC turned over responsibility for maintenance of the examination question pools for amateur radio licenses to the National Conference of Volunteer Examiner Coordinators (NCVEC). The Conference appoints a Question Pool Committee (QPC) to develop and revise the various question pools according to a schedule. As a rule, each of the 3 question pools is changed once every 4 years. The FCC requires at least ten times as many questions in each of the pools as may appear on an examination. Both the Technician Class Element 2 and General Class Element 3 written examinations contain 43 multiple-choice questions. The Extra Class Element 4 written examination has 50 questions.

OPERATOR LICENSE CLASSES AND EXAM REQUIREMENTS

Anyone is eligible to become a U.S. licensed amateur operator (including foreign nationals, if they are not a representative of a foreign government). There is no age limitation – if you can pass the examinations, you can become a ham!

Today, there are three amateur operator licenses issued by the FCC – Technician, General, and Extra. Each license requires progressively higher levels of learning and proficiency, and each gives you additional operating privileges. This is known as incentive licensing – a method of strengthening the amateur service by offering more radio spectrum privileges in exchange for more operating and electronic knowledge.

There is no waiting time required to upgrade from one amateur license class to another. Similarly, there is no required waiting time to retake a failed exam. You can even take all three examinations at one sitting if you're really brave! *Table 2-1* details the amateur service license structure and required examinations.

Table 2-1: Current Amateur License Classes and Exam Requirements

License Class	Exam Element	Type of Examination
Technician Class	2	35-question, multiple-choice written examination. Minimum passing score is 26 questions answered correctly (74%).
General Class	3	35-question, multiple-choice written examination. Minimum passing score is 26 questions answered correctly (74%).
Extra Class	4	50-question, multiple-choice written examination. Minimum passing score is 37 questions answered correctly (74%).

ABOUT THE WRITTEN EXAMS

What is the focus of each of the written examinations, and how does it relate to gaining expanding amateur radio privileges as you move up the ladder toward your Extra Class license? *Table 2-2* summarizes the subjects covered in each written examination element.

Table 2-2. Question Element Subjects

Exam Element	License Class	Subjects
Element 2	Technician	Elementary operating procedures, radio regulations, and a smattering of beginning electronics. Emphasis is on VHF and UHF operating.
Element 3	General	HF (high-frequency) operating privileges, amateur practices, radio regulations, and a little more electronics. Emphasis is on HF bands.
Element 4	Extra	Basically a technical examination. Covers specialized operating procedures, more radio regulations, formulas and heavy math. Also covers the specifics on amateur testing procedures.

No Jumping Allowed

You cannot skip over a license class or by-pass a required examination as you upgrade from Technician to General to Extra. For example, to obtain a General Class license, you must first take and pass the Element 2 written examination for the Technician Class license then take and pass the Element 3 written examination. To obtain an Extra Class license, you must first pass the Element 2 (Technician) and Element 3 (General) written examinations and then successfully pass the Element 4 (Extra) written examination.

TAKING THE ELEMENT 3 EXAM

Here's a summary of what you can expect when you go to the session to take the Element 3 written examination for your General Class license. Detailed information about how to find an exam session, what to expect at the session, what to bring to the session, and more is included in Chapter 4.

Examination Administration

All amateur radio examinations are administered by a team of at least three Volunteer Examiners (VEs) who have been accredited by a Volunteer Examiner Coordinator (VEC). The VEs are licensed hams who volunteer their time to help our hobby grow.

How to Find an On-Site or Remote Exam Session

Amateur Radio license exam sessions are offered under the auspices of an FCC approved VEC. A list of approved VECs is located in the Appendix on page 216. The W5YI-VEC and the ARRL-VEC are the two largest exam groups in the country.

In the past few years, VECs have developed the option of taking your exam on-line from the comfort of your home or office. This is a great convenience for those who live in rural areas far from on-site exam sessions.

On-site exam sessions are also offered at locations throughout the 50 states, if you prefer that in-person option. To find a session, either on-line or in-person visit:

https://w5yi-vec.org/index.php/find-an-exam-session

where you will find two links – one for remote exam sessions and one for in-person exam sessions. These links take you to sites that are updated continuously. Search for a convenient session, click on the link to that VE team, and register on-line for your exam. It is easier than ever to find and take your ham exam.

Taking the Exam

The Element 3 written exam is a multiple-choice format. The VEs will give you a test paper that contains the 35 questions and multiple choice answers and an answer sheet for you to complete. Take your time! Make sure you read each question carefully and select the correct answer. Once you're finished, double check your work before handing in your exam papers.

The VEs will score your exam immediately. You'll know before you leave the exam site whether you've passed. If you pass, you will be given a Certificate of Successful Completion of Examination (CSCE), proof that you passed your exam. Chances are very good that, if you've studied hard, you'll get that passing grade!

GETTING/KEEPING YOUR CALL SIGN

Once the VE team scores your exam and you've passed, the process of upgrading your official FCC Amateur Radio License begins – usually that same day.

At the exam site, you will complete NCVEC Form 605, which is your application to the FCC for your license. If you pass the exam, the VE team will send on the required paperwork to their VEC. The VEC reviews the paperwork then files your application with the FCC. This filing is done electronically and your license upgrade will be granted and posted on the FCC's website within a few days.

If you didn't check the "Change Call Sign" box on your NCVEC Form 605 application, you will simply keep your current call sign. However, if you do check the "Change Call Sign" box, you will receive an entry-level "Group D" call sign as if you were a newly-licensed amateur. We suggest that you don't check the "Change Call Sign" box and stick with your present call sign. If you have been operating for any period of time, your call sign is familiar to you and in some ways a part of your on-the-air identity. It can be a little difficult to become accustomed to a new call sign.

As soon as you pass your exam and have the CSCE, you are permitted to go on the air with your General Class HF privileges – even before your license upgrade appears on the FCC's Universal License System database. See Chapter 4 for more details on this process.

Vanity Call Signs

If you checked the "Change Call Sign" box on the Form 605, your call sign is assigned by the FCC's computer. Once you have that call sign, you can apply for a Vanity Call Sign if you would prefer a different letter combination. This process is explained in more detail In Chapter 4.

HOW MANY CLASSES OF LICENSES?

Once you've passed your Element 3 exam and go on the air as a new General Class operator, you'll be talking to fellow hams throughout the U.S. and around the world. Here's a summary of the new and "grandfathered" licenses that your fellow amateurs may hold and a recap of the level of expertise they have demonstrated in order to gain their licenses.

New License Classes

Following the FCC's restructuring of Amateur Radio licensing that took effect April 15, 2000, there are just three written exams and three license classes – Technician, General, and Extra. Persons who hold licenses issued prior to April 15, 2000 may continue to hold onto their license class and renew it every 10 years for as long as they wish.

"Grandfathered" Licensees

Once you get on the air with your new General Class privileges, every now and then you might meet a Novice operator while yakking on 10 meters, or sending CW on 15, 40, or 80 meters. And then there are the Advanced Class operators who may continue to hold onto their license class designation until they finally decide to move up to Extra Class. When you meet an operator holding an Advanced Class license, you know without a doubt that he had to successfully complete a 13 word per minute Morse code test along with the written exam to earn that license.

When you look at the Frequency Charts in this book, you'll see that we have updated them to reflect the expanded privileges on many high frequency bands for General Class and higher operators. We also list the sub-band privileges for Extra Class, Advanced Class, General Class, Technician Class and even the Novice.

"Paper Upgrade" to General

The FCC Rules (Part 97.505) provides credit for General Class Element 3, without examination, to those applicants who can prove they held an unexpired Technician Class license granted before March 21, 1987. No other class of license receives this element credit. You can submit a copy of your old Technician license and receive credit for the Element 3 exam to qualify for your General Class upgrade. To do so, you must attend a VE testing session, pay the exam fee and submit your documentation and application through the normal VE to VEC session process to receive what is commonly referred to as a General Class "paper upgrade."

To see if you qualify for any of these opportunities to regain your former license privileges, or for a "paper upgrade" to General Class, contact the W5YI VEC at 800-669-9594.

Element Credit for Prior Licenses

Recent rule changes by the FCC make it possible for hams whose licenses have expired to regain their priviliges simply by taking and passing the Element 2 Technician Class written exam. If you were licensed as a General, passing the Tech exam will earn you a new General Class license. If you were Advanced, passing the Tech exam will also get you a new General Class license. And if you were an Extra, passing the Tech exam will earn you a new Extra Class license!

This rule applies to those with expired General, Advanced, and Extra Class licenses that are beyond the two-year grace period. In order to take advantage of this, you must show proof of holding your expired license. If you do not have a copy of your old license, one resource to help verify your former status is to e-mail call sign historian Pete Varounis, NL7XM, at **twelveVDC@aol.com**.

Paperless Licenses

Effective February 17, 2015 the FCC no longer routinely issues/mails a paper license document to Amateur Radio licensees and other WTB licensed services. The Commission maintains that the official Amateur Radio license authorization is the electronic record that exists in its Universal Licensing System Database. Licensees may access their current, official authorization, and print out an unofficial "reference copy" of their license, using the FCC ULS License Search feature at: **http://wireless.fcc.gov/uls.**

The FCC will provide a paper license to those who notify the Commission that they prefer to receive one. To notify the FCC that you want a license mailed to you, contact the FCC at 877-480-3201 between 8:00 a.m. to 6:00 p.m. Eastern time Monday through Friday (except Federal holidays). You can also request a paper license by logging into the ULS license record using your FRN and CORES password and selecting to receive a paper copy by mail. If you do not know your CORES password, you can reset it on the FCC website: **https://apps.fcc.gov/coresWeb**

IT'S EASY!

The primary pre-requisite for passing any amateur radio operator license exam is the "will" to do it. If you follow our suggestions in this book, your chances of passing the General Class exam are excellent.

The 2007 FCC rule changes that eliminated the Morse code test requirement for General Class make it even easier for you to earn your General Class license and enjoy voice privileges on the high frequency bands that were expanded in those same changes.

When you become a General Class operator, GET ON THE AIR! Operating is an important step to becoming a good ham and ultimately a candidate for the highest license – Amateur Extra Class. But, GET ON THE AIR and enjoy your new General Class worldwide HF privileges!

Gordo and Chip work the Hawaii tropo duct, 2500 mile DX on VHF and UHF!

3

Getting Ready for the Exam

Your General Class written examination will consist of 35 multiple-choice questions taken from the 430 questions that make up the 2023-2027 Element 3 question pool. Each question on your examination and the multiple-choice answer will be identical to those contained in this book.

This chapter contains the official, complete 430-question FCC Element 3 General Class question pool from which your examination will be taken. Of the 35 questions, you must get 74% of the questions correct – which means you must answer 26 questions correctly in order to pass.

Your examination will be administered by a team of 3 or more Volunteer Examiners (VEs) – amateur radio operators who are accredited by a Volunteer Examiner Coordinator (VEC). You will receive a Certificate of Successful Completion of Examination (CSCE) when you pass the examination. This is official proof that you have passed the exam and it will be given to you before you leave the exam center.

With this completed form in hand, you can begin operating with General Class privileges immediately using your current call sign with "temporary AG."

THE 2023-2027 QUESTION POOL

The Element 3 General Class question pool contained in this book is valid from July 1, 2023, through June 30, 2027.

The 430 questions and distracters in the new General Class question pool were developed by the National Conference of Volunteer Examiner Coordinators' Question Pool Committee (NCVEC-QPC). The QPC Chairman is Roland Anders, K3RA, and the QPC members are Maria Somma,AB1FM and Larry Pollock, NB5X.

The QPC encourages amateur radio operators throughout the country to submit revised questions for the amateur radio pools to the committee. If you have any suggestions for new or revised questions, you can send them to Gordo, and he'll be happy to forward them on to the QPC. Gordo's address is on page 205.

WHAT THE EXAMINATION CONTAINS

The examination questions and the multiple-choice answers (one correct answer and three "distracters") for all license class levels are public information. They are widely published and are identical to those in this book. *There are no "secret" questions.* FCC rules prohibit any examiner or examination team from making any changes to any questions, including any numerical values. No numbers, words, letters, or punctuation marks can be altered from the published question pool. By studying all 430 Element 3 questions in this book, you will be reading the same exact questions that will appear on your 35-question Element 3 written examination. But which 35 out of the 430 total questions?

Table 3-1. FCC Element 3 General Class Question Pool

Subelement	Topic	Total Questions	Exam Questions
G1	Commission's Rules	57	5
G2	Operating Procedures	60	5
G3	Radio Wave Propagation	37	3
G4	Amateur Radio Practices	60	5
G5	Electrical Principles	40	3
G6	Circuit Components	24	2
G7	Practical Circuits	38	3
G8	Signals and Emissions	43	3
G9	Antennas and Feedlines	46	4
G0	Electrical and RF Safety	25	2
TOTALS		430	35

Table 3-1 shows how the 35 question examination for Element 3 will be compiled from the question pool. For example, for the Element 3 examination, three questions from the 35 total exam questions will be taken from subelement G8, Signals and Emissions (one from each of the three topics in subelement G8). On subelement G1, Commission's Rules, you will have 5 exam questions on your test. Rusty on electrical principles? Your test will have only 3 questions from subelement G5.

The question pool is divided into 10 subelements which are each divided into topics. Each subelement covers a different subject with each topic covering a part of that subject. You can review the complete list of subelement topics in the Question Pool Syllabus found on page 222 of this book.

All Volunteer Examination teams use the same question pool. This uniformity in material ensures common examinations throughout the country. Most exams are computer-generated so that while the specific questions will vary, the combination of questions will not. The computer selects one question from each topic within each subelement for your Element 3 exam.

Trust us, every question on your Element 3 exam will look very familiar to you by the time you finish studying this book

QUESTION CODING

Each and every question in the 430 question Element 3, General Class pool is numbered using a **code.** *The coded numbers and letters reveal important facts about each question!*

The numbering code always contains 5 alphanumeric characters to identify each question. Here's how to read the question number so you know the subelement and topic that it is from and you can see exactly how the computer selects one question out of each topic for your exam. Once you know this information, you can increase your odds of achieving a "max" score on the exam, especially if there is a specific group of questions which seems impossible for you to understand.

Let's pick a typical question out of the pool – G1A04 – and let us show you how this numbering code works:

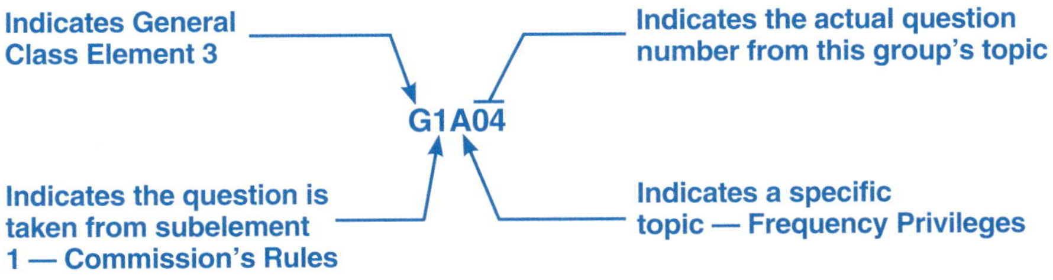

Figure 3-1. Examination Question Coding

- The first character "G" identifies the license class question pool from which the question is taken. "T" would be for Technician. "G" is for General, and "E" would be for Extra.
- The second digit, a "1", identifies the subelement number, 1 through 0. General subelement 1 deals with FCC Rules.
- The third character, "A", indicates the topic area within the subelement. Topic "A" deals with your General Class frequency privileges.
- The fourth and fifth digits indicate the actual question number within the subelement topic's group. The "04" indicates this is the fourth question about frequency privileges, and within the topic area of Commission's Rules. There are 11 individual questions in topic area G1A, *but only one question out of this topic group will appear on the test.*

Here's the Secret Study Hint

Only one exam question will be taken from any single group! A computer-generated test is set up to take only one question from each topic. It cannot skip a topic, nor can it take any more than one question from that topic.

If you decide to skip a topic completely because you are having trouble understanding the subject, guess what – how many questions out of any one topic? That's right, only one per topic. This means you are not going to get hammered on any Element 3 test with a whole bunch of questions dealing with a specific topic. Great secret, huh?

Study Time

How long will it take you to prepare for your upcoming exam?

The General Class question pool in this book is valid from July 1, 2023, through June 30, 2027. It contains a total of 430 questions – but don't panic! Most questions are repeated several different ways, and these "repeats" reinforce what you already learned. It is probably going to take about 30 days to work through this book and prepare for your General Class exam.

QUESTIONS REARRANGED FOR SMARTER LEARNING

The first thing you'll notice when you look at how the Element 3 question pool is presented in this book is that we have completely rearranged the entire General Class question pool to precisely follow Gordo's weekend ham radio training classes. This rearrangement will take you logically through each and every one of the 430 questions with their answers exactly as you will see them on an Element 3 exam. The questions are arranged here into 18 subjects in a way that eliminates the need for you to jump back and forth between topics or subelements to match up questions on similar subjects

For example, we have taken all of the questions in the pool about where you can operate your ham radio and grouped them together into one section that allows you to better understand all of the material that relates to this subject. This arrangement of the questions follows a natural learning process

Trust us, the reorganization of all of the test questions in the pool has been tested and finely-tuned in hundreds of my weekend classes. This method of learning WORKS! You will probably cut your study time in half simply by following the questions as presented here in our book!

Each and every Element 3 question is in this book. A cross-reference of all 430 questions is found on pages 223 to 224 of the book.

This book – and our General Class audio course – contain all 430 General Class questions, 4 possible answers, the noted correct answer, and our upbeat description of how the correct answer works into the real world of amateur radio. We highlight ***KEY WORDS*** that will help you remember the correct answer and provide you with a fast review of the entire question pool just before you sit for the big General Class exam.

We also include many web addresses that can provide you with hours of fascinating study on selected "hot topics" that will help you really understand the real world of ham radio. You can visit a site while you study, or visit after you've earned your General Class license and are on the air.

When you visit some of these websites, it may not be immediately apparent why we are suggesting that you go there. Some addresses take you to the sites of local ham clubs. Most of these are specialty clubs, and they contain lots of information on how to operate on repeaters, or satellites, or provide educational resources on learning about electronics or antennas or how radios work.

And a disclaimer – while we have worked hard to make sure all of these addresses are current at the time of publication, websites move, addresses change, or sites simply go away. If you find an address that doesn't work, feel free to drop us an e-mail so we can update it for the next printing of this book. And if you know of a website that you think is a gem, send us that information and we'll consider it for our next printing.

Here's my e-mail address:
masterpubl@aol.com

How to Read the Questions

Using an actual question from page 28, here is a guide to explain what it is you will be studying as you go through all of the Q&As in the book:

Official Q&A

G1C05 What is the limit for transmitter power on the 28 MHz band for a General Class operator??

A. 100 watts PEP output. C. 1500 watts PEP output.
B. 1000 watts PEP output. D. 2000 watts PEP output.

Novice and Technician Class operators are restricted to 200 watts on high frequency bands; however, as a General Class operator you can run up to ***1500 watts PEP*** (Peak Envelope Power) output. [97.313] **ANSWER C.**

FCC Part 97 Rule Citation — Correct Answer — Key Words To Remember

Topic Areas

Here is a list of our 18 topic areas showing the page where it starts in the book. Again, there is a complete cross reference list of the Q&As in numerical order on pages 223 to 224 in the Appendix, along with the official Question Pool Syllabus.

STUDY SUGGESTIONS

Finally, as you get ready to start studying the questions, here are some suggestions to make your learning easier:

1. Read over each multiple-choice answer carefully. Some answers start out looking good, but turn bad during the last 2 or 3 words. If you speed read the answers, you could very easily go for a wrong answer because you didn't read them all the way through. Also, don't count on the multiple-choice answers always appearing in the exact same A-B-C-D order on your actual computer-generated test. While they won't change any words in the answers, they will sometimes scramble the A-B-C-D order.
2. Give this book to a friend, and ask him or her to read you the correct answer. You then reply with the question wording.

3. Mark the heck out of your book! When the pages begin to fall out, you're probably ready for the exam!
4. Our book is available on audio CDs, too. So if you'd like to listen to Gordo and Eric read the questions and answers to you while you're driving your car, riding your bike, or laying on the beach, we can do that for you. The CD symbol, disk number, and track number at the beginning of each topic section keys this book to the audio book. You can get this book on audio CD where you purchased this book, or by calling 800-669-9594, or by visiting www.w5yi.org.

   CD 1 TRACK 2

5. Highlight the keywords one week before the test. Then speed read the brightly highlighted keywords twice a day before the exam.

Are you ready to work through the 430 Q & A's? Put a check mark by the easy ones that you may already know the answer for, and put a little circle by any question that needs a little bit more study. Save your highlighting work until a few days before your upcoming test. Work the Q & A's for about 30 minutes at a time. We'll drop in a little bit of humor to keep you on track; and if you actually need Gordo's live words of encouragement, you can call him on the phone Monday through Thursday, 10:00 a.m. to 4:00 p.m. (California time), 714-549-5000.

THE QUESTION POOL, PLEASE

Okay, this is the big moment – your General Class, Element 3, question pool. Don't freak out and get overwhelmed with the prospect of learning 430 Q & A's. You will find that the topic content is repeated many times, so you're really going to breeze through this test without any problem!

Your Passing CSCE

G1D09 How long is a Certificate of Successful Completion of Examination (CSCE) valid for exam element credit?

A. 30 days
B. 180 days
C. 365 days
D. For as long as your current license is valid

When you pass your exam, your examiners will all sign a Certificate of Successful Completion of Examination (CSCE). With the signed CSCE in hand, you are good to go on the air immediately with your new privileges! This CSCE is proof-positive that you passed the exam just in case there is a paperwork error down the line. Your license usually is upgraded within two weeks, so the ***365-day*** period of this ***CSCE*** applies only in rare cases where paperwork gets lost. [97.9(b)] **ANSWER C.**

When you pass your exam, you'll receive your CSCE and lots of congratulations!

G1D06 Until an upgrade to General class is shown in the FCC database, when must a Technician licensee identify with "AG" after their call sign?

A. Whenever they operate using General class frequency privileges
B. Whenever they operate on any amateur frequency
C. Whenever they operate using Technician frequency privileges
D. A special identifier is not required if their General class license application has been filed with the FCC

Until your call sign appears on the Universal Licensing System data base, ***add the special identifier "AG"*** when you operate using General Class privileges. You don't need to append this identifier when operating within Technician frequency privileges, just ***when using your new General Class frequencies***. [97.119(f)(2)] **ANSWER A.**

G1D03 On which of the following band segments may you operate if you are a Technician class operator and have an unexpired Certificate of Successful Completion of Examination (CSCE) for General class privileges?

A. Only the Technician band segments until your upgrade is posted in the FCC database
B. Only on the Technician band segments until you have a receipt for the FCC application fee payment
C. On any General or Technician class band segment
D. On any General or Technician class band segment except 30 meters and 60 meters

Once you pass your General Class written examination, you are good to ***go on the air on all General Class*** segments of the worldwide ***bands plus your present Technician frequencies***. Keep our book handy to reference the frequencies for General Class operations on each band. [97.9(b)] **ANSWER C.**

G1D01 Who may receive partial credit for the elements represented by an expired amateur radio license?

A. Any person who can demonstrate that they once held an FCC-issued General, Advanced, or Amateur Extra class license that was not revoked by the FCC
B. Anyone who held an FCC-issued amateur radio license that expired not less than 5 and not more than 15 years ago
C. Any person who previously held an amateur license issued by another country, but only if that country has a current reciprocal licensing agreement with the FCC
D. Only persons who once held an FCC issued Novice, Technician, or Technician Plus license

In 2014, the FCC issued a new rule that allows ***General, Advanced, and Extra Class*** hams who have let their license expire by more than 2 years to ***regain their original license level*** by simply taking and passing the Technician Class Element 2 exam. This means that granddad, who had an Extra Class license back in the '50s, can now get back to that Extra Class level just by studying up on the current Element 2 using our book and passing the Technician "entry level" exam to become an Extra Class again! [97.501, 97.505(a)] **ANSWER A.**

G1D11 What action is required to obtain a new General class license after a previously held license has expired and the two-year grace period has passed?

A. They must have a letter from the FCC showing they once held an amateur or commercial license
B. There are no requirements other than being able to show a copy of the expired license
C. Contact the FCC to have the license reinstated
D. The applicant must show proof of the appropriate expired license grant and pass the current Element 2 exam

A previously-licensed amateur radio operator may get back to their expired General Class or higher license simply by ***passing the current Element 2 Technician Class exam***. The applicant will need to show proof his or her original license. This could be the old license itself, an old Callbook listing, or proof of an old license from a look-up service, such as that provided by The W5YI-VEC. Call them at 1-800-669-9594. Another resource for this service is provided by call sign historian Pete Varounis, NL7XM. Email him at **twelveVDC@aol.com**. [97.505] **ANSWER D.**

Ham operator Dick Bruno, N6ISY, veteran West Coast public service communicator, works new upgrades on High Frequency.

Your New General Bands

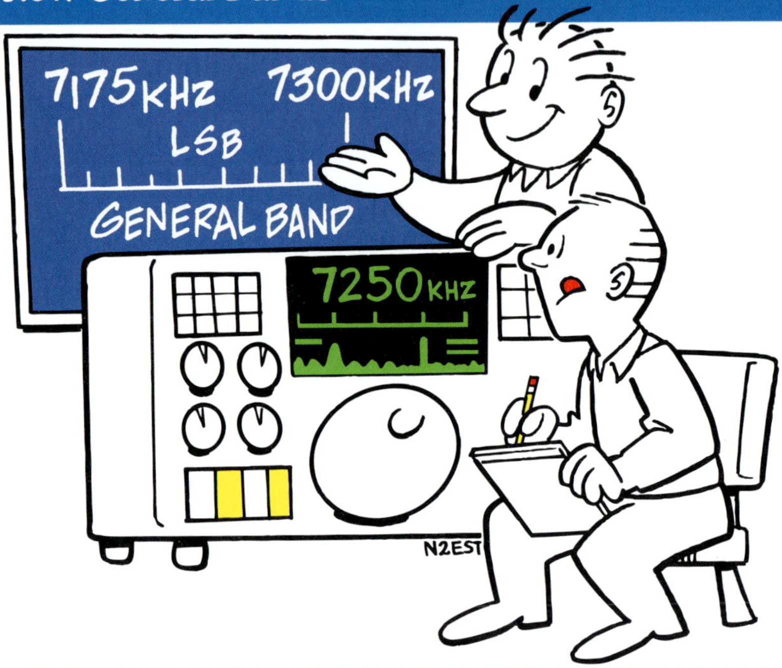

Elmer Point: Here are the formulas that you need to convert frequency to wavelength, and wavelength to frequency:

Converting Frequency to Wavelength

To find wavelength (λ) in meters if you know frequency (f) in megahertz (MHz), Solve:

$$\lambda(\text{meters}) = \frac{300}{f(\text{MHz})}$$

Converting Wavelength to Frequency

To find frequency (f) in megahertz (MHz) if you know wavelength (λ) in meters, Solve:

$$f(\text{MHz}) = \frac{300}{\lambda(\text{meters})}$$

G1A01 On which HF and/or MF amateur bands are there portions where General class licensees cannot transmit?

A. 60 meters, 30 meters, 17 meters, and 12 meters
B. 160 meters, 60 meters, 15 meters, and 12 meters
C 80 meters, 40 meters, 20 meters, and 15 meters
D. 80 meters, 20 meters, 15 meters, and 10 meters

When you pass your General Class exam, you will gain privileges on every High Frequency (HF) and Medium Frequency (MF) band. ***On 80 meters, 40 meters, 20 meters, and 15 meters***, the Extra and Advanced class operators have expanded privileges where we cannot transmit. The color charts show our General Class band privileges in yellow and blue. Just remember 80,40,20, and 15 meter bands have red areas, where we cannot transmit. [97.301(d)] **ANSWER C.**

G1A08 Which HF bands have segments exclusively allocated to Amateur Extra licensees?

A. All HF bands
B. 80 meters, 40 meters, 20 meters, and 15 meters
C All HF bands except 160 meters and 10 meters
D. 60 meters, 30 meters, 17 meters, and 12 meters

While a General Class license gives you privileges on each and every amateur radio band, there is some prime radio “real estate” available only to ***Amateur Extras on 80, 40, 20, and 15 meters.*** Though these sections are small, they are where a lot of “juicy” DX is to be found, and is a good incentive to getting your Amateur Extra ticket. [97.301(b)] **ANSWER B.**

G1A11 When General class licensees are not permitted to use the entire voice portion of a band, which portion of the voice segment is available to them?

A. The lower frequency portion
B. The upper frequency portion
C. The lower frequency portion on frequencies below 7.3 MHz, and the upper portion on frequencies above 14.150 MHz
D. The upper frequency portion on frequencies below 7.3 MHz, and the lower portion on frequencies above 14.150 MHz

Study our band plan charts and see where your privileges begin and end. ***Voice privileges***, or “phone,” on all bands are always at the ***upper frequency portion of the band***. (The one exception here is on 160 meters, where phone is allowed anywhere in the band (1.8-2.0 MHz) [97.301] **ANSWER B.**

Voice (phone) privileges are always at the top end of the bands.

G1A07 On which amateur frequencies in the 10-meter band may stations with a General class control operator transmit CW emissions?

A. 28.000 MHz to 28.025 MHz only
B. 28.000 MHz to 28.300 MHz only
C. 28.025 MHz to 28.300 MHz only
D. The entire band

With only one minor exception, radio amateurs are permitted to transmit CW on *any* frequency where they are allowed to operate. CW is still the “default” mode of operation, as far as the FCC is concerned. As a General Class licensee, you are allowed to use CW over the ***entire 10-meter band***, although CW is more likely to be found near the “bottom” (lowest frequency region) of any amateur band. [97.305(a)] **ANSWER D.**

G1A10 What portion of the 10-meter band is available for repeater use?

A. The entire band
B. The portion between 28.1 MHz and 28.2 MHz
C. The portion between 28.3 MHz and 28.5 MHz
D. The portion above 29.5 MHz

The 10-meter amateur band is a big amateur band, a whole 1.7 MHz wide, by far the biggest HF band in the entire amateur radio spectrum. There is plenty of "elbow room" for experimenting with different modes on the 10-meter band. ***The upper 200 kHz of the band, beginning at 29.5 MHz is available for repeater operation.*** It is possible (and perfectly legal!) to work distant 10-meter repeaters via ionospheric "skip," and a great deal of fun to do so. Tune to 29.6 MHz for FM simplex contacts, and tune up to hear FM repeater outputs, minus 100 kHz lower transmit split. Eric in Alaska may answer you! [97.205(b)] **ANSWER D.**

G1C05 What is the limit for transmitter power on the 28 MHz band for a General Class control operator?

A. 100 watts PEP output
B. 1000 watts PEP output
C. 1500 watts PEP output
D. 2000 watts PEP output

Novice and Technician Class operators are restricted to 200 watts on high frequency bands; however, as a General Class operator you can run up to ***1500 watts PEP*** (Peak Envelope Power) output. [97.313] **ANSWER C.**

G1E02 When may a 10-meter repeater retransmit the 2-meter signal from a station that has a Technician class control operator?

A. Under no circumstances
B. Only if the station on 10-meters is operating under a Special Temporary Authorization allowing such retransmission
C. Only during an FCC-declared general state of communications emergency
D. Only if the 10-meter repeater control operator holds at least a General class license

Technician Class operators have no privileges between 29.500 to 29.700 MHz where 10 meter repeaters operate. As a General Class operator, you can set up a home station as a cross-band relay system. This could allow a Technician on the 2-meter band to end up transmitting and receiving on the 10-meter band. Think of all the excitement you could give Technician Class operators on 2 meters when the 10 meter FM segment of the band is open for worldwide skywave communications. This is perfectly legal to do provided a ***General Class, or higher, control operator*** stays at the control point of your station. [97.205(b)] **ANSWER D.**

G1C02 What is the maximum transmitter power an amateur station may use on the 12-meter band?

A. 50 watts PEP output
B. 200 watts PEP output
C. 1500 watts PEP output
D. An effective radiated power equivalent to 100 watts from a half-wave dipole

On the ***12 meter band***, you can run the legal limit of ***1500 watts*** PEP output. [97.313] **ANSWER C.**

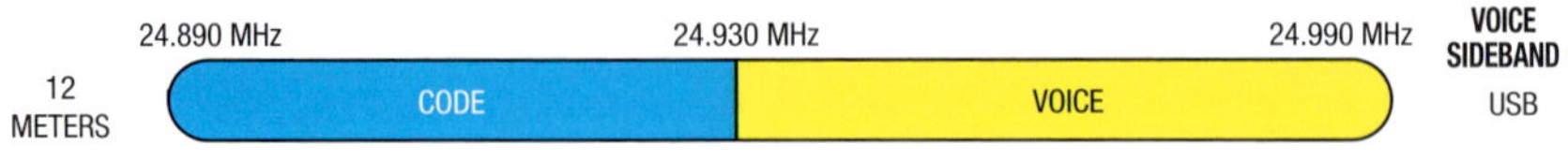

G1A09 Which of the following frequencies is within the General class portion of the 15-meter band?

A. 14250 kHz
B. 18155 kHz
C. 21300 kHz
D. 24900 kHz

The ***15 meter band*** is at 21 MHz (21000 kHz), so ***21300 kHz*** is a great frequency for voice operations to regularly work the world in the morning and afternoon. [97.301(d)] **ANSWER C.**

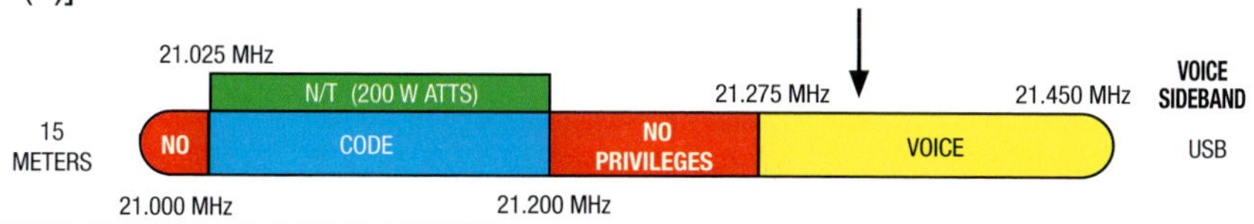

G1A02 On which of the following bands is phone operation prohibited?

A. 160 meters
B. 30 meters
C. 17 meters
D. 12 meters

As a new General, you can operate throughout the entire 30 meter band using CW and DATA emissions with power output limited to 200 watts. ***No phone (voice) activity is allowed on 30 meters***. [97.305] **ANSWER B.**

G1A03 On which of the following bands is image transmission prohibited?

A. 160 meters
B. 30 meters
C. 20 meters
D. 12 meters

Image transmissions include popular slow-scan television and facsimile. On ***30 meters, image transmissions are prohibited.*** [97.305] **ANSWER B.**

G1A05 On which of the following frequencies are General class licensees prohibited from operating as control operator?

A. 7.125 MHz to 7.175 MHz
B. 28.000 MHz to 28.025 MHz
C. 21.275 MHz to 21.300 MHz
D. All of the above

The ***40 meter frequencies between 7.125 MHz and 7.175 MHz are allocated to Amateur Extra and (grandfathered) Advanced class licensees only, and so are "out of bounds" to*** General Class control operators. It is always a good idea to have a chart of amateur radio frequency allocations near your operating position as a reminder of where your "borders" are. [97.301(d)] **ANSWER A.**

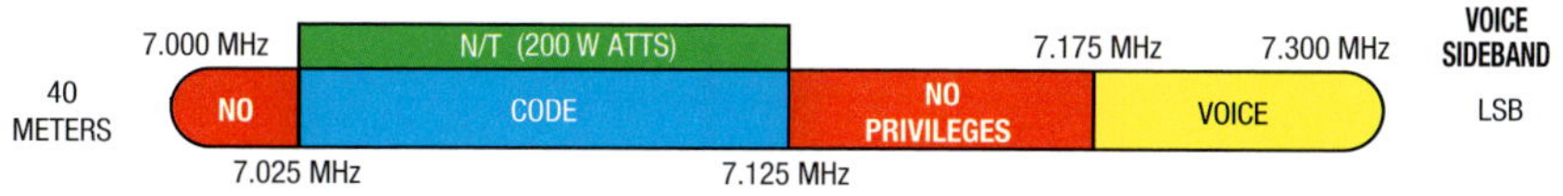

G1C01 What is the maximum transmitter power an amateur station may use on 10.140 MHz?

A. 200 watts PEP output
B. 1000 watts PEP output
C. 1500 watts PEP output
D. 2000 watts PEP output

On the ***30 meter*** CW and Data ***band***, only ***200 watts*** peak envelope power output is allowed in accordance with FCC rules. [97.313(c)(1)] **ANSWER A.**

THREE SIMPLE RULES FOR 60 METERS

When operating 60 meters, it is crucial that you transmit on the correct frequency within the authorized channel. Compliance with the rules when using Single Sideband phone or sound card digital modes is very straightforward. CW operation is slightly different. 60 Meter channels are assigned by the bottom table, where the frequency represents the VFO display (suppressed carrier) frequency of your transceiver:

VOICE USB
- Channel 1: 5330.5 kHz
- Channel 2: 5346.5 kHz
- Channel 3: 5357.0 kHz
- Channel 4: 5371.5 kHz
- Channel 5: 5403.5 kHz

If you heed the following three rules, you will be in compliance with the FCC regulations:

(1) Phone Operation: Set your transmitter to Upper Sideband (USB) and your VFO to display the frequency of the chosen channel from the table. Be sure your transmitter is set to limit the bandwidth to 2.8 kHz. Check your operator's manual if you are unsure about how to do this. Most modern rigs default to this setting, but READ THE MANUAL!

(2) Sound Card Digital Modes: Set your transmitter to USB, select the channel frequency on your VFO, and click on 1.5 kHz on your waterfall or spectrum display. This will place your transmitted signal properly in the CENTER of the channel.

(3) CW operation: Place your transmitted signal in the CENTER of the channel, 1.5 kHz above the assigned carrier frequency shown in the table. Depending on your particular transceiver, this MAY OR MAY NOT correspond to your VFO display frequency! READ YOUR OPERATOR'S MANUAL TO BE SURE.

The diagram above shows the position of your transmitted signal within a 60 meter channel.

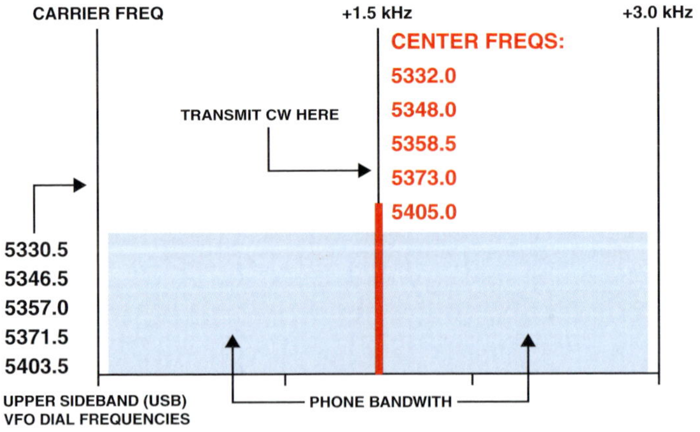

One final note: If you're using ***non-sound card digital modes***, such as "old school" RTTY with direct FSK modulation, you must assure that your transmitted signal is exactly centered in the channel, using any reliable means at your disposal.

G1A04 Which of the following amateur bands is restricted to communication only on specific channels, rather than frequency ranges?

A. 11 meters
B. 12 meters
C. 30 meters
D. 60 meters

The 60 meter ham band is shared with a few government stations on a non-interference basis – they can interfere with us, but we cannot interfere with them! Ham operators are authorized ***5 discrete channels***, which are great frequencies for passing regional radio traffic. ***60 meters*** is the only band where we have been assigned specific channel allocations, and we may now use digital and voice on each of these channels. [97.303(h)] **ANSWER D.**

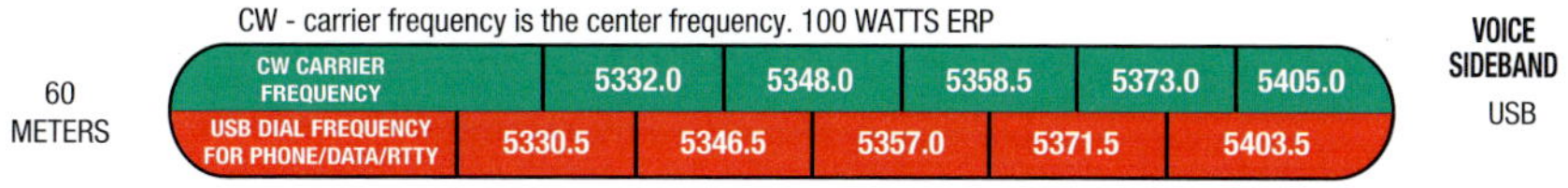

G1C03 What is the maximum bandwidth permitted by FCC rules for amateur radio stations transmitting on USB frequencies in the 60-meter band?

A. 2.8 kHz
B. 5.6 kHz
C. 1.8 kHz
D. 3 kHz

On the ***60 meter band***, there are five channels allocated on specific frequencies with a ***maximum bandwidth of 2.8 kHz.*** [97.303(h)(1)] **ANSWER A.**

G1C09 What is the maximum power limit on the 60-meter band?

A. 1500 watts PEP
B. 10 watts RMS
C. ERP of 100 watts PEP with respect to a dipole
D. ERP of 100 watts PEP with respect to an isotropic antenna

The 60 meter band is one of the few amateur radio bands that has limitations on effective radiated power (ERP), rather than transmitter power. A 60-meter station must not exceed ***ERP of 100 watts PEP with respect to a dipole.*** [97.313(i)] **ANSWER C.**

G1C04 Which of the following is required by the FCC rules when operating in the 60-meter band?

A. If you are using an antenna other than a dipole, you must keep a record of the gain of your antenna
B. You must keep a record of the date, time, frequency, power level, and stations worked
C. You must keep a record of all third-party traffic
D. You must keep a record of the manufacturer of your equipment and the antenna used

FCC rules require 60 meter band, 5-channel operation not to exceed 100 watts effective radiated power as measured on a dipole antenna. On a dipole, gain is zero, so 100 watts into the dipole from your transmitter will not exceed 100 watts ERP. However, ***if you're transmitting using a beam antenna***, you will need to turn your power output down to correspond with the amount of gain the beam exhibits. If the beam offers 3 dB gain in the forward direction, this 2 times increase in ERP will require you to reduce your transmitter ERP to half of 100 watts. You then must ***note this in your station's logbook***. [97.303(i)] **ANSWER A.**

G1A06 Which of the following applies when the FCC rules designate the amateur service as a secondary user on a band?

A. Amateur stations must record the call sign of the primary service station before operating on a frequency assigned to that station
B. Amateur stations may use the band only during emergencies
C. Amateur stations must not cause harmful interference to primary users and must accept interference from primary users
D. Amateur stations may only operate during specific hours of the day, while primary users are permitted 24-hour use of the band

Both our 30 meter and 60 meter bands are shared, and authorized government users always have priority. They are primary on the band, which means ***we must not cause harmful interference to primary government users.*** [97.303] **ANSWER C.**

G1C06 What is the limit for transmitter power on the 1.8 MHz band?

A. 200 watts PEP output
B. 1000 watts PEP output
C. 1200 watts PEP output
D. 1500 watts PEP output

As a new General Class operator, you are permitted to run up to ***1500 watts*** of Peak Envelope Power (PEP) output on all bands other than 60 meters and 30 meters. However, by FCC rules, you should always run the minimum power necessary to make the contact. [97.313] **ANSWER D.**

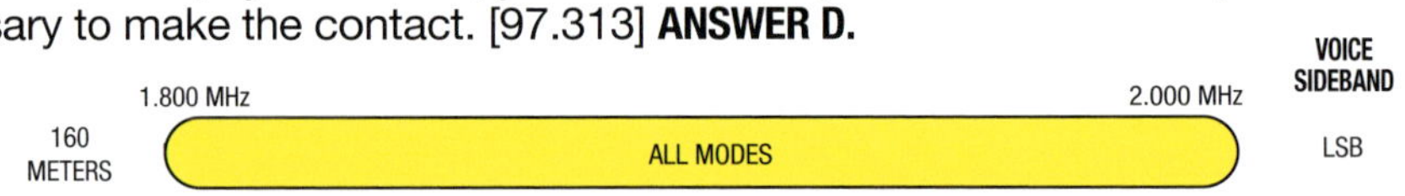

G1E06 The frequency allocations of which ITU region apply to radio amateurs operating in North and South America?

A. Region 4
B. Region 3
C. Region 2
D. Region 1

The International Telecommunications Union (ITU) has divided the world into three large regions. North and South America are in ***ITU Region 2***. While radio frequency allocations are fairly uniform in most of the world, differences in the allocations do exist within in the different ITU areas due to regional requirements. [97.301, ITU Radio Regulations] **ANSWER C.**

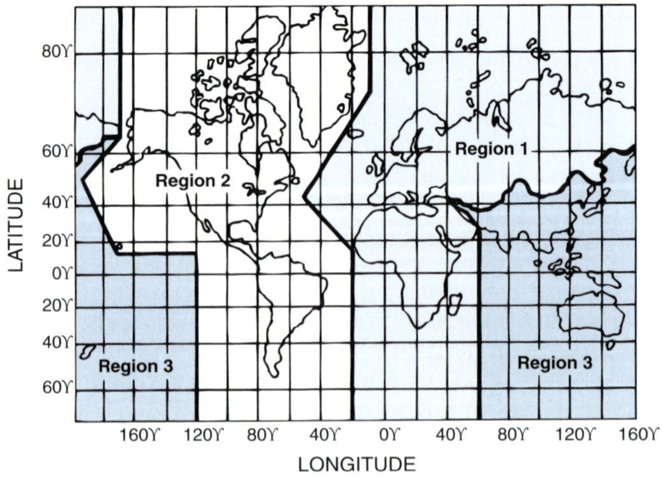

ITU Regions

FCC Rules

G2D08 Why do many amateurs keep a station log?

A. The FCC requires a log of all international contacts
B. The FCC requires a log of all international third-party traffic
C. The log provides evidence of operation needed to renew a license without retest
D. To help with a reply if the FCC requests information about your station

Whenever a control operator lets a guest ham operate his equipment, he writes down details of who the other operator was in his ***station log***. This way, if the FCC should ask who was the control operator or third party during a transmission on a given date and time, he will be able to look it up and have solid information about what went out over the airwaves at your station! **ANSWER D.**

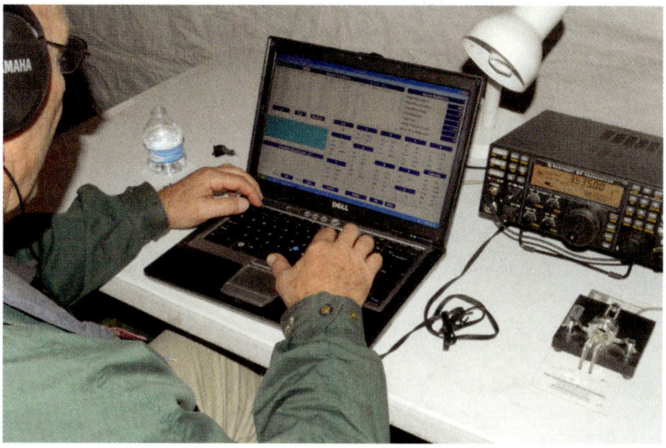

Keeping a station log on a computer makes it easy to look up a past HF contact.

ham apps — As a radio amateur, you should not only know where you are, but also when you are. You need an accurate clock in your shack. The Precise-Time app gives your logbook accurate time and your choice of time zones includes Greenwich (UTC) time. **https://itunes.apple.com/au/app/emerald-time/id290384375?mt=8**

G2D01 What is the Volunteer Monitor Program?

A. Amateur volunteers who are formally enlisted to monitor the airwaves for rules violations
B. Amateur volunteers who conduct amateur licensing examinations
C. Amateur volunteers who conduct frequency coordination for amateur VHF repeaters
D. Amateur volunteers who use their station equipment to help civil defense organizations in times of Emergency

The Volunteer Monitoring Program is replacing the original Amateur Auxiliary program under the American Radio Relay League and the FCC. ***Volunteer monitoring hams*** are registered with the ARRL and undergo formal training to ***assist all hams in self-regulation and adherence to the FCC's rules and regulations***. **ANSWER A.**

G2D02 Which of the following are objectives of the Volunteer Monitor Program?

A. To conduct efficient and orderly amateur licensing examinations
B. To provide emergency and public safety communications
C. To coordinate repeaters for efficient and orderly spectrum usage
D. To encourage amateur radio operators to self-regulate and comply with the rules

The benchmark of the amateur service is ***self-regulation and compliance*** with the rules. All hams help other hams stay on the straight and narrow. The Volunteer Monitor Program streamlines the exchange of information between formally enlisted hams to the ARRL and the FCC. **ANSWER D.**

G2D03 What procedure may be used by Volunteer Monitors to localize a station whose continuous carrier is holding a repeater on in their area?

A. Compare vertical and horizontal signal strengths on the input frequency
B. Compare beam headings on the repeater input from their home locations with that of other Volunteer Monitors
C. Compare signal strengths between the input and output of the repeater
D. All these choices are correct

The tried and true method of *triangulation* is the most reliable method of determining the location of a transmitter. This is often necessary when attempting to locate a transmitter which is "hung up," transmitting an unmodulated carrier on a local repeater. This involves ***comparing beam headings on the repeater input from their home locations with that of other Volunteer Monitors.*** It is important to recognize that a Volunteer Monitor is NOT an FCC agent or a "radio cop." The job of a Volunteer Monitor is simply to inform an operator of improper operation or faulty equipment. **ANSWER B.**

Elmer Point: Volunteer Monitoring Program operators know the Part 97 Rules and Regulations inside and out. You should, too! The FCC rules are written in plain language providing fun reading to see all that the FCC encourages you to do on the air. Call 800-669-9594, and tell them Gordo and Eric want you to read the FCC Part 97 Rule book.

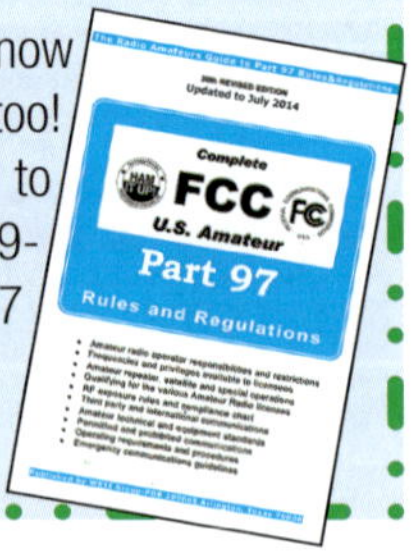

G1B11 Who or what determines "good engineering and good amateur practice," as applied to the operation of an amateur station in all respects not covered by the Part 97 rules?

A. The FCC
B. The control operator
C. The IEEE
D. The ITU

Only ***the Federal Communications Commission (FCC)*** can decide what meets "good engineering and good amateur practice." [97.101(a)] **ANSWER A.**

G1B06 Under what conditions are state and local governments permitted to regulate amateur radio antenna structures?

A. Under no circumstances, FCC rules take priority
B. At any time and to any extent necessary to accomplish a legitimate purpose of the state or local entity, provided that proper filings are made with the FCC
C. Only when such structures exceed 50 feet in height and are clearly visible 1,000 feet from the structure
D. Amateur Service communications must be reasonably accommodated, and regulations must constitute the minimum practical to accommodate a legitimate purpose of the state or local entity

Antennas are a necessity for radio amateurs. While we hams consider any form of antenna a thing of great beauty, there are many "civilians" who consider amateur radio and other antennas unsightly or dangerous. However, local communities must reasonably accommodate amateur radio antennas when no other compelling safety or other considerations are present. The precise wording for this policy is ***Amateur Service communications must be reasonably accommodated, and regulations must constitute the minimum practical to accommodate a legitimate purpose of the state or local entity.*** What the legitimate purpose of the state or local entity often is a matter of hotly-debated review and legislation, and the rules are not "chiseled in granite" yet. It is best to keep yourself informed of local activity and legislation on this matter. [97.15(b), PRB-1, 101 FCC 2d 952 (1985)] **ANSWER D.**

G1B01 What is the maximum height above ground for an antenna structure not near a public use airport without requiring notification to the FAA and registration with the FCC?

A. 50 feet
B. 100 feet
C. 200 feet
D. 250 feet

The FCC works closely with the FAA when it comes to towers taller than 200 feet. Although you do not need FCC approval for towers less than ***200 feet tall***, you may need approval from your city or homeowner's association. [97.15(a)] **ANSWER C.**

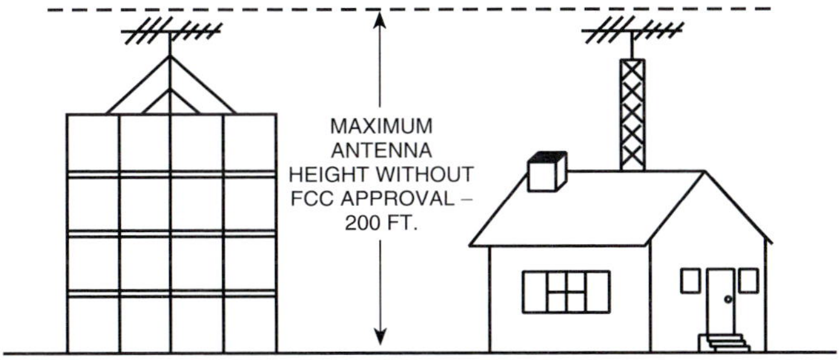

Maximum antenna height

G1B05 Which of the following one-way transmissions are permitted?

A. Unidentified test transmissions of less than 10 seconds in duration
B. Transmissions to assist with learning the International Morse code
C. Regular transmissions offering equipment for sale, if intended for amateur radio use
D. All these choices are correct

The Federal Communications Commission (FCC) has provided well-defined differences between commercial and amateur radio frequency usage. Broadcasting is one activity that is, with a few exceptions, confined to the commercial radio world. One notable exception to this rule is the permitting of ***transmissions necessary to assist learning the International Morse code***, most notably by the ARRL's flagship station W1AW. [97.111((5)(b)] **ANSWER B.**

G1B07 What are the restrictions on the use of abbreviations or procedural signals in the amateur service?

A. Only "Q" signals are permitted
B. They may be used if they do not obscure the meaning of a message
C. They are not permitted
D. They are limited to those expressly listed in Part 97 of the FCC rules

Common abbreviations, "Q" codes, and other phrases such as "73," "QRZ?," or "Please QSL" that ***do not obscure the meaning of our communications*** are perfectly acceptable on the ham bands. Popular "Q" codes are given on page 56. Here is the list of common prowords. [97.113(a)(4)] **ANSWER B.**

Proword	Meaning
Affirmative	Yes
All after	Say again all after ______
All before	Say again all before ______
Break	Used to separate message heading, text and ending
Break	Stop transmitting
Correct	That is correct
Figures	Numerals follow
From	Originator follows
Groups	Numeral(s) indicating number of text words follows
Incorrect	That is incorrect
Initial	Single letter follows
I say again	I repeat
I spell	Phonetic spelling follows
Message follows	A message which requires recording follows
More to follow	I have more traffic for you
Negative	No, not received
Number	Message number (in numerals) follows
Out	End of transmission, no answer required or expected
Over	End of transmission, answer is expected. Go ahead. Transmit.
Roger	I have received your transmission satisfactorily
Say again	Repeat
Slant	Slant bar
This is	This transmission is from the station whose call sign follows
Time	File time or date-time group of the message follows
To	Addressee follows
Wait	Short pause
Wait out	Long pause
Word after	Say again word after ______
Word before	Say again word before ______

MARS – Army Radiotelephone Prowords

G1B08 When is it permissible to communicate with amateur stations in countries outside the areas administered by the Federal Communications Commission?

A. Only when the foreign country has a formal third-party agreement filed with the FCC
B. When the contact is with amateurs in any country except those whose administrations have notified the ITU that they object to such communications
C. Only when the contact is with amateurs licensed by a country which is a member of the United Nations, or by a territory possessed by such a country
D. Only when the contact is with amateurs licensed by a country which is a member of the International Amateur Radio Union, or by a territory possessed by such a country

As a new General Class operator, you can work hundreds of countries and become an expert in DX, plus learn a little bit of a foreign language! ***As long as neither their nor our administration has notified the International Telecommunications Union(ITU) that ham communications are forbidden***, you are okay to work any ham in that foreign country. [97.111(a)(1)] **ANSWER B.**

G1D05 When operating a US station by remote control from outside the country, what license is required of the control operator?

A. A US operator/primary station license
B. Only an appropriate US operator/primary license and a special remote station permit from the FCC
C. Only a license from the foreign country, as long as the call sign includes identification of portable operation in the US
D. A license from the foreign country and a special remote station permit from the FCC

The Internet has created the ability to operate an amateur radio station from the other side of the globe; an increasingly popular method for hams to operate their home station while residing in or visiting a foreign country. For such operation a ***U.S. operator/primary license is required, and as always the control operator*** needs to be in actual control of any transmissions. [97.7] **ANSWER A.**

G1D12 When operating a station in South America by remote control over the internet from the US, what regulations apply?

A. Those of both the remote station's country and the FCC
B. Those of the remote station's country and the FCC's third-party regulations
C. Only those of the remote station's country
D. Only those of the FCC

In most cases, it is the actual physical location of the amateur radio transmitting equipment that determines who has jurisdiction over the rules and regulations. If operating a DX station from the comforts of home, ***it is only the rules of the remote station's country*** that apply. [97.507] **ANSWER C.**

G1E01 Which of the following would disqualify a third party from participating in sending a message via an amateur station?

A. The third party's amateur license has been revoked and not reinstated
B. The third party is not a US citizen
C. The third party is speaking in a language other than English
D. All these choices are correct

You are not allowed to let a "third party" talk over your equipment if they were previously licensed as a ham and their ***license has been revoked***. Don't let them "con" you into letting them speak through your station! [97.115(b)(2)] **ANSWER A.**

G1E05 What are the restrictions on messages sent to a third party in a country with which there is a Third-Party Agreement?

A. They must relate to emergencies or disaster relief
B. They must be for other licensed amateurs
C. They must relate to amateur radio, or remarks of a personal character, or messages relating to emergencies or disaster relief
D. The message must be limited to no longer than 1 minute in duration and the name of the third party must be recorded in the station log

During a third party traffic exchange only transmissions of ***personal messages are allowed***. In an emergency, messages relating to ***disaster relief are also allowed***. [97.115(a)(2), 97.117] **ANSWER C.**

G1E09 Under what circumstances are messages that are sent via digital modes exempt from Part 97 third-party rules that apply to other modes of communication?

A. Under no circumstances
B. When messages are encrypted
C. When messages are not encrypted
D. When under automatic control

Third party traffic rules have remained essentially unchanged throughout the history of Amateur Radio, and are unlikely to be changed significantly in the foreseeable future. You must not perform any third party traffic handling with any entity that does not have a third party agreement. ***No exceptions!*** [97.115] **ANSWER A.**

G1E12 When may third-party messages be transmitted via remote control?

A. Under any circumstances in which third party messages are permitted by FCC rules
B. Under no circumstances except for emergencies
C. Only when the message is intended for licensed radio amateurs
D. Only when the message is intended for third parties in areas where licensing is controlled by the FCC

A third party agreement has nearly always been required when transmitting third party traffic in another country. A recent rule change has allowed remote control of a third party station, ***if such transmissions are already permitted by FCC rules.*** This is another exciting development made possible by the Internet and related technology. [97.115] **ANSWER A.**

Be a VE

G1D02 What license examinations may you administer as an accredited Volunteer Examiner holding a General class operator license?

A. General and Technician
B. None, only Amateur Extra class licensees may be accredited
C. Technician only
D. Amateur Extra, General, and Technician

As a new General Class operator, we hope you will apply for Volunteer Examiner accreditation. As a VE accredited General Class operator, you and 2 other accredited VE General Class (or higher) operators could administer an Element 2 ***Technician Class*** examination. [97.509(b)(3)(i)] **ANSWER C.**

World famous Gordo graduate, Dr. Tamitha Skov, www.spaceweatherwoman.com is proud of her CSCE!

G1D07 Volunteer Examiners are accredited by what organization?

A. The Federal Communications Commission
B. The Universal Licensing System
C. A Volunteer Examiner Coordinator
D. The Wireless Telecommunications Bureau

Individual ***Volunteer Examiners are accredited by a Volunteer Examiner Coordinator***. The largest VECs are the American Radio Relay League (ARRL) and the W5YI-VEC organizations. [97.509(b)(1)] **ANSWER C.**

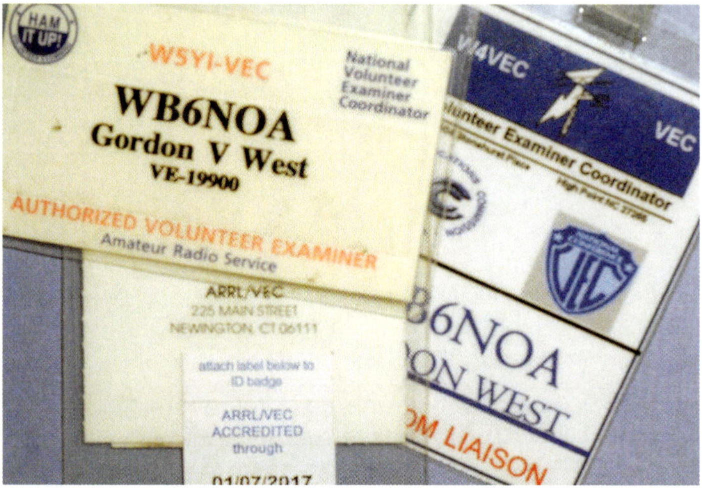

Look for the official "VEC Seal of Approval" when you go to your exam session. VEC examiners work hard to maintain the integrity and quality of the amateur radio exams.

G1D04 Who must observe the administration of a Technician class license examination?

A. At least three Volunteer Examiners of General class or higher
B. At least two Volunteer Examiners of General class or higher
C. At least two Volunteer Examiners of Technician class or higher
D. At least three Volunteer Examiners of Technician class

As a VE accredited General Class operator, ***you and 2 other accredited General Class (or higher) volunteer examiners*** may administer Technician Class Element 2 FCC examinations. [97.509(3)(i)(c)] **ANSWER A.**

G1D08 Which of the following criteria must be met for a non-US citizen to be an accredited Volunteer Examiner?

A. The person must be a resident of the US for a minimum of 5 years
B. The person must hold an FCC granted amateur radio license of General class or above
C. The person's home citizenship must be in ITU region 2
D. None of these choices is correct; a non-US citizen cannot be a Volunteer Examiner

Non U.S. citizens may become volunteer examiners if they ***hold an FCC-granted General Class license*** or higher. [97.509(b)(3)] **ANSWER B.**

G1D10 What is the minimum age that one must be to qualify as an accredited Volunteer Examiner?

A. 16 years
B. 18 years
C. 21 years
D. There is no age limit

There is no age limit to obtain a ham license; however, ***Volunteer Examiners must be at least 18 years old***. [97.509(b)(2)] **ANSWER B.**

Elmer Point: Our listing of Volunteer Exam Coordinators will lead you to a phone number of your local area testing team. Look for it in the Appendix on page 216. Testing teams are always looking for examinees, so they'll be delighted to hear that you want to take an exam. And once you're a General, you may want to join them as an examiner! **Visit: www.w5yi-vec.org**

VEs Can Teach Ham Classes

When the VEC Program first began, FCC rules prohibited Volunteer Examiners from teaching amateur radio classes. This rule was rescinded many years ago, and today many VEs also teach ham radio classes for new applicants, as well as licensed hams upgrading to General and Extra. The only issue is that you must teach the entire question pool, not the actual exam to be given.

Want to teach? The W5YI Group has a program just for you!

HamInstructor.com is a support program that provides FREE teaching materials for every license class. These include Instructor Guides tied to the Gordon West study manuals; pre-study homework you can use to encourage students to "work their book" before class; frequency charts and other materials for handouts; and most of all, discounts on bulk purchases of the Gordon West study manuals, to save you or your club money providing the instruction materials.

To learn more, and to become a registered instructor, visit:
www.haminstructor.com.

Elmer Point: Take your exam at home – or from your office – on-line!! It's easy to do. Ham Radio VECs have developed remote testing to make it easier than ever to access you General Class Element 3 exam site. Go to the following website where you can search for an on-line exam session:
https://w5yi-vec.org/index.php/find-an-exam-session

Elmer Point: "Roger on your QTH, and fine business on your new rig. Hope you can QSL our QSO, and I wish you very seven three." Say what? Huh? Here's a glossary with a sampling of ham radio lingo that you'll hear when you're on the air!

CQ CQ CQ this is a station on HF looking for anyone to have a nice friendly contact
CQDX CQDX CQDX this is a station calling ONLY for a contact to a foreign station, not looking for a USA contact
Old Man this really doesn't mean you are old, but rather a term for a fellow ham radio operator
YL usually an unmarried lady
XYL usually a married lady
Harmonics your children
73 best regards to you
88 an affectionate hug to a YL or XYL
Ham a licensed amateur radio operator (with every ham having his or her own idea of this term's origin)
ARRL American Radio Relay League, our number one, non-profit organization that you should join.
APRS Automatic Position Reporting System - automatic GPS radio tracking, usually on 10 MHz HF
DX a station a LONG way away
Break only use this word to break into a conversation with emergency or priority traffic. To enter a conversation politely, use only your callsign, never "Break".
CQ contest you can answer this call if you are familiar with the precise "exchange" the other operator is looking for.
QRZed who is the station calling me?
Down 10 move down in frequency 10 kHz
5 9 9 your signal report is strong, loud, and clear!
In the Mud your signal is extremely weak
QRM interference from another station on a close frequency
QTH your station location
QSL please send me a QSL card (also…I agree)
QRN power line or automobile static
QRU does anyone have traffic for me?
QRP low power station
QRT going off the air
QRX stand by - I need to do something
QSB your signal is fading in and out
QSO a communications contact
QST calling all ham radio operators
QSY we need to move off this frequency
TVI interfering with a television set
Heil a premier after-market microphone system
HF worldwide high frequency bands
MARS Military Affiliate Radio Service
Nets regular frequency meeting spot at a certain time for all interested hams
OO an official observer monitoring for rule violations
My Shack your home radio location
Mobile in motion driving down the road with a big HF rig
Ragchew having a long winded conversation
RFI every time I transmit, my windshield wipers self-activate!
Handi-ham an active radio ham who has overcome physical challenges
Splatter maybe turn down your microphone gain
Traffic an incoming message for you
HI HI radio laughter on CW

Voice Operation

G2B06 How can you avoid harmful interference on an apparently clear frequency before calling CQ on CW or phone?

A. Send "QRL?" on CW, followed by your call sign; or, if using phone, ask if the frequency is in use, followed by your call sign
B. Listen for 2 minutes before calling CQ
C. Send the letter "V" in Morse code several times and listen for a response, or say "test" several times and listen for a response
D. Send "QSY" on CW or if using phone, announce "the frequency is in use," then give your call sign and listen for a response

Soon you will be a General Class operator on the high frequency airwaves. Sometimes, propagation allows you to hear only half of a conversation. So a good way to double check that a frequency is clear for your use is to ***send "QRL?" on CW***, followed by your call sign, or ***on phone simply ask, "Is the frequency in use?"*** followed by your call sign. This will make you one great operator! **ANSWER A.**

G2B07 Which of the following complies with commonly accepted amateur practice when choosing a frequency on which to initiate a call?

A. Listen on the frequency for at least two minutes to be sure it is clear
B. Identify your station by transmitting your call sign at least 3 times
C. Follow the voluntary band plan
D. All these choices are correct

First, double ***check that you are following the band plan*** and will be transmitting within your privileges. Then, before placing a call on a frequency, listen for about one minute to make sure that specific frequency is open. Finally, ask if the frequency is in use and give your call sign. Repeat the question and your call sign about 3 times and listen between the calls. Now you can be relatively sure that the frequency is open for you to call CQ. **ANSWER C.**

G2B01 Which of the following is true concerning access to frequencies?

A. Nets have priority
B. QSOs in progress have priority
C. Except during emergencies, no amateur station has priority access to any frequency
D. Contest operations should yield to non-contest use of frequencies

High frequency nets most always take place at a scheduled time on a published frequency. But what happens if that frequency is already in use by hams who don't realize that the net takes place on that frequency every day? The courteous net controller would politely interrupt and encourage the two operators to join in on the net that "is soon to begin on this frequency." If the other two stations are unable to hear the request or don't wish to move, considering that ***no one has priority access to frequencies,*** the only option is to conduct the net on a nearby clear frequency. As a new General Class operator, be a courteous ham and always relinquish your frequency for a published and popular net. [97.101(b), (c)] **ANSWER C.**

G2A08 What is the recommended way to break into a phone contact?

A. Say "QRZ" several times, followed by your call sign
B. Say your call sign once
C. Say "Breaker Breaker"
D. Say "CQ" followed by the call sign of either station

When you hear a conversation between two hams, a polite way to join this QSO (communication) is to simply ***say your call sign in between transmissions as one station turns it over to the other station***. Say your call sign in a cheerful manner, making it sound like you wish to enter the conversation in a friendly way. **ANSWER B.**

G2D11 Why are signal reports typically exchanged at the beginning of an HF contact?

A. To allow each station to operate according to conditions
B. To be sure the contact will count for award programs
C. To follow standard radiogram structure
D. To allow each station to calibrate their frequency display

The signal report (RST) has always been one of the most important "ingredients" of any ham radio QSO. An HONEST signal report is extremely important for the other station, especially if it is a DX station, which relies on this information to ***optimize equipment and operating procedure according to conditions***. Giving the signal report at the very beginning of the QSO will help the station to optimally aim his antenna, adjust power level, and even determine CW transmitting speed. **ANSWER A.**

G2D05 Which of the following indicates that you are looking for an HF contact with any station?

A. Sign your call sign once, followed by the words "listening for a call"—if no answer, change frequency and repeat
B. Say "QTC" followed by "this is" and your call sign—if no answer, change frequency and repeat
C. Repeat "CQ" a few times, followed by "this is," then your call sign a few times, then pause to listen, repeat as necessary
D. Transmit an unmodulated carried for approximately 10 seconds, followed by "this is" and your call sign, and pause to listen—repeat as necessary

---

When it comes to maintaining good relations with your fellow radio amateurs the "prime directive" is "always listen before transmitting." Once you determine that the frequency is clear, the best way to establish a contact is to ***repeat "CQ" a few times, followed by "this is," then your call sign a few times, then pause to listen, repeat as necessary***. Many hams rely on the time-honored 3x3x3 pattern: CQ three times, your call sign three times, and the whole thing three times. When conditions are good, you might not need as many calls; when they are bad, you might need a lot more. Patience is always a virtue in amateur radio! **ANSWER C.**

G2A11 Generally, who should respond to a station in the contiguous 48 states calling "CQ DX"?

A. Any caller is welcome to respond
B. Only stations in Germany
C. Any stations outside the lower 48 states
D. Only contest stations

The term "CQ" is used by hams to "fish" for a new station to answer their call. Say your "CQ" with a smile and sound excited about making the call to anyone hearing you. A drab, lifeless "CQ" is like fishing with old bait. If you hear someone calling ***"CQ DX,"*** this means they are not looking for just any stateside contact; but rather, they are ***seeking calls only from very distant or foreign stations.*** These usually are very experienced operators, so stay tuned and learn from the "pros" how to call out and get rare "DX" responses. **ANSWER C.**

G2B08 What is the voluntary band plan restriction for US stations transmitting within the 48 contiguous states in the 50.1 MHz to 50.125 MHz band segment?

A. Only contacts with stations not within the 48 contiguous states
B. Only contacts with other stations within the 48 contiguous states
C. Only digital contacts
D. Only SSTV contacts

It is important to begin your General Class worldwide band operations in accordance with both the FCC rules and voluntary band plans. Most high frequency bands have a spot where stateside hams will ***call and listen only for foreign country DX stations***. For example, 1830 to 1850 kHz in the 160 meter band has long been recognized as the DX window for that band – same for 6 meters, 50.1 to 50.125 MHz – no idle chit-chatting here! Use the DX window as a great spot to listen for worldwide DX. **ANSWER A.**

G2D09 Which of the following is required when participating in a contest on HF frequencies?

A. Submit a log to the contest sponsor
B. Send a QSL card to the stations worked, or QSL via Logbook of The World
C. Identify your station according to normal FCC regulations
D. All these choices are correct

Contesting is a major amateur radio activity for a great number of hams. It is a good way to improve your communications skills while having a great deal of fun in the process. You must always obey all FCC rules and ***identify your station according to normal FCC regulations***. Also, you should check with the specific requirements of any contest before the contest starts! Nearly every contest requires that you submit a log to the contest sponsor, and QSL the stations worked (either electronically, or by old fashioned paper). **ANSWER C.**

G4A12 Which of the following is a common use of the dual-VFO feature on a transceiver?

A. To allow transmitting on two frequencies at once
B. To permit full duplex operation—that is, transmitting and receiving at the same time
C. To transmit on one frequency and listen on another
D. To improve frequency accuracy by allowing variable frequency output (VFO) operation

The dual VFO feature on the modern transceiver with same-band receive allows you to ***transmit on one frequency, and listen on another*** when working "split." With the right radio, you can even add a professional headset from Heil Sound that will put one frequency in your left ear and another in your right ear. That's how the pro DXers work split! **ANSWER C.**

Most modern HF rigs have two VFOs to make it easy to work SPLIT mode.

G2B03 What is good amateur practice if propagation changes during a contact creating interference from other stations using the frequency?

A. Advise the interfering stations that you are on the frequency and that you have priority
B. Decrease power and continue to transmit
C. Attempt to resolve the interference problem with the other stations in a mutually acceptable manner
D. Switch to the opposite sideband

On the worldwide General Class ham bands, propagation will sometimes cause stations that you did not hear moments ago on the same frequency to all of a sudden come in right on top of your ongoing contact. Be a good ham and ***attempt to resolve the interference in a friendly manner.*** **ANSWER C.**

G2B05 When selecting an SSB transmitting frequency, what minimum separation should be used to minimize interference to stations on adjacent frequencies?

A. 5 Hz to 50 Hz
B. 150 Hz to 500 Hz
C. 2 kHz to 3 kHz
D. Approximately 6 kHz

When operating single sideband, your emission will take up approximately 3 kHz of bandwidth. Always ***stay at least 2 kHz to 3 kHz away from any other station*** that is using an adjacent frequency. **ANSWER C.**

G4D10 How close to the lower edge of a band's phone segment should your displayed carrier frequency be when using 3 kHz wide LSB?

A. At least 3 kHz above the edge of the segment
B. At least 3 kHz below the edge of the segment
C. At least 1 kHz below the edge of the segment
D. At least 1 kHz above the edge of the segment

On the 40 meter band, we would want to operate ***lower sideband*** and transmit at least ***3 kHz above our band edge*** of 7.175 MHz. This keeps all of the signal within the frequency range for General Class privileges. **ANSWER A.**

G4D08 What frequency range is occupied by a 3 kHz LSB signal when the displayed carrier frequency is set to 7.178 MHz?

A. 7.178 MHz to 7.181 MHz
B. 7.178 MHz to 7.184 MHz
C. 7.175 MHz to 7.178 MHz
D. 7.1765 MHz to 7.1795 MHz

7.178 MHz is in the 40 meter band where we usually operate lower sideband, which means our signal will extend DOWN 3 kHz from 7.178 MHz. We would then occupy ***7.175 to 7.178 MHz***. **ANSWER C.**

G4D11 How close to the upper edge of a band's phone segment should your displayed carrier frequency be when using 3 kHz wide USB?

A. At least 3 kHz above the edge of the band
B. At least 3 kHz below the edge of the band
C. At least 1 kHz above the edge of the segment
D. At least 1 kHz below the edge of the segment

When operating voice SSB on upper sideband, ***stay at least 3 kHz down*** from the top edge frequency of the band. **ANSWER B.**

G4D09 What frequency range is occupied by a 3 kHz USB signal with the displayed carrier frequency set to 14.347 MHz?

A. 14.347 MHz to 14.647 MHz
B. 14.347 MHz to 14.350 MHz
C. 14.344 MHz to 14.347 MHz
D. 14.3455 MHz to 14.3485 MHz

On the 20 meter band (14.347 MHz) a USB (upper sideband) signal will extend UP 3 kHz. It will occupy ***14.347 up to 14.350 MHz***. **ANSWER B.**

G2D10 What is QRP operation?

A. Remote piloted model control
B. Low-power transmit operation
C. Transmission using Quick Response Protocol
D. Traffic relay procedure net operation

Many ham operators on worldwide frequencies enjoy operating ***QRP*** – the Q code for ***low power operation***. Hams get a big kick out of working all the way around the world with less power than that used by a tiny night-light 4 watt bulb. You can look for QRP operations at specific spots on the band plan. **ANSWER B.**

G2A10 Which of the following statements is true of VOX operation versus PTT operation?

A. The received signal is more natural sounding
B. It allows "hands free" operation
C. It occupies less bandwidth
D. It provides more power output

Most worldwide radios have a voice-operated relay circuit, abbreviated ***"VOX."*** If you have a big base station microphone, this is a neat ***"hands-free"*** circuit to minimize you having to reach over to depress the push-to-talk switch. Just be sure you never leave the VOX circuit on when you are not right at your turned-on equipment! **ANSWER B.**

Using a headset with an attached mike on VOX will keep both hands free when you're taking on the worldwide bands.

G1E04 Which of the following conditions require a licensed amateur radio operator to take specific steps to avoid harmful interference to other users or facilities?

A. When operating within one mile of an FCC Monitoring Station
B. When using a band where the Amateur Service is secondary
C. When a station is transmitting spread spectrum emissions
D. All these choices are correct

It is always the amateur radio operator's responsibility to prevent harmful interference to others. So, if you are within a mile of an FCC monitoring station, or operating on a band where the amateur service is secondary, or experimenting with spread spectrum emissions, you want to be sure that you are not causing harmful interference. You do not want the FCC knocking on your door. ***All of these choices are correct***. [97.13(b), 97.303, 97.311(b)] **ANSWER D.**

G2A05 Which mode of voice communication is most commonly used on the HF amateur bands?

A. Frequency modulation
B. Double sideband
C. Single sideband
D. Single phase modulation

When you gain your new privileges on High Frequency, the majority of voice communications are done as ***single sideband, SSB***. **ANSWER C.**

G2A06 Which of the following is an advantage of using single sideband, as compared to other analog voice modes on the HF amateur bands?

A. Very high-fidelity voice modulation
B. Less subject to interference from atmospheric static crashes
C. Ease of tuning on receive and immunity to impulse noise
D. Less bandwidth used and greater power efficiency

The advantages of ***single sideband*** are that it ***occupies less spectrum*** than other transmission modes making it possible for more people to operate on frequencies that are closer together and ***is power efficient, which can make your signal travel a long way on skywaves.*** **ANSWER D.**

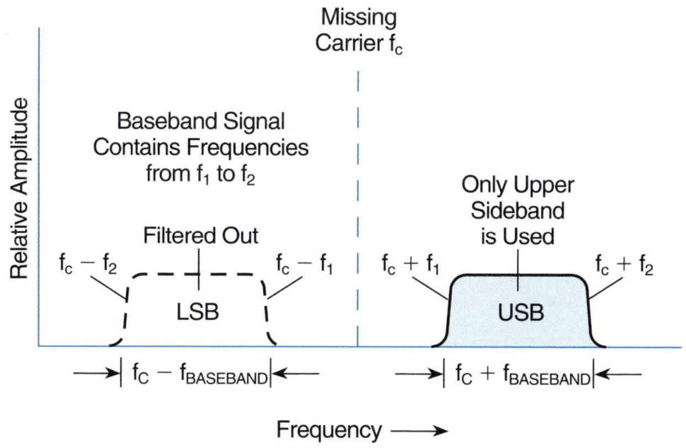

SSB signals are Amplitude Modulated (AM) with the carrier and one sideband suppressed.

G2A07 Which of the following statements is true of single sideband (SSB)?

A. Only one sideband and the carrier are transmitted; the other sideband is suppressed
B. Only one sideband is transmitted; the other sideband and carrier are suppressed
C. SSB is the only voice mode authorized on the 20-, 15-, and 10-meter amateur bands
D. SSB is the only voice mode authorized on the 160-, 75-, and 40-meter amateur bands

When we transmit using ***SSB***, only one sideband signal, approximately 2.8 kHz wide, is sent out over the air. The ***opposite sideband is suppressed***. There is ***no carrier*** in a properly-adjusted SSB signal. This means your radio gets a complete rest during each break in your syllables, which saves power and is great for battery operation in the field. **ANSWER B.**

G2A04 Which mode is most commonly used for voice communications on the 17- and 12-meter bands?

A. Upper sideband
B. Lower sideband
C. Suppressed sideband
D. Double sideband

Since ***17 and 12 meters*** are higher in frequency than 20 meters, we always use ***upper sideband***. Equipment limitations from long ago established the tradition of using USB for frequencies above 20 meters and LSB for frequencies below the 20 meter band. Although equipment today has changed, the tradition remains. **ANSWER A.**

G2A01 Which mode is most commonly used for voice communications on frequencies of 14 MHz or higher?

A. Upper sideband
B. Lower sideband
C. Suppressed sideband
D. Double sideband

14 MHz is in the 20 meter band. On 20, 17, 15, 12, and 10 meters, plus the 5 channels on the 60 meter band, plus VHF and UHF weak signal operations, we use ***upper sideband***. By tradition, and to easily make contacts, use upper sideband on frequencies from 14 MHz and higher, including 60 meters. **ANSWER A.**

ham apps

Slow Scan TV is capable of delivering surprisingly high resolution images over HF, if you have lots of time! If you haven't played with amateur SSTV, you've missed out on a lot of unusual fun. SSTV is quirky with a relatively small but dedicated "club" within ham radio. Some of amateur radio's greatest ingenuity was dedicated to the challenge of sending images over very limited bandwidth. Fortunately, unlike half a century ago, you don't need a shack full of bulky, temperamental hardware! SSTV Pad makes experimenting with this unique mode a snap. SSTV is allowed anywhere HF phone is allowed, but should be restricted to the suggested band plan frequencies. 14.230 kHz is one common SSTV "watering hole." **http://www.blackcatsystems.com/software/sstv.html**

G2A03 Which mode is most commonly used for SSB voice communications in the VHF and UHF bands?

A. Upper sideband
B. Lower sideband
C. Suppressed sideband
D. Double sideband

When you upgrade to General Class, we hope you will continue to stay active on the VHF and UHF bands, too. If you operate weak signal on ***VHF and UHF, use upper sideband for voice***. Traditionally, on any frequency above 20 meters (14 MHz) voice operations are on upper sideband while on any frequency below 20 meters voice operations are on lower sideband. **ANSWER A.**

Modern HF transceivers automatically select the correct sideband, a feature that lets new General Class operators really enjoy field day!

G2A02 Which mode is most commonly used for voice communications on the 160-, 75-, and 40-meter bands?

A. Upper sideband
B. Lower sideband
C. Suppressed sideband
D. Double sideband

We use ***lower sideband (LSB) on 160, 75, and 40 meters***. While it is not illegal to use lower sideband on 20 meters and above, good operating procedure always indicates that you should "go with the flow" and use the proper sideband. When operating LOWER sideband be sure to remain safely ABOVE the lower phone band edge. **ANSWER B.**

G2A09 Why do most amateur stations use lower sideband on the 160-, 75-, and 40-meter bands?

A. Lower sideband is more efficient than upper sideband at these frequencies
B. Lower sideband is the only sideband legal on these frequency bands
C. Because it is fully compatible with an AM detector
D. It is commonly accepted amateur practice

Remember that the choice of upper and lower sideband is by gentleman's agreement. On the ***160, 75, and 40 meter bands, commonly accepted amateur practice is to use lower sideband***. Most modern amateur worldwide high-frequency equipment automatically selects upper sideband for the bands 20 meters and up, and lower sideband for the bands 40 meters and down. **ANSWER D.**

SIDEBAND	FREQUENCY BAND IN METERS								
USB			60		20	17	15	12	10
LSB	160	75/80		40					

Sideband Usage on Amateur Radio Bands

G2D07 Which of the following are examples of the NATO Phonetic Alphabet?

A. Able, Baker, Charlie, Dog
B. Adam, Boy, Charles, David
C. America, Boston, Canada, Denmark
D. Alfa, Bravo, Charlie, Delta

Some hams like to get "creative" or "cute" with their phonetics. While there's no law that requires the use of standard phonetics, there's no valid reason not to. The use of random phonetics is one sign of "liddy" behavior, which we trust you would want to avoid. The purpose of universally agreed upon and standardized phonetics is to make communications clear to all involved, especially when band conditions are poor. The NATO Phonetic Alphabet is the standard you should use, and it begins with ***Alfa, Bravo, Charlie, Delta***. **ANSWER D.**

NATO International Phonetic Alphabet

A – Alfa – AL fah
B – Bravo – BRAH voh
C – Charlie – CHAR lee
D – Delta – DELL tah
E – Echo – ECK ohh
F – Foxtrot – FOKS trot
G – Golf – GOLF
H – Hotel – HOH tel
I – India – IN dee ah
J – Juliet – JEW lee ett
K – Kilo – KEY loh
L – Lima – LEE mah
M – Mike – MIKE
N – November – NO vem ber
O – Oscar – OSS car
P – Papa – PAH pah
Q – Quebec – KEH beck
R – Romeo – ROW me o
S – Sierra – SEE air rah
T – Tango – TANG go
U – Uniform – YOU nee form
V – Victor – VICK tah
W – Whiskey – WISS key
X – X-ray – ECKS ray
Y – Yankee – YANG kee
Z – Zulu – ZOO loo

Elmer Point: As a brand new General, spend a few days on the air LISTENING before you go on the air. Look at this band plan, and then tune in to hear how everything has its place on the radio dial. One of the best ways to complete your first transmission using your new General Class privileges is to answer an upbeat CQ call. Double-check to make sure you are within your General Class privileges, and check the band plan to make sure you are not answering a station looking only for foreign DX.

160 Meters (1.8 – 2.0 MHz)

1.800-2.000	CW
1.800-1.810	Digital Modes
1.810	CW QRP calling frequency
1.843-2.000	SSB, SSTV and other wideband modes
1.910	SSB QRP
1.995-2.000	Experimental
1.999-2.000	Beacons

80 Meters (3.5 – 4.0 MHz)

3.500-3.510	CW DX window
3.560	QRP CW calling frequency
3.570-3.600	RTTY/Data
3.585-3.600	Automatically controlled data stations
3.590	RTTY/Data DX
3.790-3.800	DX window
3.845	SSTV
3.885	AM calling frequency
3.985	QRP SSB calling frequency

40 Meters (7.0 – 7.3 MHz)

7.030	QRP CW calling frequency
7.040	RTTY/Data DX
7.070-7.125	RTTY/Data
7.100-7.105	Automatically controlled data stations
7.171	SSTV
7.173	D-SSTV
7.285	QRP SSB calling frequency
7.290	AM calling frequency

30 Meters (10.1 – 10.15 MHz)

10.130-10.140	RTTY/Data
10.140-10.150	Automatically controlled data stations

20 Meters (14.0 – 14.35 MHz)

14.060	QRP CW calling frequency
14.070-14.095	RTTY/Data/FT8
14.095-14.099	Automatically controlled data stations
14.100	IBP/NCDXF beacons
14.1005-14.112	Automatically controlled data stations
14.230	SSTV
14.233	D-SSTV
14.236	Digital Voice
14.285	QRP SSB calling frequency
14.286	AM calling frequency

17 Meters (18.068 – 18.168 MHz)

18.100-18.105	RTTY/Data
18.105-18.110	Automatically controlled data stations
18.110	IBP/NCDXF beacons
18.162.5	Digital Voice

15 Meters (21.0 – 21.45 MHz)

21.060	QRP CW calling frequency
21.070-21.110	RTTY/Data
21.090-21.100	Automatically controlled data stations
21.150	IBP/NCDXF beacons
21.340	SSTV
21.385	QRP SSB calling frequency

12 Meters (24.89 – 24.99 MHz)

24.920-24.925	RTTY/Data
24.925-24.930	Automatically controlled data stations
24.930	IBP/NCDXF beacons

10 Meters (28.0 – 29.7 MHz)

28.060	QRP CW calling frequency
28.070-28.120	RTTY/Data
28.120-28.189	Automatically controlled data stations
28.190-28.225	Beacons
28.200-28.300	Beacons
28.385	QRP SSB calling frequency
28.680	SSTV
29.000-29.200	AM
29.300-29.510	Satellite downlinks
29.520-29.580	Repeater inputs
29.600	FM simplex
29.620-29.680	FM repeater outputs

Wider digital bandwidths may be found above parts of the RTTY / data sub-bands.

CW Lives

G2B04 When selecting a CW transmitting frequency, what minimum separation from other stations should be used to minimize interference to stations on adjacent frequencies?

A. 5 Hz to 50 Hz
B. 150 Hz to 500 Hz
C. 1 kHz to 3 kHz
D. 3 kHz to 6 kHz

When ***operating CW***, try to separate yourself from other CW transmissions by at least ***150 to 500 Hz***. This will give your CW signal a distinct tonal difference from the other station and hopefully not cause interference. **ANSWER B.**

G2C06 What does the term "zero beat" mean in CW operation?

A. Matching the speed of the transmitting station
B. Operating split to avoid interference on frequency
C. Sending without error
D. Matching the transmit frequency to the frequency of a received signal

When a net control station asks everyone to ***"zero beat"*** their CW operation, it is asking you to ***match their frequency*** so that everyone's CW tone will sound about the same. **ANSWER D.**

G2C05 What is the best speed to use when answering a CQ in Morse code?

A. The fastest speed at which you are comfortable copying, but no slower than the CQ
B. The fastest speed at which you are comfortable copying, but no faster than the CQ
C. At the standard calling speed of 10 wpm
D. At the standard calling speed of 5 wpm

Ready to try your first CW CQ? Send at a relatively slow rate, and expect that any other station will send at this slow rate in their response to your CQ. Same thing applies in reverse. If you hear a station sending CQ at a very slow speed, chances are they are brand new on Morse code, so ***send back*** to them ***at the same speed***. **ANSWER B.**

G2C07 When sending CW, what does a "C" mean when added to the RST report?

A. Chirpy or unstable signal
B. Report was read from an S meter rather than estimated
C. 100 percent copy
D. Key clicks

If someone sends you an RST report of 5-9-9 ***C, it means your signal is unstable or chirping***, probably due to an inadequate power supply or operating from a low battery. **ANSWER A.**

Elmer Point: The S meter on the front of your radio indicates signal strength. S-9 is much stronger than S-5, and S-1 is relatively weak, but it will be up to your own ears and brain to judge readability. R-2 means you can make out the signal with difficulty. R-5 is a loud and clear signal report. A great report would be 5 by 9. A bad one might be 3 by 3. Sometimes hams will generalize for strength, readability and CW tone as Q-5. Let's hope you always get a 5 by 9! Here's the how the RST Signal Reporting System works:

The RST system is a way of reporting on the quality of a received signal by using a three digit number. The first digit indicates Readability (R), the second digit indicates received Signal Strength (S), and the third digit indicates Tone (T).

READABILITY (R) for Voice + CW
1 – Unreadable
2 – Barely readable, occasional words distinguishable
3 – Readable with considerable difficulty
4 – Readable with practically no difficulty
5 – Perfectly readable

SIGNAL STRENGTH (S) for Voice + CW
1 – Faint, barely perceptible signals
2 – Very weak signals
3 – Weak signals
4 – Fair signals
5 – Fairly good signals
6 – Good signals
7 – Moderately strong signals
8 – Strong signals
9 – Extremely strong signals

TONE* (T) Use on CW only
1 – Very rough, broad signals, 60 cycle AC may be present
2 – Very rough AC tone, harsh, broad
3 – Rough, low-pitched AC tone, some trace of filtering
5 – Filtered, rectified AC note, musical, ripple modulated
6 – Slight trace of filtered tone but with ripple modulation
7 – Near DC tone but trace of ripple modulation
8 – Good DC tone, may have slight trace of modulation
9 – Purest, perfect DC tone with no trace of ripple or modulation

*The TONE report refers only to the purity of the signal, and has no connection with its stability or freedom from clicks or chirps. If the signal has the characteristic steadiness of crystal control, add X to the report (e.g., RST 469X). If it has a chirp or "tail" (either on "make" or "break") add C (e.g., RST 469C). If it has clicks or other noticeable keying transients, add K (e.g., 469K). If a signal has both chirps and clicks, add both C and K (e.g., 469CK).

G2C02 What should you do if a CW station sends "QRS?"

A. Send slower
B. Change frequency
C. Increase your power
D. Repeat everything twice

If you are sending code to another station and they respond ***"QRS,"*** this means for you to please ***send*** at a ***slower*** rate. **ANSWER A.**

G2C04 What does the Q signal "QRL?" mean?

A. "Will you keep the frequency clear?"
B. "Are you operating full break-in?" or "Can you operate full break-in?"
C. "Are you listening only for a specific station?"
D. "Are you busy?" or "Is this frequency in use?"

Q signals are radio "shorthand" for common requests and questions encountered in radio communications. They were developed when CW was the most common mode of amateur radio communication and are still standard practice for CW operation. QRL is among the most common Q signals. Without a question mark it means, "This frequency is in use." With a question mark, it asks, ***"Is this frequency in use?"*** **ANSWER D.**

G2C10 What does the Q signal "QRN" mean?

A. Send more slowly
B. Stop sending
C. Zero beat my signal
D. I am troubled by static

QRN is another very common Q signal and it means, ***"I am troubled by static."*** With a question mark it asks, "Are you troubled by static?" A complete list of Q Signals is on page 58. Some of these are used quite often and will become very familiar to you when you work CW. Others are used very little. **ANSWER D.**

G2C11 What does the Q signal "QRV" mean?

A. You are sending too fast
B. There is interference on the frequency
C. I am quitting for the day
D. I am ready to receive

The Q code ***"QRV" means*** that you are ***ready***, with pen or computer at hand, ***to receive*** the incoming message. If you send "QRV?" you are asking "are there any messages holding for my station?" **ANSWER D.**

G2C09 What does the Q signal "QSL" mean?

A. Send slower
B. We have already confirmed the contact
C. I have received and understood
D. We have worked before

The term ***"QSL"*** has several meanings in ham radio. On CW and sometimes voice it means that I have received and understood your message. And if the other station asks for a QSL, they are asking you to send a QSL card with your call sign on the front and QSO details on the back. QSL cards are fun to collect. All General Class hams should have their own QSL card. If you ever receive a QSL card, you should always send one back! **ANSWER C.**

POPULAR Q SIGNALS

Given below are a number of Q signals whose meanings most often need to be expressed with brevity and clarity in amateur work. (Q abbreviations take the form of questions only when each is sent followed by a question mark.)

QRG Will you tell me my exact frequency (or that of ____)? Your exact frequency (or that of ____) is ____ kHz.
QRH Does my frequency vary? Your frequency varies.
QRI How is the tone of my transmission? The tone of your transmission is _____ (1. Good; 2. Variable; 3. Bad).
QRJ Are you receiving me badly? I cannot receive you. Your signals are too weak.
QRK What is the intelligibility of my signals (or those of _____)? The intelligibility of your signals (or those of _____) is _____ (1. Bad; 2. Poor; 3. Fair; 4. Good; 5. Excellent).
QRL Are you busy? I am busy (or I am busy with _____). Please do not interfere.
QRM Is my transmission being interfered with? Your transmission is being interfered with _____ (1. Nil; 2. Slightly; 3. Moderately; 4. Severely; 5. Extremely).
QRN Are you troubled by static? I am troubled by static _____ (1-5 as under QRM).
QRO Shall I increase power? Increase power.
QRP Shall I decrease power? Decrease power.
QRQ Shall I send faster? Send faster (_____ WPM).
QRS Shall I send more slowly? Send more slowly (_____WPM).
QRT Shall I stop sending? Stop sending.
QRU Have you anything for me? I have nothing for you.
QRV Are you ready? I am ready.
QRW Shall I inform ____ that you are calling on ____ kHz? Please inform ____ that I am calling on ____ kHz.
QRX When will you call me again? I will call you again at _____ hours (on _____ kHz).
QRY What is my turn? Your turn is numbered _____.
QRZ Who is calling me? You are being called by _____ (on _____ kHz).
QSA What is the strength of my signals (or those of _____)? The strength of your signals (or those of _____) is _____ (1. Scarcely perceptible; 2. Weak; 3. Fairly good; 4. Good; 5. Very good).
QSB Are my signals fading? Your signals are fading.
QSD Is my keying defective? Your keying is defective.
QSG Shall I send _____ messages at a time? Send _____ messages at a time.
QSK Can you hear me between your signals and if so can I break in on your transmission? I can hear you between my signals; break in on my transmission.
QSL Can you acknowledge receipt? I am acknowledging receipt.
QSM Shall I repeat the last message which I sent you, or some previous message? Repeat the last message which you sent me [or message(s) number(s) _____].
QSN Did you hear me (or _____) on _____ kHz? I heard you (or _____) on _____ kHz.
QSO Can you communicate with _____ direct or by relay? I can communicate with _____ direct (or by relay through _____).
QSP Will you relay to _____? I will relay to _____.
QST General call preceding a message addressed to all amateurs and ARRL members. This is in effect "CQ ARRL."
QSU Shall I send or reply on this frequency (or on _____ kHz)?
QSW Will you send on this frequency (or on _____ kHz)? I am going to send on this frequency (or on _____ kHz).
QSX Will you listen to _____ on _____ kHz? I am listening to _____ on _____ kHz.
QSY Shall I change to transmission on another frequency? Change to transmission on another frequency (or on _____ kHz).
QSZ Shall I send each word or group more than once? Send each word or group twice (or _____ times).
QTA Shall I cancel message number _____? Cancel message number _____.
QTB Do you agree with my counting of words? I do not agree with your counting of words. I will repeat the first letter or digit of each word or group.
QTC How many messages have you to send? I have messages for you (or for _____).
QTH What is your location? My location is _____.
QTR What is the correct time? The time is _____.

Source: ARRL

G2C03 What does it mean when a CW operator sends "KN" at the end of a transmission?

A. No US stations should call
B. Operating full break-in
C. Listening only for a specific station or stations
D. Closing station now

When a station turns the communication back to you and sends ***"KN"*** at the end of their transmission, it ***means that they want only you to respond*** and all other stations to stand by. **ANSWER C.**

G2C08 What prosign is sent to indicate the end of a formal message when using CW?

A. SK
B. BK
C. AR
D. KN

The ***end of a CW formal message*** usually includes ***"AR."*** This lets all operators know that the formal message has been sent completely. See the list of common CW abbreviations on page 233 of the Appendix. **ANSWER C.**

G4A10 What is the function of an electronic keyer?

A. Automatic transmit/receive switching
B. Automatic generation of dots and dashes for CW operation
C. To allow time for switching the antenna from the receiver to the transmitter
D. Computer interface for PSK and RTTY operation

That brand new radio you rewarded yourself with in preparation for successfully passing your General exam will likely have a built-in ***electronic keyer***. Sure, you could set the keyer to accept your granddad's old J-38 straight key, but why not try your CW skills with paddles, where your thumb and finger create ***dots and dashes*** with a single touch? **ANSWER B.**

Newer HF rigs have the electronic keyer built in. Older radios can take an external CW keyer box.

G2C01 Which of the following describes full break-in CW operation (QSK)?

A. Breaking stations send the Morse code prosign "BK"
B. Automatic keyers, instead of hand keys, are used to send Morse code
C. An operator must activate a manual send/receive switch before and after every transmission
D. Transmitting stations can receive between code characters and elements

You will begin your adventures with CW transmissions using VOX mode to turn on the transmitter when you start keying and turn it off a few seconds after you stop keying. This is called semi-break-in. When you really get good at CW, you can set your transceiver to operate CW in the ***QSK full break-in mode***. In this mode, the transmitting station can hear interruptions during code characters being sent. **ANSWER D.**

G1B03 Which of the following is a purpose of a beacon station as identified in the FCC rules?

A. Observation of propagation and reception
B. Automatic identification of repeaters
C. Transmission of bulletins of general interest to amateur radio licensees
D. All these choices are correct

Beacon stations are important for the study of ***propagation and reception*** from the ionosphere. Always try to stay clear of beacon stations when selecting a frequency on which to transmit. Beacon stations are found at 14.100 MHz, 28.200 - 28.300 MHz, and on the 2 meter band below 144.300 MHz. These are one- way transmissions. Six meter beacons are great for determining a band opening! [97.3(a)(9)] **ANSWER A.**

G1E10 Why should an amateur operator normally avoid transmitting on 14.100, 18.110, 21.150, 24. 930 and 28.200 MHz?

A. A system of propagation beacon stations operates on those frequencies
B. A system of automatic digital stations operates on those frequencies
C. These frequencies are set aside for emergency operations
D. These frequencies are set aside for bulletins from the FCC

Beacon stations are indispensable for determining HF band openings, especially during years of low or non-existent sunspots. HF propagation can be sporadic during these times, and hams can use all the help they can get to "catch" these rare openings. In addition, radio beacons are useful for many types of radio science and research. The "high band" HF bands, (20, 17, 15, 12, and 10 meters) include 14.100, 18.110, 21.150, 24.930 and 28.200 MHz. ***A system of propagation beacon stations operates on these frequencies***. Courteous amateur radio operation calls for leaving those frequencies clear for beacon operation. [97.101] **ANSWER A.**

G1B10 What is the power limit for beacon stations?

A. 10 watts PEP output
B. 20 watts PEP output
C. 100 watts PEP output
D. 200 watts PEP output

Beacon stations used for propagation surveys must never transmit more than ***100 watts*** peak envelope power ***(PEP) output***. [97.203(c)] **ANSWER C.**

G1B02 With which of the following conditions must beacon stations comply?

A. No more than one beacon station may transmit in the same band from the same station location
B. The frequency must be coordinated with the National Beacon Organization
C. The frequency must be posted on the internet or published in a national periodical
D. All these choices are correct

Beacon stations are important for the study of propagation. Do not transmit on beacon band plan frequencies. Ham operators are permitted to put up only a ***single beacon signal in the same band from a single location.*** [97.203(b)] **ANSWER A.**

Radio Beacon Stations

Slot	Country	Call	14.100	18.110	21.150	24.930	28.200	Operator
1	United Nations	4U1UN	00:00	00:10	00:20	00:30	00:40	UNRC
2	Canada	VE8AT	00:10	00:20	00:30	00:40	00:50	RAC
3	USA	W6WX	00:20	00:30	00:40	00:50	01:00	NCDXF
4	Hawaii	KH6WO	00:30	00:40	00:50	01:00	01:10	UHRO
5	New Zealand	ZL	00:40	00:50	01:00	01:10	01:20	NZART
6	Australia	VK8	00:50	01:00	01:10	01:20	01:30	W1A
7	Japan	JA21CY	01:00	01:10	01:20	01:30	01:40	JARL
8	China	BY	01:10	01:20	01:30	01:40	01:50	CRSA
9	Russia	UA	01:20	01:30	01:40	01:50	02:00	TBO
10	Sri Lanka	4S7B	01:30	01:40	01:50	02:00	02:10	RSSL
11	South Africa	ZS6DN	01:40	01:50	02:00	02:10	02:20	ZS6DN
12	Kenya	5Z4B	01:50	02:00	02:10	02:20	02:30	RSK
13	Israel	4X6TU	02:00	02:10	02:20	02:30	02:40	U of Tel Aviv
14	Finland	OH2B	02:10	02:20	02:30	02:40	02:50	U oh Helsinki
15	Madeira	CS3B	02:20	02:30	02:40	02:50	00:00	ARRM
16	Argentina	LU4AA	02:30	02:40	02:50	00:00	00:10	RCA
17	Peru	OA4B	02:40	02:50	00:00	00:10	00:20	RCP
18	Venezuela	YV5B	02:50	00:00	00:10	00:20	00:30	RCV

The 10-second, phase-3, message format is: “W6WX dah-dah-dah-dah” — each “dah” lasts a little more than one second. W6WX is transmitted at 100 watts, then each “dah” is attenuated in order, beginning at 100 watts, then 10 watts, then 1 watt, and finally 0.1 watt. *Courtesy CQ Magazine*

G1B09 On what HF frequencies are automatically controlled beacons permitted?

A. On any frequency if power is less than 1 watt
B. On any frequency if transmissions are in Morse code
C. 21.08 MHz to 21.09 MHz
D. 28.20 MHz to 28.30 MHz

The 10-meter band is a very large HF band with plenty of room for activities not available on the other HF bands. Operating a beacon is one of these, and unattended (automatically controlled) beacons are permitted between ***28.20 to 28.30 MHz.*** These beacons can be heard in many parts of the country, and are very useful for determining if HF propagation paths exist. [97.203(d)] **ANSWER D.**

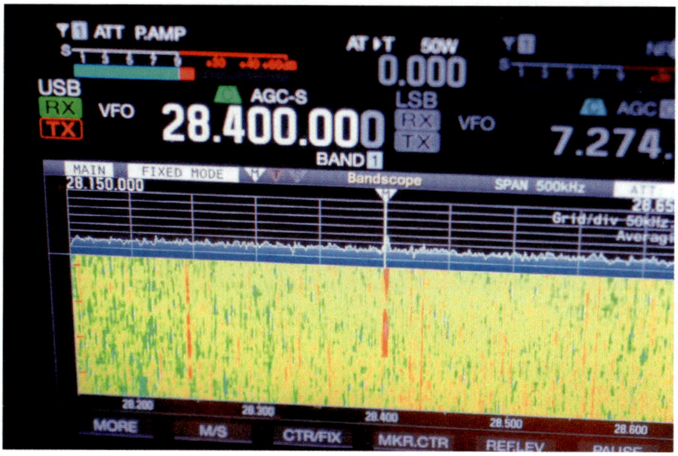

G4A02 What is the benefit of using the opposite or "reverse" sideband when receiving CW?

A. Interference from impulse noise will be eliminated
B. More stations can be accommodated within a given signal passband
C. It may be possible to reduce or eliminate interference from other signals
D. Accidental out-of-band operation can be prevented

We encourage you to learn Morse code. In the back of this book is a complete chapter on learning the code. On-air code practice is a great way to boost your copying speed. Sometimes when receiving a weak CW signal you hear interference, too. Try this trick. ***Switch*** between upper and lower ***sideband*** to see if one of the sideband filters pulls in the CW signal better and ***reduces the interference*** from other signals. That's right – you can still hear CW in the SSB mode. Just be sure to go back to CW mode when you are ready to transmit. Many if not most modern SSB transceivers have a "reverse CW" function to allow one to transmit on the opposite sideband as well, in the CW mode. **ANSWER C.**

G8B09 Why is it good to match receiver bandwidth to the bandwidth of the operating mode?

A. It is required by FCC rules
B. It minimizes power consumption in the receiver
C. It improves impedance matching of the antenna
D. It results in the best signal-to-noise ratio

When you switch modes on your new radio, appropriate filters fall into place giving you the ***best signal-to-noise ratio***. You might be able to select tighter CW bandwidths to further improve signal-to-noise ratios. **ANSWER D.**

ham apps

Morse Decoder

While no Morse code decoder is as good as a well-trained ear, under good conditions with "machine sent" code, such as code practice sessions from W1AW, some of these decoders work pretty well.

https://itunes.apple.com/us/app/morsedecoder/id313071325?mt=8

Increasing your CW Proficiency

Many new radio amateurs are surprised when they hear so much CW activity on the amateur bands. It's almost as if a lot of hams actually *like* to use CW, even though they don't have to know CW anymore! Can this possibly be true?

Absolutely! CW is a lot of fun and shows no signs of going away any time soon. It's a lot *more* fun, however, when you're good at it! How do you get good at it? Practice, and lots of it. But it helps to have a good start. Get some good CW practice CDs with *random groups*. The advantage of random groups is that it forces you to copy code *perfectly*, not just "sort of." It's also helpful to use the Farnsworth method in which individual characters are sent at a very high speed, while words are sent at a much lower rate. This helps you avoid "plateaus" and forces you to listen to the sound of complete characters, rather than "counting" dots and dashes. The Farnsworth method works!

Nothing builds up CW proficiency like formal traffic handling. See if you can check into one of the regional NTS CW traffic nets. Contests can help; but contest operation is rather "bursty" and will not guarantee that you will be able to consistently operate for a long time with high accuracy and speed. Also, in a contest, you already have a pretty good idea what's coming next, whereas traffic handling is more like the random groups you practiced!

Get the best key or keyer you can afford. You can operate up to about 30 words per minute with a first rate straight key. A bad straight key will make 20 wpm a real challenge! But if you decide a straight key isn't your cup of tea, be assured that code sent with an electronic keyer is "real CW" too!

In Chapter 5 of this book, Gordo gives you a fun way to learn CW, beginning with the most common letters. He also has recorded an 8-CD audio course for learning Morse code. Call 800-669-9594 to learn more and order a set for yourself.

You can also learn CW on-line! You can even track your progresson your computer. Visit these websites:

http://aa9pw.com/morsecode

www.dxzone.com/catalog/Operating_Modes/Morse_code/Learning_Morse_Code

Digital Operating

G8C04 Which of the following describes Baudot code?

A. A 7-bit code with start, stop, and parity bits
B. A code using error detection and correction
C. A 5-bit code with additional start and stop bits
D. A code using SELCAL and LISTEN

Give me FIVE! This is a good way to remember ***Baudot is a 5 bit code*** with additional start and stop bits. Give me FIVE! **ANSWER C.**

G2E06 What is the most common frequency shift for RTTY emissions in the amateur HF bands?

A. 85 Hz
B. 170 Hz
C. 425 Hz
D. 850 Hz

Almost all ***ham radio RTTY*** transmissions use a ***170 Hz shift***. Commercial broadcast stations on shortwave use larger frequency shifts. **ANSWER B.**

G8C11 How are the two separate frequencies of a Frequency Shift Keyed (FSK) signal identified?

A. Dot and dash
B. On and off
C. High and low
D. Mark and space

While FSK signals could reasonably be called "High and Low" because of their relative frequencies, there is a specific LOGICAL significance to MARK and SPACE. This is true whether you're operating on a closed loop land line (as many RTTY circuits once were) or over the air. So, ***Mark and Space*** define the actual "1" and "0" logic states of a two-state digital system. **ANSWER D.**

G2E01 Which mode is normally used when sending RTTY signals via AFSK with an SSB transmitter?

A. USB
B. DSB
C. CW
D. LSB

If you plan to operate radioteletype (***RTTY***) using audio frequency-shift- keying (***AFSK***), your single sideband transmitter must be switched to ***LSB, lower sideband***. **ANSWER D.**

G2E14 What could be wrong if you cannot decode an RTTY or other FSK signal even though it is apparently tuned in properly?

A. The mark and space frequencies may be reversed
B. You may have selected the wrong baud rate
C. You may be listening on the wrong sideband
D. All these choices are correct

Frequency Shift Keying (FSK) is used by a number of digital modes, the oldest of which is RTTY (RadioTeleTYpe). The computer sound card is the most convenient way to try out a number of different FSK modes, as this allows you to apply the audio directly into the microphone input of a single sideband transmitter with little or no modification. The audio sound card actually creates Audio Frequency Shift Keying (AFSK) which is converted to "true" FSK in a properly-aligned SSB transmitter. ***Reversing the MARK and SPACE*** audio tones has exactly the same effect as having the SSB ***transmitter on the wrong sideband.*** Although some software is capable of detecting "reversed" tones, not all sound card programs are that "smart." So if you encounter difficulty decoding an FSK signal of any kind, try reversing the sideband or the audio tones. Also, be sure you're set for the ***right baud rate***. While RTTY is standard at 45 baud, other digital modes have multiple available transmission (baud) rates. **ANSWER D.**

G2E05 What is the standard sideband for JT65, JT9, FT4, or FT8 digital signal when using AFSK?

A. LSB
B. USB
C. DSB
D. SSB

A number of conventions dictate amateur radio standard usage when there are no specific FCC rules that apply. Such conventions generally come about for a good reason, and unless there's a compelling reason to depart from them, it's best to follow the convention. Since the advent of sound card digital modes, it is conventional to ***use upper sideband (USB) for HF digital operation, regardless of the band***. **ANSWER B.**

G7C10 What is an advantage of using I-Q modulation with software-defined radios (SDRs)?

A. The need for high resolution analog-to-digital converters is eliminated
B. All types of modulation can be created with appropriate processing
C. Minimum detectible signal level is reduced
D. Automatic conversion of the signal from digital to analog

One of the neat things about working with I and Q signals is that you can determine the precise phase angle of not only the I and Q signals (shifted by 90 degrees), but by any phase angle in between! This allows countless varieties of phase shift modulation to be implemented. In fact, ***all types of modulation can be created with appropriate processing***, **ANSWER B.**

G2E08 In what segment of the 20-meter band are most digital mode operations commonly found?

A. At the bottom of the slow-scan TV segment, near 14.230 MHz
B. At the top of the SSB phone segment, near 14.325 MHz
C. In the middle of the CW segment, near 14.100 MHz
D. Between 14.070 MHz and 14.100 MHz

PSK31 was the first popular sound card digital mode, followed quickly by countless other sound card digital modes. No elaborate setup or interface connections are necessary for sound card modes, which is why they are so popular. If you haven't played around with ***digital modes***, the best place to find a lot of activity is on ***14.070 MHz and 14.100 MHz***. Be sure your receiver is set to upper sideband. **ANSWER D.**

ham apps

Here are a couple of apps for decoding PSK31 that require no physical connection to your receiver:
http://www.blackcatsystems.com/ipad/iPad_PSK31_Pad.html
https://play.google.com/store/apps/details?id=com.wolphi.psk31&hl=en

---

G8C08 Which of the following statements is true about PSK31?

A. Upper case letters are sent with more power
B. Upper case letters use longer Varicode bit sequences and thus slow down transmission
C. Error correction is used to ensure accurate message reception
D. Higher power is needed as compared to RTTY for similar error rates

When RTTY was king of the digital modes, only CAPITAL letters were available. To the uninitiated, "plain" RTTY looks like you're always yelling! PSK31 has the entire character set available, but with a price. If you try "yelling" in PSK31, you slow down considerably, ***because capital letters have longer codes!*** So, use caps when you need to, but not all the time. **ANSWER B.**

G8C13 What is indicated on a waterfall display by one or more vertical lines on either side of a data mode or RTTY signal?

A. Long path propagation
B. Backscatter propagation
C. Insufficient modulation
D. Overmodulation

PSK31 is noted for being a very narrowband mode. On a waterfall display, a proper PSK31 signal will appear as a single thin line. The appearance of ***one or more vertical lines*** on either side of the received signal is an indication of intermodulation distortion, generally ***resulting from overmodulation*** of the transmitter. To avoid overmodulation, you should always use just enough audio to achieve between 25% and 50% of the available peak envelope power (PEP) that your SSB transmitter can provide. PSK31 is a weak signal mode. You will be surprised just how little power is needed for effective communications. **ANSWER D.**

G8C14 Which of the following describes a waterfall display?

A. Frequency is horizontal, signal strength is vertical, time is intensity
B. Frequency is vertical, signal strength is intensity, time is horizontal
C. Frequency is horizontal, signal strength is intensity, time is vertical
D. Frequency is vertical, signal strength is horizontal, time is intensity

A waterfall display is a special type of spectral display. It shows the demodulated audio frequency of a radio signal using one of the many sound card digital modes. Unlike a standard display of a spectrum analyzer or panadapter, the waterfall display has memory; it will show a record of radio events over a significant period of time. The standard waterfall display shows ***frequency along the horizontal axis, intensity by means of color, and time by vertical "scrolling."*** The waterfall display can show you a lot of information about what's happening near your receive frequency. **ANSWER C.**

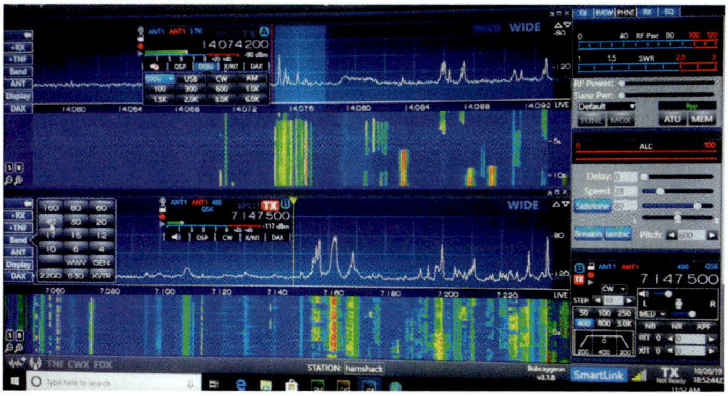

G8A12 What is QPSK modulation?

A. Modulation using quasi-parallel to serial conversion to reduce bandwidth
B. Modulation using quadra-pole sideband keying to generate spread spectrum signals
C. Modulation using Fast Fourier Transforms to generate frequencies at the first, second, third, and fourth harmonics of the carrier frequency to improve noise immunity
D. Modulation in which digital data is transmitted using 0-, 90-, 180- and 270-degrees phase shift to represent pairs of bits

Whenever working with digital modes, Q almost always means *quadrature*, which means a phase shift of 90 degrees or some multiple thereof. ***QPSK stands for Quadrature Phase Shift Keying, which means the information is applied by shifting the phase of a radio frequency signal by some multiple of 90 degrees***. **ANSWER D.**

G8A06 Which of the following is characteristic of QPSK31?

A. It is sideband sensitive
B. Its encoding provides error correction
C. Its bandwidth is approximately the same as BPSK31
D. All these choices are correct

QPSK31 was one of the first digital modes to take full advantage of I/Q modulation. The symbols of a QPSK31 signal are shifted by 90 degrees, in comparison with the more basic PSK31, which uses 180 degree phase shifting. Because there are more symbols per character with QPSK31 than PSK31, it takes more bits or phase shifts to convey the same amount of information, but this does provide a slight advantage over "plain vanilla" PSK31 when it comes to error handling. Unlike the "regular" PSK31, which doesn't care what sideband you use, QPSK31 cares deeply; you must use upper sideband (USB). Here is a great link to all the gory details about every digital HF mode: **http://ac4m.us/BPSK31.html** **ANSWER D.**

G8A01 How is direct binary FSK modulation generated?

A. By keying an FM transmitter with a sub-audible tone
B. By changing an oscillator's frequency directly with a digital control signal
C. By using a transceiver's computer data interface protocol to change frequencies
D. By reconfiguring the CW keying input to act as a tone generator

While the method of using an SSB transmitter to convert an AFSK signal to an FSK signal is pretty much universal these days, there's still something to be said for generating FSK the old, direct way. One advantage of "old school" FSK is that it allows you to use very powerful and efficient Class C RF amplifiers. This method is still in common use by serious RTTY contesters and DXers. The most direct way of ***creating FSK is to shift the frequency of an oscillator*** by "keying in" a small amount of capacitance across its resonant tuned circuit. If the oscillator is a low powered solid state circuit, it can be keyed directly with a digital gate chip. **ANSWER B.**

G8C12 Which type of code is used for sending characters in a PSK31 signal?

A. Varicode
B. Viterbi
C. Volumetric
D. Binary

PSK31 is actually a rather unusual code. It is optimized for very narrow bandwidths. ***PSK31 uses*** a code known as ***Varicode*** for its different symbol lengths. **ANSWER A.**

G4A11 Why should the ALC system be inactive when transmitting AFSK data signals?

A. ALC will invert the modulation of the AFSK mode
B. The ALC action distorts the signal
C. When using digital modes, too much ALC activity can cause the transmitter to overheat
D. All these choices are correct

Sound card digital modes work by applying AFSK signals to the input of a properly aligned single sideband transmitter, which then become FSK signals. An FSK

Elmer Point: Down on the digital frequencies you'll hear data activity, and with a simple sound card program you can decode all of the excitement. There are some regular digital contests, too, giving you a great way to begin transmitting and receiving data with other stations needing contact points. Here's a list of some of the bigger data contests:

- New Years' Day RTTY Contest
- First weekend in January ARRL RTTY Roundup
- First weekend in February Low Power Digital Contest
- Second weekend in February Worldwide RTTY Call Letter Prefix Contest
- Second weekend in March RTTY Sprint
- Third weekend in April PSK-31 Activity weekend
- Third weekend in July North American RTTY Activity weekend
- First weekend in September PSK-31 Contest
- First weekend in October Hellschreiber Contest

signal should consist of two and only two frequencies. Intermodulation distortion, usually resulting from ***overdriving an SSB transmitter will create additional frequencies*** near the desired ones. These additional products can make the signal difficult or impossible to decode, and can also cause interference to nearby stations if "intermod" is severe enough. When using sound card modes, the ALC should be disabled or the audio level reduced to the point where no ALC action occurs. The proper drive level for a sound card mode is when the PEP output power of the transmitter is between 25% to 50% of its maximum capable PEP. When in doubt, keep the drive on the low side. **ANSWER B.**

G8B08 Why is it important to know the duty cycle of the mode you are using when transmitting?

A. To aid in tuning your transmitter
B. Some modes have high duty cycles that could exceed the transmitter's average power rating
C. To allow time for the other station to break in during a transmission
D. To prevent overmodulation

Hooking-up your high-frequency ham transceiver to your computer opens up a whole new world for receiving and sending data signals. Receiving is almost a direct connection to your computer through the sound card, but sending data may require an external modem. Sending data using on-and-off handshake modes like PACTOR II or G-TOR cycles your transceiver to transmit and receive for a duty cycle (on transmit) of perhaps 50%. But other modes like PSK31 and MFSK16 are transmitting a constant key-down data stream without interruption. Now your ***duty cycle is 100%*** and the heat sinks on the back of your transceiver are going to get roasty-toasty. To keep your equipment from going into meltdown, consider adding an external fan and reducing power output to the point the rear heat sinks won't fry eggs. If you get the heat sinks so warm that you can't touch them, you could ***exceed the transmitter's average power rating***, leading to an expensive repair of your solid state final amplifier transistors. **ANSWER B.**

G8B10 What is the relationship between transmitted symbol rate and bandwidth?

A. Symbol rate and bandwidth are not related
B. Higher symbol rates require wider bandwidth
C. Lower symbol rates require wider bandwidth
D. Bandwidth is half the symbol rate

You know why big boats go so slow out of the harbor, right? If they went any faster they would create big wakes that would upset every other boat on either side of them. Same thing for ham ***radio digital modes*** – if you're going to ***send fast***, you'll need to go to higher bands that will permit the ***faster sending speed and wider bandwidth***. **ANSWER B.**

G1C08 What is the maximum symbol rate permitted for RTTY or data emission transmitted at frequencies below 28 MHz?

A. 56 kilobaud
B. 19.6 kilobaud
C. 1200 baud
D. 300 baud

RTTY and data emissions below ***28 MHz*** (below the 10 meter band) must creep along no faster than ***300 baud***. This slow symbol rate is required to minimize bandwidth allocation on the very crowded high-frequency bands. [97.307(f)(3)] **ANSWER D.**

G1C10 What is the maximum symbol rate permitted for RTTY or data emission transmissions on the 10-meter band?

A. 56 kilobaud
B. 19.6 kilobaud
C. 1200 baud
D. 300 baud

On ***10 meters*** we are permitted to increase RTTY and data emission transmission speeds to ***1200 baud***. This is 4 times faster than the slower speed required on frequencies below the 10 meter band. [97.305(c) and [97.307(f)(4)] **ANSWER C.**

Maximum Symbol (Baud) Rate for Amateur Bands

Amateur Band (meters)	Maximum Symbol Rate (bauds)
160 to 12 m	300 bauds
10 m	1200 bauds
6 and 2 m	19,600 bauds
1.25 and 0.70 m	56,000 bauds
33 cm and higher	Not Specified

G8C03 What part of a packet radio frame contains the routing and handling information?

A. Directory
B. Preamble
C. Header
D. Trailer

Within the ***header*** are ***routing addresses and handling information*** for digipeaters that direct your packet over a specific route – even coast-to-coast and worldwide! If you are into APRS (Automatic Position/Packet Reporting System), you can set up your packet header for local or wide-area relay of your position report. **ANSWER C.**

ham apps

EchoLink

As hard as it may be to believe, there are some places where there's no direct access to any repeater. Echolink lets you work thousands of remote repeaters around the world through the Internet. The use of Echolink requires that you register as a bona fide, licensed radio amateur before you are allowed access to the Echolink network. This prevents unlicensed operators from activating distant repeaters, as you are the control operator, even if you're a continent away **https://itunes.apple.com/us/app/echolink/id350688562?mt=8**

IRLP

Similar but different from Echolink, IRLP also lets you connect to repeaters via the Internet, but with a somewhat different protocol. Recent developments allow the Echolink and IRLP networks to "play together." **www.winsystem.org**

G1E11 On what bands may automatically controlled stations transmitting RTTY or data emissions communicate with other automatically controlled digital stations?

A. On any band segment where digital operation is permitted
B. Anywhere in the non-phone segments of the 10-meter or shorter wavelength bands
C. Only in the non-phone Extra Class segments of the bands
D. Anywhere in the 6-meter or shorter wavelength bands, and in limited segments of some of the HF bands

In most cases, a control operator must be physically present at one end of any radio circuit or link. In other words, normally, automatically controlled relay stations can't talk to one another directly. The exceptions to this are on the ***6-meter and shorter wavelength bands***, as well as a few ***specially designated "slots" on some of the HF bands***. In all cases, however, there must be a control operator at some point in the total radio link. [97.221, 97.305] **ANSWER D.**

G1E03 What is required to conduct communications with a digital station operating under automatic control outside the automatic control band segments?

A. The station initiating the contact must be under local or remote control
B. The interrogating transmission must be made by another automatically controlled station
C. No third-party traffic may be transmitted
D. The control operator of the interrogating station must hold an Amateur Extra class license

All amateur radio communications must be made by a ***control operator***. Sometimes it can be a bit tricky determining the identity of the control operator. In the case of Echolink or IRLP, the control operator may be located clear across the country from the actual transmitter. If you "bring up" a distant repeater from your Echolink computer, you are the control operator responsible for what goes out over the air. Now, while there are amateur sub-bands allocated specifically to automatic control, Echolink or IRLP transmission do not fall under this exception; they occur in "normal" ham bands. [97.221] **ANSWER A.**

G1C07 What must be done before using a new digital protocol on the air?

A. Type-certify equipment to FCC standards
B. Obtain an experimental license from the FCC
C. Publicly document the technical characteristics of the protocol
D. Submit a rule-making proposal to the FCC describing the codes and methods of the technique

Encrypted radio signals are prohibited on any amateur radio band; this is one of the major, important differences between Amateur Radio and commercial radio. The use of encryption is contrary to the very nature of amateur radio, which, from the very beginning, was intended to be fully open. To avoid falling under the "no encryption" rules, hams using new digital modes must ***publicly document the technical characteristics of the protocol*** so that any licensed radio amateur may decode the transmissions with non-proprietary equipment. [97.309(a)(4)] **ANSWER C.**

G6B12 Which of these connector types is commonly used for low frequency or dc signal connections to a transceiver?

A. PL-259
B. BNC
C. RCA Phono
D. Type N

Your new General Class High Frequency world wide transceiver has a lot of jacks on the rear. Read the manual! The ***RCA Phono jack*** on the rear is sometimes used for amplifier keying, yet sometimes used for an external low frequency receive long wire, or sometimes for dc signal connections to your radio. Read the manual! **ANSWER C.**

G2E12 Which of the following describes Winlink?

A. An amateur radio wireless network to send and receive email on the internet
B. A form of Packet Radio
C. A wireless network capable of both VHF and HF band operation
D. All of the above

Winlink is an automatic ***messaging network, using VHF and HF bands***. Winlink itself does not define the actual protocol used, and this has gone through several changes over the years. VARA is the latest and most common protocol, running "underneath" the Winlink system. **ANSWER D.**

G2E13 What is another name for a Winlink Remote Message Server?

A. Terminal Node Controller
B. Gateway
C. RJ-45
D. Printer/Server

A ***Winlink Remote Message Server*** is a ***gateway*** between the Internet and an amateur radio net. **ANSWER B.**

G2E02 What is VARA?

A. A low signal-to-noise digital mode used for EME (moonbounce)
B. A digital protocol used with Winlink
C. A radio direction finding system used on VHF and UHF
D.A DX spotting system using a network of software defined radios

WinLink is one of the most popular automatic message relaying modes. ***VARA is a specific digital protocol used by WinLink***, which provides a transparent, familiar email-type interface. **ANSWER B.**

G2E10 Which of the following is a way to establish contact with a digital messaging system gateway station?

A. Send an email to the system control operator
B. Send QRL in Morse code
C. Respond when the station broadcasts its SSID
D. Transmit a connect message on the station's published frequency

A gateway is an interface between different communications systems, such as between the Internet and Amateur Radio. Winlink is one of the most popular gateway technologies, combining email and (normally) HF radio. Gateway HF stations operate on specific published frequencies. To access one of these gateways from a remote HF station, ***transmit a connect command*** via your Winlink client software. Once connected, the HF link is "transparent;" from your terminal it looks just like you're on an Internet email client. **ANSWER D.**

Elmer Point: Want to learn more about how digital electronics work – from DSP systems to your computer, and all those gizmos inside your new HF radio? Get a copy of **Basic Digital Electronics** by Al Evans. You can pick-up a copy at your local ham radio dealer, on-line at www.w5yi.org, or by calling The W5YI Group at 800-669-9594.

G2E09 How do you join a contact between two stations using the PACTOR protocol?

A. Send broadcast packets containing your call sign while in MONITOR mode
B. Transmit a steady carrier until the PACTOR protocol times out and disconnects
C. Joining an existing contact is not possible, PACTOR connections are limited to two stations
D. Send a NAK code

PACTOR and a number of other digital modes operate in a connected mode. In this mode, "handshaking" or "acknowledgment" perform error correction in an extremely reliable manner. The downside to this is that ***the connected mode only works between two stations***. This is why PACTOR is very effective for automatic relaying, but is not suitable for real time "ragchewing." There are a number of other digital modes, however, that are suitable to roundtables and general conversation. **ANSWER C.**

G2E03 What symptoms may result from other signals interfering with a PACTOR or VARA transmission?

A. Frequent retries or timeouts
B. Long pauses in message transmission
C. Failure to establish a connection between stations
D. All these choices are correct

While most HF digital modes are fairly robust and generally include some kind of error correction, no system is perfect. Just the quirks of HF propagation itself present a challenge to most HF digital modes. When interference from other transmissions are in the mix, it's sometimes amazing HF "digi" works at all! An HF communications link undergoing interference can suffer symptoms ranging from ***long pauses*** in message transmissions, frequent message ***retries and timeouts*** to complete ***connection failures***. Digital technology is pretty amazing, but it's still subject to the laws of physics, some of which you have no control over! **ANSWER D.**

G8C06 What action results from a failure to exchange information due to excessive transmission attempts when using an ARQ mode?

A. The checksum overflows
B. The connection is dropped
C. Packets will be routed incorrectly
D. Encoding reverts to the default character set

Sometimes it's good to know when to quit, even if you're an automatic relay station! PACTOR and WINMOR, both common protocols for the Winlink service, will make numerous attempts to establish or maintain an HF link, and can usually do so under the most horrendous conditions. When it is clearly fruitless to attempt continuing on, PACTOR and WINMOR know when to quit. Both modes will deliberately ***drop the connection*** after a predetermined number of tries. **ANSWER B.**

G8C05 In an ARQ mode, what is meant by a NAK response to a transmitted packet?

A. Request retransmission of the packet
B. Packet was received without error
C. Receiving station connected and ready for transmissions
D. Entire file received correctly

PACTOR is an exciting data mode that leads to near-perfect reception of a message. The transmitted message is sent in short bursts, allowing the receiving station to quickly transmit ACK for perfect copy, or ***NAK***, meaning ***"send it again, Sam, I missed a few characters."*** This back-and-forth between two PACTOR stations leads to error free copy. **ANSWER A.**

G8C10 How does forward error correction (FEC) allow the receiver to correct data errors?

A. By controlling transmitter output power for optimum signal strength
B. By using the Varicode character set
C. By transmitting redundant information with the data
D. By using a parity bit with each character

Forward error correction, abbreviated FEC, is achieved by ***sending each character twice***. This allows the receiver to correct errors by double-checking the received data. The data mode AMTOR B (amateur teleprinting over radio) uses FEC. **ANSWER C.**

G8C07 Which of the following narrow-band digital modes can receive signals with very low signal-to-noise ratios?

A. MSK144
B. FT8
C. AMTOR
D. MFSK32

One of the unbreakable laws of physics (and amateur radio) is NFL… No Free Lunch. As you strive to extract minuscule signals from beneath the noise floor there is a price to pay, and that price is time. Extremely weak signal methods, either digital (***FT8***) or analog, such as the venerable lock-in amplifier, need time to do their magic, sometimes lots of it. Data speeds are low, as is the bandwidth. But it's a price most hams are willing to pay to be able to communicate under the most abominable conditions imaginable! **ANSWER B.**

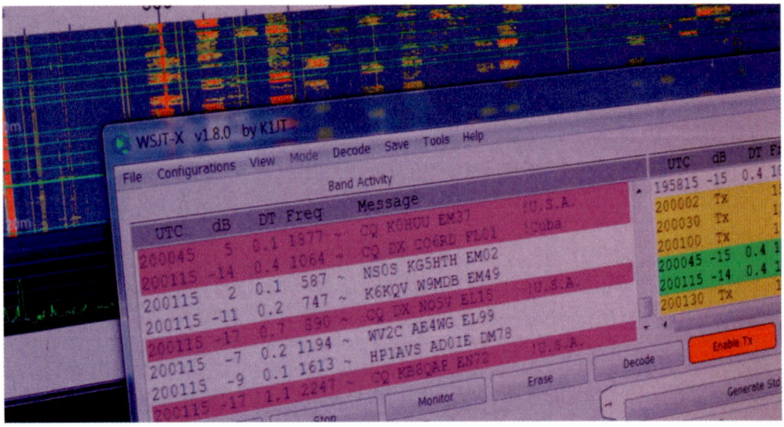

G8A09 What type of modulation is used by FT8?

A. 8-tone frequency shift keying
B. Vestigial sideband
C. Amplitude compressed AM
D. 8-bit direct sequence spread spectrum

Elsewhere, we sang the praises of I/Q modulation, and how you can determine any degree of phase shifting with an I/Q demodulator. FT8 takes a different approach by using an ***8-tone frequency shift keying scheme***. The frequency shifting is slow enough you can easily hear it; it's been described by some hams as a space alien orchestra tuning up. **ANSWER A.**

G2E07 Which of the following is required when using FT8?

A. A special hardware modem
B. Computer time accurate to within approximately 1 second
C. Receiver attenuator set to -12 dB
D. A vertically polarized antenna

Because FT8 is a structured digital mode, it requires fairly precise timing, specifically ***computer time accurate within approximately 1 second***. You don't need your own atomic clock to achieve this accuracy; you can manually set your computer time using the WWV or WWVH broadcast "tick" at the top of the minute. But if you have network time protocol working on your computer, this is even better. **ANSWER B.**

G8C15 What does an FT8 signal report of +3 mean?

A. The signal is 3 times the noise level of an equivalent SSB signal
B. The signal is S3 (weak signals)
C. The signal-to-noise ratio is equivalent to +3dB in a 2.5 kHz bandwidth
D. The signal is 3 dB over S9

Operating FT8 for a while really drives home the point that signal-to-noise ratio is FAR more important than merely signal strength, when it comes to communications effectiveness. S/N needs to be qualified by the bandwidth, which in the case of ***FT8 is 2.5 kHz***...about the same bandwidth as a typical SSB signal…also the bandwidth your receiver should be set to for best FT8 performance. The built-in number crunching in WSJT gives you a real time S/N reading in dB, for any incoming signal. Naturally, the bigger the number, the "better" the signal...even if it "sounds" weak. **ANSWER C.**

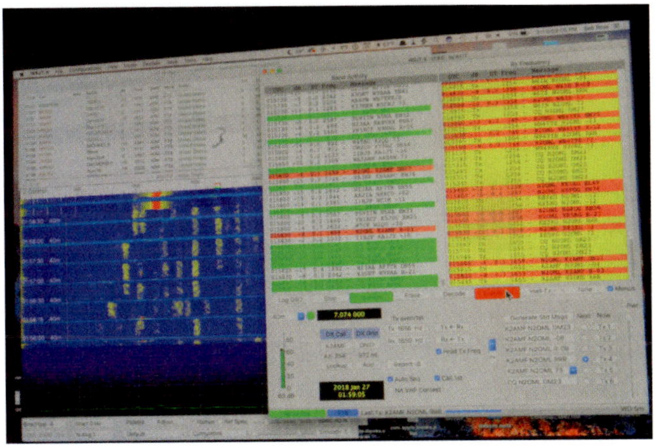

G2E04 Which of the following is good practice when choosing a transmitting frequency to answer a station calling CQ using FT8?

A. Always call on the station's frequency
B. Call on any frequency in the waterfall except the station's frequency
C. Find a clear frequency during the same time slot as the calling station
D. Find a clear frequency during the alternate time slot to the calling station

Working DX on HF, ***it is standard good practice to operate "split" allowing the DX station's CQ to be heard outside of the inevitable responding pileup***. However with FT8 (and other FT modes), one uses a time split, rather than a frequency split as commonly used with CW or phone. Find a clear frequency, and transmit on the opposite time slot as the DX station calling CQ. **ANSWER D.**

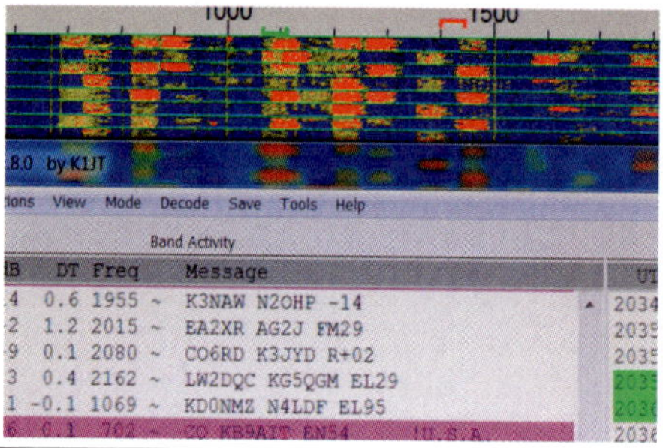

When decoded on a computer screen, FT8 provides basic information about the received signal's call sign, grid location, and signal report. Learn more at: https://physics.princeton.edu/pulsar/k1jt/

G2E15 Which of the following is a common location for FT8?

A. Anywhere in the voice portion of the band
B. Anywhere in the CW portion of the band
C. Approximately 14.074 MHz to 14.077 MHz
D. Approximately 14.110 MHz to 14.113 MHz

Most FT8 operation on the "traditional" (non-WARC) bands takes place about 70-75KHz above the bottom of the band. On 20 meters, the FT8 "watering hole" is between 14.074 and 14.077 MHz. If you are using the popular WSJT software suite, the "watering hole" FT8 frequencies are already programmed in. Just click on the BAND, and your rig (if properly configured) will put you right in the center of the action. **ANSWER C.**

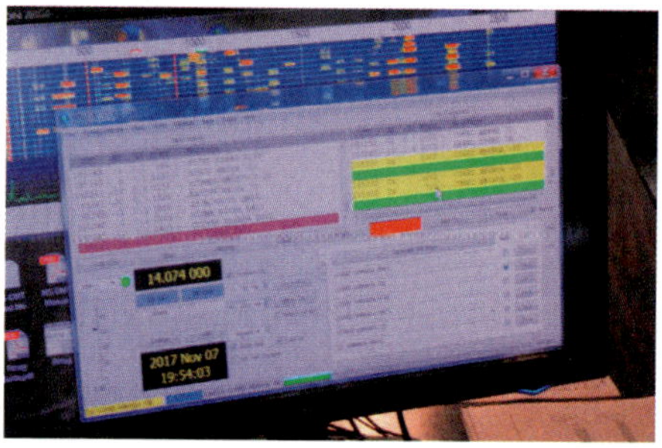

G1E08 What is the maximum PEP output allowed for spread spectrum transmissions?

A. 100 milliwatts
B. 10 watts
C. 100 watts
D. 1500 watts

Spread Spectrum (or SS) is a mode where a radio signal is "hopped" over a relatively large frequency range. This method allows two or more conversations to occupy the same bandwidth with minimal interference. However, this technique must be used with caution in the few places on the amateur bands where it is allowed, particularly in spectrum shared with non-amateur services. The power limit for ***SS is 10 watts PEP*** at the transmitter output. [97.313(j)] **ANSWER B.**

G1E07 In what part of the 2.4 GHz band may an amateur station communicate with non-licensed Wi-Fi stations?

A. Anywhere in the band
B. Channels 1 through 4
C. Channels 42 through 45
D. No part

Amateur and commercial radio fall under two entirely separate sets of rules and have completely different frequency allocations. While there are some gateway technologies that allow amateur radio to indirectly interface with commercial radio equipment, in ***no part*** of the 2.4 GHz band may amateurs directly communicate with unlicensed Wi-Fi stations, (or vice versa). While this restriction is not limited to 2.4 GHz, this is this part of the radio spectrum where unlicensed operators would be most tempted to communicate with licensed radio amateurs because of the profusion of unlicensed equipment in this frequency range. [97.111] **ANSWER D.**

G8C01 On what band do amateurs share channels with the unlicensed Wi-Fi service?

A. 432 MHz
B. 902 MHz
C. 2.4 GHz
D. 10.7 GHz

Wi-Fi is one service that uses spread spectrum (SS) modulation, which allows multiple stations to actually occupy the same channel with nearly no interference. Because of the unique properties of SS, the amateur and commercial allocations can be shared at ***2.4 GHz.*** There is no physical reason why this frequency sharing can't work on other frequencies as well, but for now frequency sharing is only allowed on this band. **ANSWER C.**

WHAT'S A WIFI MESH?

MESH networks are forming all over the country, especially after fires in California silenced local internet hot spots and in cold climates, like Chicago, where lots of WiFi systems around the city have frozen.

Hams on 2.4 GHz have formed ARDEN – Amateur Radio Disaster Emergency Network – a MESH of specially-modified 2.4 GHz WiFi routers using ham frequencies to relay local data and video signals "to get the message out." When the internet is down in a local area, these ARDEN MESH networks provide high speed data and video connections between ham radio relay stations until the signal reaches a working internet connection via router "hops."

To learn more, we suggest reading ***High Speed Multimedia for Amateur Radio*** by Glen Popiel, KW5GP, available from the ARRL and on Amazon as both a physical and Kindle book.

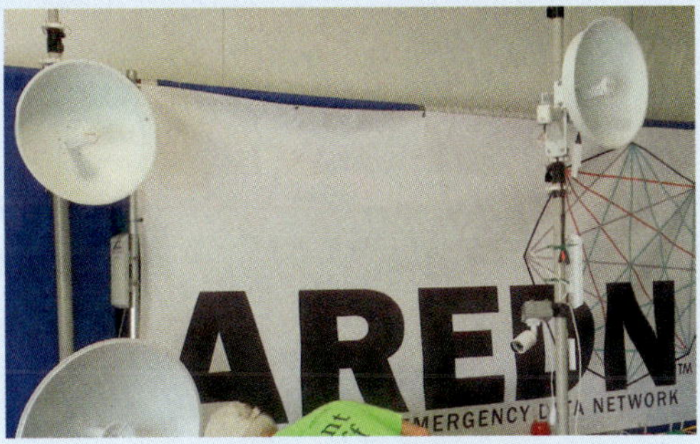

G8C09 Which is true of mesh network microwave nodes?

A. Having more nodes increases signal strengths
B. If one node fails, a packet may still reach its target station via an alternate node
C. Links between two nodes in a network may have different frequencies and bandwidths
D. More nodes reduce overall microwave out of band interference

Mesh networks, by their very nature, have multiple paths between any two nodes. This is true whether they're microwave networks, or down on the lower UHF frequencies. Mesh modems are designed to work out different paths automatically (aren't you glad you don't have to figure out all the software that does this?) By the way, a mesh is just one of several possible topologies for interconnecting nodes; other common ones being the star and daisy chain. **ANSWER B.**

G2E11 What is the primary purpose of an Amateur Radio Emergency Data Network (AREDN) mesh network?

A. To provide FM repeater coverage in remote areas
B. To provide real time propagation data by monitoring amateur radio transmissions worldwide
C. To provide high-speed data services during an emergency or community event
D. To provide DX spotting reports to aid contesters and DXers

Mesh networks such as the ***Amateur Radio Emergency Data Network (AREDN)*** allow one to create an ad hoc network on-the-fly, without having to deal with complex network configuration. This allows one to set up a functioning network quickly, as in the case of an emergency. AREDN uses commercial-off-the-shelf (COTS) equipment, requiring no modification other than downloadable software. **ANSWER C.**

G8A13 What is a link budget?

A. The financial costs associated with operating a radio link
B. The sum of antenna gains minus system losses
C. The sum of transmit power and antenna gains minus system losses as seen at the receiver
D. The difference between transmit power and receiver sensitivity

In any radio system, there are a number of gains and losses associated with achieving a given signal strength at a receiver some distance from a transmitter. Although financial costs are certainly associated with the so-called link budget, this is not what we mean when we talk about link budget. Gains of a system can be amplifier gain, antenna gain (both transmitting and receiving), and receiver gain. Losses can be transmission line losses (at both ends), propagation losses, and miscellaneous system losses. This is where the dB is your friend. If you convert all your gains and losses into dB, everything becomes a simple addition (or subtraction) problem. **ANSWER C.**

G8A14 What is link margin?

A. The opposite of fade margin
B. The difference between received power level and minimum required signal level at the input to the receiver
C. Transmit power minus receiver sensitivity
D. Receiver sensitivity plus 3 dB

In any communications system, it's nice to have a little more capability than you actually need. One can fairly easily determine how much signal is needed at a receiver's input terminals for decent communications. One can also figure out how much *weaker* the signal can be and still obtain usable communications. ***The difference between these two figures is the link margin***. One can incorporate the link budget (G8A13) to determine which components affect your link margin the most, and what you need to improve it. The link margin is usually expressed in dB. **ANSWER B.**

G8C16 Which of the following provide digital voice modes?

A. WSPR, MFSK16, and EasyPAL
B. FT8, FT4, and FST4
C. Winlink, PACTOR II, and PACTOR III
D. DMR, D-STAR, and SystemFusion

While most of the dozens of digital modes are text (keyboard) modes, whether affording "real time" communications, or "buffered" communications like Winlink, there are a few digital audio (voice) modes, ***the most popular of which are DMR, D-Star and SystemFusion***. Most digital voice modes rely on some form of commercial infrastructure (such as the Internet) for their functioning, while most of the keyboard digital modes do not. **ANSWER D.**

DIGITAL ACCESSORIES

The following websites are excellent places for you to look for digital accessories for your ham radio and computer. Thanks to Don Wilson, N9ZGE, for sharing this with us.

AH-4	www.icomamerica.com/en/downloads/Default.aspx?Category=136
Airmail	www.siriuscyber.net/ham/
ATV	www.kh6htv.com/
Digipan	www.digipan.net/
DX Engineering	www.dxengineering.com/Parts.asp?ID=1128&PLID=182&SecID=152& DeptID=42&PartNo=DXE-CSB-COMBO
Farallon Elecronics	www.farallon.us/webstore/
Ferrite Beads	www.audiosystemsgroup.com/publish.htm
FTDI Drivers	www.ftdichip.com/FTDrivers.htm
Ham Radio Deluxe	www.ham-radio-deluxe.com/
IC-718	www.icomamerica.com/en/products/amateur/hf/718/default.aspx
MFJ-1270C	www.mfjenterprises.com/
MicroHam	www.microham-usa.com/Products/USB3.html
N4PY	www.n4py.com/
Palomar-Ferrite Cores	www.palomar-engineers.com/
PrintScreen	www.gadwin.com/download/
PTC-IIusb	www.scs-ptc.com/shop/categories/modems-en
QuickMix	www.brothersoft.com/quickmix-10463.html
RIGblaster P&P	www.westmountainradio.com/product_info.php?products_id=pnp
RigExpert	www.rigexpert.com/index?s=standard
RMS Express & Paclink	www.winlink.org/winlinkexpress
SignaLink USB	www.tigertronics.com/
TM-271	www.kenwood.com/usa
TM-271 Data Mod	www.kenwood.com/usa
TM-271 Data Mod	www.kenwood.com/usa
TNC-X	www.tnc-x.com/
Two Meter Antenna	www.mfjenterprises.com/Product.php?productid=MFJ-1750
USB to Serial Converter	www.ftdichip.com/Products/Cables/USBRS232.htm
WSJT modes	http://psysics.princeton.edu/pulsar/kljt/

Emergency

G2B02 What is the first thing you should do if you are communicating with another amateur station and hear a station in distress break in?

A. Inform your local emergency coordinator
B. Acknowledge the station in distress and determine what assistance may be needed
C. Immediately decrease power to avoid interfering with the station in distress
D. Immediately cease all transmissions

Act immediately to handle a station in distress. Find out WHO is in distress, WHERE they are located, and WHAT assistance may be needed. If it's a boat, find out how many persons are on board and instruct everyone to put on their personal flotation device. **ANSWER B.**

G1B04 Which of the following transmissions is permitted for all amateur stations?

A. Unidentified transmissions of less than 10 seconds duration for test purposes only
B. Automatic retransmission of other amateur signals by any amateur station
C. Occasional retransmission of weather and propagation forecast information from US government stations
D. Encrypted messages, if not intended to facilitate a criminal act

As a general rule, broadcasting is prohibited on amateur radio frequencies. Broadcasting is defined as a one-way transmission to multiple recipients without establishing a contact with any particular station. One example of permissible amateur radio broadcasting is the code practice transmissions from W1AW. Recently, the FCC rules now include the ***occasional retransmission of weather and propagation forecast information from U.S. government stations*** in the short list of permitted amateur radio broadcasts. [97.113(c)] **ANSWER C.**

G2B09 Who may be the control operator of an amateur station transmitting in RACES to assist relief operations during a disaster?

A. Only a person holding an FCC-issued amateur operator license

B. Only a RACES net control operator

C. A person holding an FCC-issued amateur operator license or an appropriate government official

D. Any control operator when normal communication systems are operational

Radio Amateur Civil Emergency Service (***RACES***) is a public service by ***licensed amateur radio operators*** to provide volunteer communications to government agencies in time of extraordinary need. The Federal Emergency Management Agency (FEMA) provides planning guidance and technical assistance for establishing a RACES unit of licensed amateur radio operators at the state and local government levels. Only licensed amateur radio operators with a current RACES authorization may be the control operator at a RACES station. [97.407(a)] **ANSWER A.**

Amateur Radio has a long, friendly history with all our military and civilian services through MARS, RACES, and other similar auxiliary services. Here, ham operator and pilot Jeff, N6JSV, is ready for a helicopter disaster drill for city RACES training using an APRS handheld radio.

G2B11 How often may RACES training drills and tests be routinely conducted without special authorization?

A. No more than 1 hour per month

B. No more than 2 hours per month

C. No more than 1 hour per week

D. No more than 2 hours per week

Radio Amateur Civil Emergency Service (RACES) and the Amateur Radio Emergency Service (ARES) are the two most popular "official" amateur radio emergency vehicles. While regular ***training drills are important for keeping in practice, RACES rules say training drills and tests be routinely conducted for no more than 1 hour per week without special authorization***. [97.407(d)(4)] **ANSWER C.**

G2B10 Which of the following is good amateur practice for net management?

A. Always use multiple sets of phonetics during check-in
B. Have a backup frequency in case of interference or poor conditions
C. Transmit the full net roster at the beginning of every session
D. All these choices are correct

Net operation is as old as amateur radio itself, and there are a number of good practices developed over the decades for ***good amateur practice for net management***. One of the long-standing good practices is to have a backup frequency in case of interference or other poor conditions. Occasionally changing net frequencies not only increases overall network reliability, but also prevents corrosion from setting in on your VFO dial! **ANSWER B.**

Ham Hint: As an ARES or RACES member, you can expect to be on the air at least once or twice a week on your specific net time. Once a month you will attend a local meeting, and regularly you will accrue additional training to make you a better emergency responder. You will have a distinctive uniform, a set callout plan when you are informed that a major emergency has occurred nearby, and a ham radio "grab-and-go" kit that will keep you on the air for at least 48 hours on your assignment. Above all, you must be a REGULAR on the repeater, a REGULAR when it comes to in-person training sessions, and a REGULAR in accruing additional training available to your unit.

Website Resources

▼ IF YOU'RE LOOKING FOR	▼ THEN VISIT
All About RACES	www.USRACES.org
Military Radio Groups	www.ARMYMARS.org
More About Joining ARES	www.ARRL.org/ARES
ARRL Emergency Volunteers	www.ARRL.org/Volunteer

The Effect of the Ionosphere on Radio Waves

To help you with the questions on radio wave propagation, here is a brief explanation on the effect the ionosphere has on radio waves.

The ionosphere is the electrified atmosphere from 40 miles to 400 miles above the Earth. You can sometimes see it as "northern lights." It is charged up daily by the sun, and does some miraculous things to radio waves that strike it. Some radio waves are absorbed during daylight hours by the ionosphere's D layer. Others are bounced back to Earth. Yet others penetrate the ionosphere and never come back again. The wavelength of the radio waves determines whether the waves will be absorbed, refracted, or will penetrate and pass through into outer space. Here's a quick way to memorize what the different layers do during day and nighttime hours:

The D layer is about 40 miles up. The D layer is a Daylight layer; it almost disappears at night. D for Daylight. The D layer absorbs radio waves between 1 MHz to 7 MHz. These are long wavelengths. All others pass through.

The E layer is also a daylight layer, and it is very Eccentric. E for Eccentric. Patches of E layer ionization may cause some surprising reflections of signals on both high frequency as well as very-high frequency. The E layer height is usually 70 miles.

The F1 layer is one of the layers farthest away. The F layer gives us those Far away signals. F for Far away. The F1 layer is present during daylight hours, and is up around 150 miles. The F2 layer is also present during daylight hours, and it gives us the Furthest range. The F2 layer is 250 miles high, and it's the best for the Farthest range on medium and short waves. At nighttime, the F1 and F2 layers combine to become just the F layer at 180 miles. This F layer at nighttime will usually bend radio waves between 1 MHz and 15 MHz back to earth. At night, the D and E layers disappear.

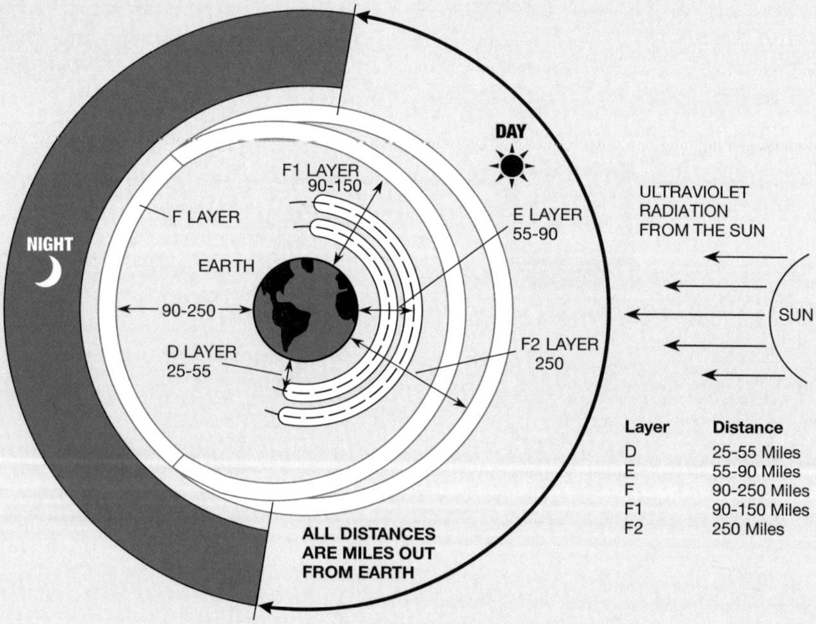

Layer	Distance
D	25-55 Miles
E	55-90 Miles
F	90-250 Miles
F1	90-150 Miles
F2	250 Miles

Ionosphere Layers

Source: *Antennas — Selection and Installation,* © 1986, Master Publishing, Inc., Niles, Illinois

Skywave Excitement!

G3C03 Why is skip propagation via the F2 region longer than that via the other ionospheric regions?

A. Because it is the densest
B. Because of the Doppler effect
C. Because it is the highest
D. Because of temperature inversions

The higher the altitude of the ionospheric region refracting the high frequency radio waves, the greater the radio range. The ***F2*** region is the ***highest region*** and gives the ***longest propagation***. **ANSWER C.**

G3B09 What is the approximate maximum distance along the Earth's surface normally covered in one hop using the F2 region?

A. 180 miles
B. 1,200 miles
C. 2,500 miles
D. 12,000 miles

The ***F2 region*** is our highest refractive ionospheric region, approximately 250 miles up. This gives worldwide signals their longest bounce, about ***2500 miles***. **ANSWER C.**

Elmer Point: One of the most fascinating aspects of General Class medium frequency and high frequency operation is propagation. Your HF signals are going coast to coast, thanks to Mother Nature's ionosphere. Many new General Class operators, with a modest dipole antenna, are spellbound when a station from Europe or the Far East comes in out of the noise, builds to S-9, and gives you a solid signal report with your paltry 100 watts and unity gain dipole antenna strung up to an apple tree. And just as soon as they give you that great report, the signal begins to fade away.

Welcome to propagation. This topic contains the most questions for your General Class studies. Propagation will keep you at the edge of your radio room chair when the band magically OPENS!

G3C04 What does the term "critical angle" mean, as applied to radio wave propagation?

A. The long path azimuth of a distant station
B. The short path azimuth of a distant station
C. The lowest takeoff angle that will return a radio wave to Earth under specific ionospheric conditions
D. The highest takeoff angle that will return a radio wave to Earth under specific ionospheric conditions

Have you ever skipped stones on a lake? If thrown at too great an angle to the surface of the water, the stone will not skip but rather penetrate into the water. Radio waves in the ionosphere act similarly; there is a point – ***the highest take-off angle*** – that cannot be exceeded or a radio wave will not refract back to Earth. It is the makeup of the ionosphere that determines the highest takeoff angle that will refract a high frequency signal back to Earth. You can play with different antennas all day long, but that magic refractive ionosphere is the number one key to a signal that can be heard around the world! **ANSWER D.**

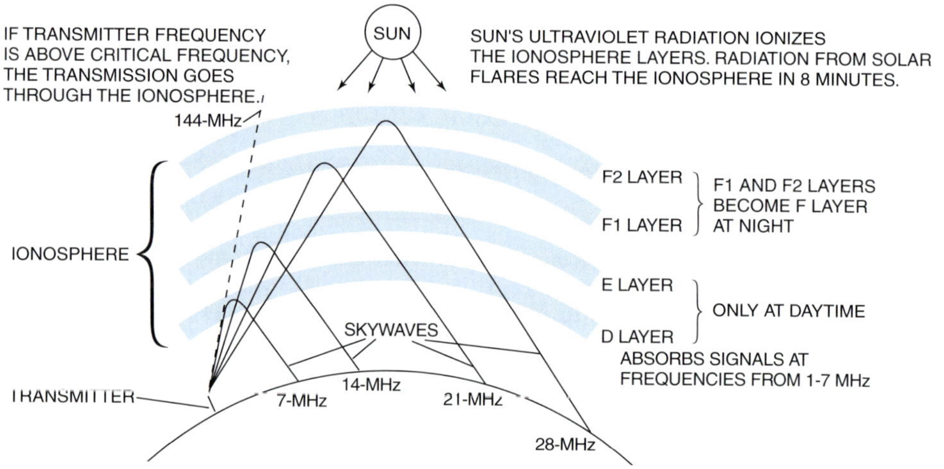

Ionosphere and Its Layers

G3C02 What is meant by the term "critical frequency" at a given incidence angle?

A. The highest frequency which is refracted back to Earth
B. The lowest frequency which is refracted back to Earth
C. The frequency at which the signal-to-noise ratio approaches unity
D. The frequency at which the signal-to-noise ratio is 6 dB

On HF, for any given "launch angle," ***there is a frequency, the critical frequency, above which all your radiated energy goes off into space, rather than being refracted back to earth***. The worst case scenario is for VIS (Vertical Incident Skywave), where the critical frequency is the lowest. A local Ionosonde is the best way to determine the critical frequency in your vicinity. **ANSWER A.**

G3B08 What does MUF stand for?

A. The Minimum Usable Frequency for communications between two points
B. The Maximum Usable Frequency for communications between two points
C. The Minimum Usable Frequency during a 24-hour period
D. The Maximum Usable Frequency during a 24-hour period

The ***maximum usable frequency (MUF)*** peaks during the day in the morning hours to the east, for working Europe, and in the afternoon and evening hours to the west, for working Asia. This is the fun of working ham radio skywaves – the ionosphere and the maximum usable frequency will constantly give us some excitement if we just keep tuned in. **ANSWER B.**

G3B07 What does LUF stand for?

A. The Lowest Usable Frequency for communications between two specific points
B. Lowest Usable Frequency for communications to any point outside a 100-mile radius
C. The Lowest Usable Frequency during a 24-hour period
D. Lowest Usable Frequency during the past 60 minutes

The term ***"lowest usable frequency"*** refers specifically to ***specific points attempting skywave contact***. If you and a buddy are separated by 500 miles and want to stay in touch on the 75/80 meter ham band using a specific frequency, you may find early morning and evening contacts loud and clear, while attempts at noon result in no contact on that frequency. This is because at noon the LUF has become many megahertz higher due to changes in the ionosphere from the effects of the Sun. Your chosen frequency is now lower than the LUF. But hang around the LUF will begin to drop quickly around sundown and your contact will be restored! **ANSWER A.**

G3B06 What usually happens to radio waves with frequencies below the LUF?

A. They are refracted back to Earth
B. They pass through the ionosphere
C. They are attenuated before reaching the destination
D. They are refracted and trapped in the ionosphere to circle Earth

During daylight hours, the lowest usable frequency for a skywave contact may be around 3 MHz. This means the 160 meter band, just under 2 MHz, will not be usable for daylight ***skywave*** contacts because they are ***attenuated before reaching the destination***. But as soon as the Sun goes down, hang on for some great DX contacts! **ANSWER C.**

G3B11 What happens to HF propagation when the LUF exceeds the MUF?

A. Propagation via ordinary skywave communications is not possible over that path
B. HF communications over the path are enhanced
C. Double-hop propagation along the path is more common
D. Propagation over the path on all HF frequencies is enhanced

When the lowest usable frequency (LUF) exceeds the maximum usable frequency (MUF), high frequency ***radio communications along a specific ionospheric signal path disappears***. This sometimes occurs with increased geomagnetic activity from sunspots. **ANSWER A.**

G3B05 How does the ionosphere affect radio waves with frequencies below the MUF and above the LUF?

A. They are refracted back to Earth
B. They pass through the ionosphere
C. They are amplified by interaction with the ionosphere
D. They are refracted and trapped in the ionosphere to circle Earth

Frequencies below the Maximum Usable Frequency (MUF) and above the Lowest Usable Frequency (LUF) are ***refracted back to Earth*** by the ionosphere. For maximum range, operate as close to MUF as possible. **ANSWER A.**

G3B02 What factors affect the MUF?

A. Path distance and location
B. Time of day and season
C. Solar radiation and ionospheric disturbances
D. All these choices are correct

Getting a signal halfway around the Earth is a ham radio tradition. But there are plenty of things to consider when attempting to make a contact – solar activity, day or night, fall or summer, and how far away the other station is located. ***All of the choices are correct***. **ANSWER D.**

G3B04 Which of the following is a way to determine current propagation on a desired band from your station?

A. Use a network of automated receiving stations on the internet to see where your transmissions are being received
B. Check the A-index
C. Send a series of dots and listen for echoes
D. All these choices are correct

The Reverse Beacon Network (RBN) is one of the greatest amateur radio tools made possible by the Internet. ***The RBN will let you determine current propagation on a desired band from your station***. The RBN is not the only system that can serve this function. A worldwide network of Digisonde® Ionosondes **http://www.digisonde.com/stationlist.php** provides a wealth of information about worldwide

Don't Forget Medium Wave

Amateur Radio started in the frequency range now known as Medium Wave (MW). Highly recommended reading is ***200 Meters and Down*** by Clinton Desoto, which explores this history. We have one full-fledged MW band, 160 meters, often called the Gentleman's Band. We also have a brand new MW band, 630 meters! (And, if you really like a challenge, we now have a brand new Low Frequency band on 2200 Meters.)

There's a world of interesting radio in the MW region. Long distance communications can be a challenge because of the antenna requirements, but reliable local operation can be had with reasonable antennas. Simple wire antennas are pretty much the norm for MW communications, or if you have a tower you can usually "load it up" on MW. We are no longer limited by the regional power restrictions that once hampered effective 160 meters communications. 160 meters is a great deal of fun and we have plenty of elbow room down there. Modern digital methods make effective MW communications far more effective than in the not-too-distant past. Give it a try!

radio propagation, but requires a little education to fully understand the data. Also, don't overlook the old reliable broadcasts from WWV, the oldest continuously operating radio broadcast station on Earth! **ANSWER A.**

G8C02 Which digital mode is used as a low-power beacon for assessing HF propagation?

A. WSPR
B. MFSK16
C. PSK31
D. SSB-SC

The Weak Signal Propagation Reporter (***WSPR***) protocol is one major component of the popular Reverse Beacon Network, which has truly revolutionized radio science. For ages, hams (and other radio experimenters) have looked for a way to monitor their own transmissions from afar. The RBN can be around when and where there are no hams, and gives us a much better picture of worldwide radio propagation. **ANSWER A.**

G3B03 Which frequency will have the least attenuation for long-distance skip propagation?

A. Just below the MUF
B. Just above the LUF
C. Just below the critical frequency
D. Just above the critical frequency

The term ***"lowest attenuation"*** means least amount of signal fading. The trick is to try to operate on the highest high frequency ham band that gives you skywave propagation to somewhere else in the country or the world. Operating ***just below the maximum usable frequency (MUF)*** will lead to some extraordinary crystal-clear communications. **ANSWER A.**

G3B10 What is the approximate maximum distance along the Earth's surface normally covered in one hop using the E region?

A. 180 miles
B. 1,200 miles
C. 2,500 miles
D. 12,000 miles

The ***E layer*** is between 50 and 90 miles up. Because it's closer to Earth, high-frequency waves don't bounce as far as they do off of the F layer. E skip is usually about ***1200 miles***. During the summertime, "sporadic E" may sometimes "short skip" as little as 600 miles. **ANSWER B.**

G3C01 Which ionospheric region is closest to the surface of Earth?

A. The D region
B. The E region
C. The F1 region
D. The F2 region

The ***D region*** (D, then E then F then F1 then F2… there is an order there) is the region ***closest to*** the surface of the ***Earth***. During daylight hours the Darn D region is usually responsible for absorbing ham radio medium-frequency skywave signals. **ANSWER A.**

Altitudes in Miles of Ionospheric Layers

	Day		
Layers	**Summer**	**Winter**	**Night**
F2	**>250**		
F1	**90-150**		
F		**90-150**	**90-250**
E	**55-90**	**55-90**	
D	**40**	**40**	

G3C11 Which ionospheric region is the most absorbent of signals below 10 MHz during daylight hours?

A. The F2 region
B. The F1 region
C. The E region
D. The D region

During the day, the Darn D region hinders distant signals. Here's an example of what it can do to your signal. The 40-meter band is a great one for 500-mile, daylight, skywave contacts. Even though they may fade in and out a little bit, they are almost always there from Sun-up to around 4:00 p.m. local time. After 4:00 p.m., the D-region associated with absorption begins to disappear, and the 40 meter band begins to "go long." Your 500-mile buddies will disappear, and next thing you hear are stations a couple thousand miles away pouring in. Then, as the 40 meter band continues on well into the night, in come the dreaded megawatt, foreign, double-sideband, shortwave broadcast stations that share our frequencies, too. What you will hear at night and in the early morning hours on 40 meters are extremely loud whistles from foreign broadcast, double-sideband, full-carrier stations, and the key to operating 40 meters in the early morning hours is finding a spot to dodge the foreign broadcast signals. **ANSWER D.**

G3C05 Why is long-distance communication on the 40-, 60-, 80-, and 160-meter bands more difficult during the day?

A. The F region absorbs signals at these frequencies during daylight hours
B. The F region is unstable during daylight hours
C. The D region absorbs signals at these frequencies during daylight hours
D. The E region is unstable during daylight hours

The Darn D region does more harm than good to medium- and high-frequency signals during daylight hours. During the day, SSB and CW operations on 160 and 80 meters are confined to ground wave coverage. On 40 meters, daytime skip distances are generally no greater than 600 miles when the ***D region*** is ***absorbing MF and HF signals***. **ANSWER C.**

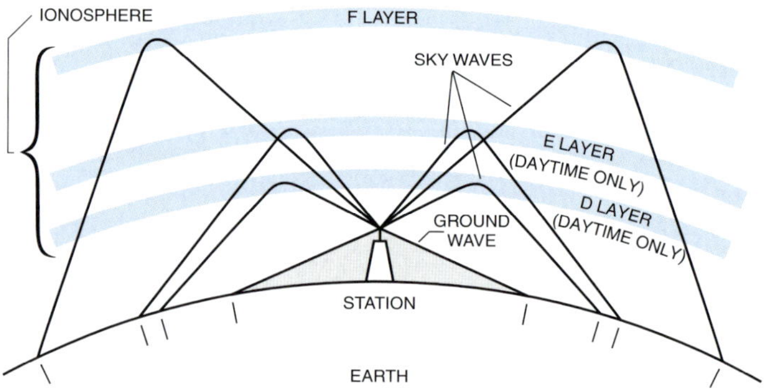

Radio Wave Propagation

Source: Mobile 2-Way Radio Communications, G. West, © 1993, Master Publishing, Inc.

G3B12 Which of the following is typical of the lower HF frequencies during the summer?

A. Poor propagation at any time of day
B. World-wide propagation during daylight hours
C. Heavy distortion on signals due to photon absorption
D. High levels of atmospheric noise or static

One of the great things about having a General Class license is that you have access to all the HF amateur bands, each with its own unique characteristics. Regardless of the prevailing conditions, there is almost always at least one band that will allow you to establish communications. During years of low solar activity, the lower frequency amateur bands will be the most useful. However, there are no perfect ham radio bands; your choice will always involve some kind of compromise. While the "low bands" are less subject to the whims of the ionosphere, noise levels are generally much higher. Especially ***during the summer, high levels of atmospheric noise or "static"*** can be prominent. This is one valid reason to operate high power; you may need all the power you can legally generate to overcome the atmospheric noise at the far end! **ANSWER D.**

G3C09 What type of propagation allows signals to be heard in the transmitting station's skip zone?

A. Faraday rotation
B. Scatter
C. Chordal hop
D. Short-path

Scatter communications (sometimes called backscatter) is one way to reach a station that is in that zone of no-reception – the skip zone. When Gordo communicates from southern California to Seattle, San Francisco is in his skip zone and will not receive his signals. But if he aims his beam antenna west toward Hawaii, some of his signal is backscattered into the Bay Area, giving him communications to a station that is too far for ground waves, and too close for normal skywaves. **ANSWER B.**

G3C08 Why are HF scatter signals in the skip zone usually weak?

A. Only a small part of the signal energy is scattered into the skip zone
B. Signals are scattered from the magnetosphere, which is not a good reflector
C. Propagation is via ground waves, which absorb most of the signal energy
D. Propagation is via ducts in the F region, which absorb most of the energy

During periods of scatter communications, ***only a fraction of the original signal is scattered*** back to those stations that are too far for ground wave reception yet too close for the main part of your signal that is being reflected by the ionosphere. The station in your skip zone gets only a very weak incoming skywave signal. **ANSWER A.**

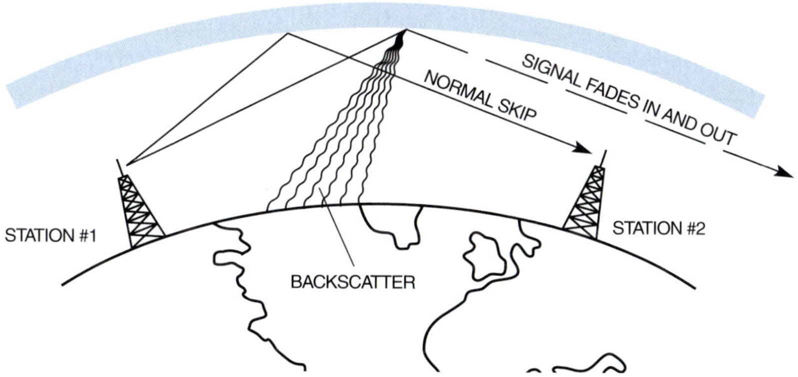

Backscatter

G3C07 What makes HF scatter signals often sound distorted?

A. The ionospheric region involved is unstable
B. Ground waves are absorbing much of the signal
C. The E region is not present
D. Energy is scattered into the skip zone through several different paths

The wavy sound of HF scatter signals, especially backscatter, is caused by the ***signal*** being ***reflected*** back ***through several radio wave paths***, creating multi- path distortion. **ANSWER D.**

Your modern HF transceiver may also include the 6 meter, 2 meter, and 440 bands. Six meters is the "Magic Band" and can offer unusual and surprising propagation. And don't forget the DX portion of 2 meters, far away from the "madding crowd," where the still small voice of weak signal operation prevails.

G3C06 What is a characteristic of HF scatter?

A. Phone signals have high intelligibility
B. Signals have a fluttering sound
C. There are very large, sudden swings in signal strength
D. Scatter propagation occurs only at night

High frequency ***scatter communications*** bounce a portion of your signal off of densely ionized patches in the ionosphere. Since the ionosphere is constantly in motion, the signals will fade in and out, much like ocean waves, resulting in a ***fluttering sound***. **ANSWER B.**

G2D04 Which of the following describes an azimuthal projection map?

A. A map that shows accurate land masses
B. A map that shows true bearings and distances from a specific location
C. A map that shows the angle at which an amateur satellite crosses the equator
D. A map that shows the number of degrees longitude that an amateur satellite appears to move westward at the equator with each orbit Long-range communications do not necessarily go in straight lines.

When we navigate our signals around the world, we need a ***chart*** that takes into account the curvature of the Earth and ***true bearings and distance from a specific location***. An azimuthal map shows your ham shack at the center of the Earth and will help you determine the shortest path between your station and that rare DX station. **ANSWER B.**

ham apps

Want the accuracy of a GPS receiver, but the "old school" feel of a magnetic compass? This compass app is just for you! A great accessory to take with you on your next 2-meter Fox Hunt! Also great for setting up your antenna rotator. **https://play.google.com/store/apps/details?id=com.gn.android.compass&hl=en**

It should come as no surprise that a lot of radio amateurs are also amateur astronomers. TheNightSky is a great way of keeping track of all those celestial objects, for fun or navigation. Between NightSky and Compass, there's no excuse to ever be lost! **https://itunes.apple.com/us/app/the-night-sky/id475772902?mt=8**

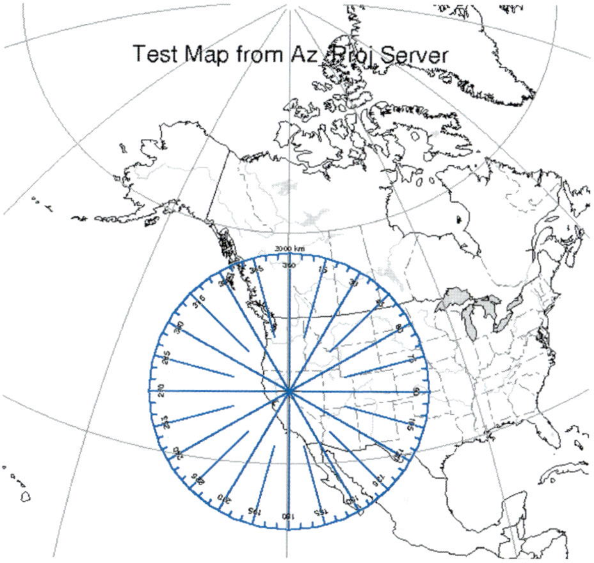

Ham operators with a beam antenna will use an azimuthal map like this one to determine short path and long path headings to reach DX stations.

G3B01 What is a characteristic of skywave signals arriving at your location by both short-path and long-path propagation?

A. Periodic fading approximately every 10 seconds
B. Signal strength increased by 3 dB
C. The signal might be cancelled causing severe attenuation
D. A slightly delayed echo might be heard

Do you have Gordo's audio course? If so, you can hear the distinctive sound of simultaneous short path and long path reception. Incoming ***signals will have a well-defined echo*** because the short path signal is coming to you from a much closer distance than the long path signal coming all the way around the globe. The echo you hear is caused by the difference in the time it takes the signal to reach you via short path and long path. **ANSWER D.**

G2D06 How is a directional antenna pointed when making a "long-path" contact with another station?

A. Toward the rising sun
B. Along the gray line
C. 180 degrees from the station's short-path heading
D. Toward the north

Some ionospheric conditions may let you to establish better communications with a distant station over a long path around the world rather than over the direct short path. If you hear the station with an echo, try turning your beam ***antenna 180 degrees*** in the opposite direction ***from the station's short path*** direction to hear whether or not the station will come in better on the long path. **ANSWER C.**

G3A01 How does a higher sunspot number affect HF propagation?

A. Higher sunspot numbers generally indicate a greater probability of good propagation at higher frequencies
B. Lower sunspot numbers generally indicate greater probability of sporadic E propagation
C. A zero sunspot number indicates that radio propagation is not possible on any band
D. A zero sunspot number indicates undisturbed conditions

Sunspots are temporary "cold" regions on the surface of the Sun, somewhat like bubbles on the surface of a vat of boiling spaghetti sauce. They emit lots of ultraviolet radiation, which is primarily responsible for creating an active ionosphere. Generally speaking, hams are happy when there are a lot of sunspots! The frequency of sunspots varies with the solar cycle. When there are ***a lot of sunspots, the "high bands" (20, 17, 15, 12, 10, and 6 meters) come alive***, while during the down times, the low bands (160, 80, 60, 40, and 30 meters) are the only bands suitable for long distance communications. But there are always exceptions, so don't put too much stock in sunspot numbers alone. Get on the air and see what's there! If you don't hear anything, always call CQ! **ANSWER A.**

Solar flares and sunspots affect radiowave propagation
Photo courtesy of N.A.S.A.

G3A10 What causes HF propagation conditions to vary periodically in a 26- to 28-day cycle?

A. Long term oscillations in the upper atmosphere
B. Cyclic variation in Earth's radiation belts
C. Rotation of the Sun's surface layers around its axis
D. The position of the Moon in its orbit

We find recurring skywave conditions about every 28 days ***in the rotation of the Sun's surface layers around its axis***. Ham operators carefully monitor solar activity and find that stronger sunspots may reappear 28 days later for more excitement on the air waves. **ANSWER C.**

G3A09 How can high geomagnetic activity benefit radio communications?

A. Creates auroras that can reflect VHF signals
B. Increases signal strength for HF signals passing through the polar regions
C. Improve HF long path propagation
D. Reduce long delayed echoes

During periods of high geomagnetic activity beautiful auroras may be viewed at night, away from city lights, as far south as latitude 37° north. The aurora itself is created when gases in our upper atmosphere are bombarded by coronal mass ejections, kind of like a neon light. Depending on which gas gets stirred up determines what color Northern Lights you may see. A trip to Alaska during equinox will usually lead to some awe-inspiring Northern Lights viewing. ***The aurora can also reflect VHF signals***, adding to the excitement. **ANSWER A.**

This aurora photo is from Chip and Janet Margelli, K7JA and KL7MF, during their week of radio fun in Coldfoot, Alaska. Geomagnetic disturbances caused by the Sun create the Northern Lights.

G3A04 Which of the following are the least reliable bands for long-distance communications during periods of low solar activity?

A. 80 meters and 160 meters
B. 60 meters and 40 meters
C. 30 meters and 20 meters
D. 15 meters, 12 meters, and 10 meters

As we begin to leave the bottom of solar cycle 24 for new solar cycle 25, we still will have a few more years of ***low solar activity and we won't hear much skywave activity on 6, 10, 12, and 15 meters.*** No problem – just switch down to 20 meters during the days, or 40 and 75 meters at night, and enjoy predictable good skywave DX without all the noise that sometimes elevated solar activity brings! This is why you are getting the General license, to enjoy all the ham bands for great worldwide signals, day and night! **ANSWER D.**

G3A05 What is the solar flux index?

A. A measure of the highest frequency that is useful for ionospheric propagation between two points on Earth
B. A count of sunspots that is adjusted for solar emissions
C. Another name for the American sunspot number
D. A measure of solar radiation with a wavelength of 10.7 centimeters

The ***solar-flux*** index is ***measured*** daily ***on a wavelength of 10.7 centimeters*** in Ottawa, Canada. You may tune into the radio propagation solar activity reports transmitted by WWV at 18 minutes past the hour. Frequencies of 10 and 15 MHz will give you best reception during the day, and 5 MHz may give you best reception at night. **ANSWER D.**

G3A12 What does the K-index measure?

A. The relative position of sunspots on the surface of the Sun
B. The short-term stability of Earth's geomagnetic field
C. The short-term stability of the Sun's magnetic field
D. The solar radio flux at Boulder, Colorado

Earth is surrounded by the magnetosphere that acts as a barrier protecting us from some of the charged particles coming from eruptions on the Sun. The magnetosphere occasionally develops holes and cracks that may allow tremendous amounts of solar energy to disturb our natural ***geomagnetic stability***. Some of the energy that penetrates the magnetosphere can be seen as auroras. A low ***K index*** means good, stable high-frequency propagation. **ANSWER B.**

G3A13 What does the A-index measure?

A. The relative position of sunspots on the surface of the Sun
B. The amount of polarization of the Sun's electric field
C. The long-term stability of Earth's geomagnetic field
D. The solar radio flux at Boulder, Colorado

The ***A-Index*** is a 24 hour averaging of the planetary K-Index, and is a great indicator of ***long term stability*** of the Earth's geomagnetic field. **ANSWER C.**

G3A03 Approximately how long does it take the increased ultraviolet and X-ray radiation from a solar flare to affect radio propagation on Earth?

A. 28 days
B. 1 to 2 hours
C. 8 minutes
D. 20 to 40 hours

Ultraviolet radiation travels at the speed of light. It takes about ***8 minutes*** for sunlight and ultraviolet rays to reach the Earth's ionosphere. Heavy sunspot activity may affect worldwide propagation for up to 3 days. **ANSWER C.**

G3A06 What is a geomagnetic storm?

A. A sudden drop in the solar flux index
B. A thunderstorm that affects radio propagation
C. Ripples in the geomagnetic force
D. A temporary disturbance in Earth's geomagnetic field

We're surrounded! Above our weather layer of the atmosphere, called the troposphere, is the ionosphere with its D layer, and above that the E layer, and on top of the E layer are the F-1 and F-2 layers. But did you know there is yet another layer up around 400 miles, called the magnetosphere? When the ***Sun sends out a coronal mass ejection***, the charged particles may ***interact with Earth's geomagnetic field***, and disrupt communications for days. **ANSWER D.**

G3A02 What effect does a sudden ionospheric disturbance have on the daytime ionospheric propagation?

A. It enhances propagation on all HF frequencies
B. It disrupts signals on lower frequencies more than those on higher frequencies
C. It disrupts communications via satellite more than direct communications
D. None, because only areas on the night side of the Earth are affected

The ***lower bands***, such as 160, 80, 40, and even 20 meters, ***become so noisy*** that it is impossible to hear any distant signals coming in from skywaves during a sudden ionospheric disturbance. **ANSWER B.**

Elmer Point: Your new HF General Class radio also offers full shortwave reception. Try 10- or 15-MHz to hear the WWV time ticks. At 18 minutes past the hour, listen to your latest ionospheric and solar weather reports! A K index between 1 to 4, and an A index of 0 to 7 means the ionosphere is quiet and very predictable for long-range skywaves. But a K index of 5 or 6 with an A index of 30 to 49 indicates that HF band conditions will become unpredictable and unstable. And hang on to your receivers – a K index of 7 to 9 or an A index of 50 and higher means the HF bands will likely be unusable for regular skywave contacts due to a major solar storm with strong geomagnetic activity disrupting HF signals. With high K and A indexes, time to go outside after dark and look for an aurora! Here's a summary of K and A Index readings:

K Index	A Index	HF Skip Conditions
K1 – K4	A0 – A7	Bands are normal
K4	A8 – A15	Bands are unsettled
K4	A16 – A30	Bands are unpredictable
K5	A30 – A50	Lower bands are unstable
K6	A50 – A99	Few skywaves below 15 MHz
K7 – K9	A100 – A400	Radio blackout is likely. Go fishing or watch for an aurora.

G3A08 How can a geomagnetic storm affect HF propagation?

A. Improve high-latitude HF propagation
B. Degrade ground wave propagation
C. Improve ground wave propagation
D. Degrade high-latitude HF propagation

During periods of major geomagnetic disturbances, high-frequency propagation over ***high-latitude paths will be degraded***. At the same time, activity on 6 meters VHF might be hopping! **ANSWER D.**

G3A11 How long does it take a coronal mass ejection to affect radio propagation on Earth?

A. 28 days
B. 14 days
C. 4 to 8 minutes
D. 15 hours to several days

We can see a sunspot in the amount of time it takes light to travel from the Sun to the Earth – 8 minutes. But this question asks about the slower moving ***sunspot charged particles*** that lumber toward Earth as part of the solar wind. This wind can take as long as ***15 hours to several days*** to begin to disturb radio wave propagation on the ham bands. This means we have almost 2 days advanced alert that band conditions may be changing. Tune into WWV at 18 minutes past the hour and listen to the 30-second solar report.

WWV 5 MHz	Best at night	WWV 15 MHz	Best days
WWV 10 MHz	Day and night	WWV & WWVH 20 MHz	Some days

You can usually tune in WWV 10 MHz during the days, but only before a big sunspot event finally hits Earth. When disruption occurs, WWV sometimes fades out completely! **ANSWER D.**

G3A14 How is long distance radio communication usually affected by the charged particles that reach Earth from solar coronal holes?

A. HF communication is improved
B. HF communication is disturbed
C. VHF/UHF ducting is improved
D. VHF/UHF ducting is disturbed

A solar coronal hole can be seen as a dark spot on the face of the Sun emitting charged particles into the solar wind. If you took your thermometer up there, there would be an extreme temperature drop within the eruption. You can actually track sunspots as they rotate around the Sun on a 27.5-day cycle. There usually is a pair of sunspots – one with a positive magnetic north field, and the other with a negative south field. Just ask Galileo – he was the first to observe these sunspots in 1610. Sunspots with a solar coronal hole will normally ***disrupt high-frequency communications***, but for the joy of 6 and 2 meter operators, they can create aberrations in the magnetosphere that will cause VHF long-range band openings. **ANSWER B.**

G3A07 At what point in the solar cycle does the 20-meter band usually support worldwide propagation during daylight hours?

A. At the summer solstice
B. Only at the maximum point
C. Only at the minimum point
D. At any point

We told you so – ***20 meters*** will ***always*** be the fun band ***for daytime skywave activity***, no matter where we are on the slow upward climb on solar cycle 25! And at night, when 20 meters fades out, turn the band switch to 40 meters, dodge the foreign broadcast carriers, and work the world into daybreak the next morning! With a General Class ham ticket, the world of skywave DX is yours to enjoy, on all ham bands! **ANSWER D.**

20 meters is an excellent daytime band for voice communications.

Shortwave Listening: Gateway to Understanding HF

For many decades, most radio amateurs got their first exposure to long distance radio communications by listening to shortwave radio. By the time we old timers got our "tickets" we had a pretty good idea of what to expect when it came to HF communications because we had spent time listening.

SWL (shortwave listening) is still alive and well throughout the world. Every radio amateur should have a shortwave radio in the shack. Excellent receivers are available for less than $100 and provide a nice break from normal ham activity, even for experienced radio amateurs. Remember, one of our reasons for existing as radio amateurs is to "promote international good will." In order to promote international good will, you have to know about the world beyond your back yard, and shortwave radio is a great way to expand your world view. By learning what's going on in other countries, when you get on the air with a ham from one of those faraway places you'll have something to talk about!

One excellent resource for you shack is ***The Worldwide Listening Guide*** by John Figliozzi. It lists English language shortwave broadcasts from around the world, and tells you how to tune into programming over the Internet and other listening options. You can obtain a copy from The W5YI Group by calling 800-669-9594 or visit www.w5yi.org.

There's a lot of interesting stuff outside of the amateur bands; take time to explore the *whole* radio spectrum!

Website Resources

IF YOU'RE LOOKING FOR	THEN VISIT
DX reference guide	www.ac6v.com
amateur radio satellite operations	www.amsat.org
the latest news about ham radio	www.arnewsline.org
microphones, headsets, and more	www.heilsound.com
Disaster preparedness & emergency comms info	www.fema.gov
DSP, antenna analyzers, and more	www.timewave.com
HF modems for digital modes	www.halcomm.com
HF modems and gear for digital modes	www.kantronics.com
digital amateur radio organization	www.tapr.org
azimuthal maps, solar information, and more	www.wm7d.net
software defined radios	www.flex-radio.com

CD 3 TRACK 1

Your HF Transmitter

G8A05 What type of modulation varies the instantaneous power level of the RF signal?

A. Power modulation
B. Phase modulation
C. Frequency modulation
D. Amplitude modulation

The instantaneous power level of the signal varies with ***amplitude modulation***. **ANSWER D.**

G7C02 What output is produced by a balanced modulator?

A. Frequency modulated RF
B. Audio with equalized frequency response
C. Audio extracted from the modulation signal
D. Double-sideband modulated RF

A balanced modulator is used in both transmitters and receivers, as well as all kinds of instrumentation. ***The basic balanced modulator when supplied with an RF carrier and an audio signal produces a double sideband (suppressed carrier) signal***. If followed up with a bandpass filter tuned to one of the sideband frequencies, it now becomes a single sideband generator (more precisely a single-sideband suppressed-carrier) generator. The most common implementation of the balanced modulator in modern ham gear is the modular DBM, or double-balanced mixer. **ANSWER D.**

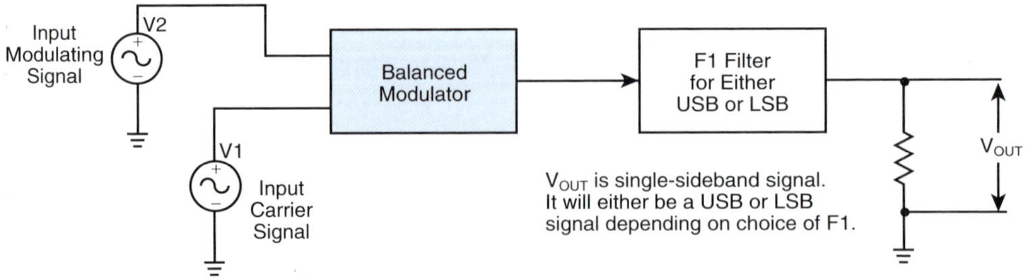

G7C03 What is one reason to use an impedance matching transformer at a transmitter output?

A. To minimize transmitter power output
B. To present the desired impedance to the transmitter and feed line
C. To reduce power supply ripple
D. To minimize radiation resistance

When impedances are matched, we have the greatest amount of power transfer. An ***impedance matching transformer*** allows us to precisely match radio stages ***to present the desired impedance to the the transmitter and feed line.*** Always remember the NFL principle of transformers: No Free Lunch. While a properly matched transformer can minimize losses, you never get any more power out of it than you put into it. The product of voltage and current on the output can never be more than the product of voltage and current on the input. If you step up the voltage, the current must go down, and vice versa. **ANSWER B.**

G7C01 What circuit is used to select one of the sidebands from a balanced modulator?

A. Carrier oscillator
B. Filter
C. IF amplifier
D. RF amplifier

The ***balanced modulator*** produces an upper and lower sideband signal, with the carrier reduced to near zero. The upper and lower sideband signals are then fed ***into*** a narrow ***filter*** network which cancels out either the upper or the lower sideband signal based on other settings of the radio. **ANSWER B.**

G8A07 Which of the following phone emissions uses the narrowest bandwidth?

A. Single sideband
B. Vestigial sideband
C. Phase modulation
D. Frequency modulation

The phone emission that uses the ***least bandwidth is single sideband (SSB)***, usually about 2.8 kHz. The modern high frequency ham radio may include adjustable transmit SSB filter networks that can decrease the amount of occupied bandwidth on transmit from the normal 2.8 kHz down to 2.6 kHz. While the resulting signal sounds void of bass response, its narrow 2.6 kHz of bandwidth really helps get the signal through to a distant station when noise levels are high. **ANSWER A.**

G4D01 What is the purpose of a speech processor in a transceiver?

A. Increase the apparent loudness of transmitted voice signals
B. Increase transmitter bass response for more natural-sounding SSB signals
C. Prevent distortion of voice signals
D. Decrease high-frequency voice output to prevent out-of-band operation

The ***speech processor*** on modern transceivers should be used with caution. Too much processing may distort your signal. But just a little bit of speech processing could ***increase the apparent loudness of a transmitted voice signals*** and your average power. When conditions are good, turn the processor off! Speech processing is like sending an e-mail in all upper-case letters! Turn it off! **ANSWER A.**

G4D02 How does a speech processor affect a single sideband phone signal?

A. It increases peak power
B. It increases average power
C. It reduces harmonic distortion
D. It reduces intermodulation distortion

Turning on your transceiver's ***speech processor*** will not increase PEP output power if you are 100 percent modulated. It will ***increase the average power,*** which many times will make your signal sound "too hot" for comfort. Stay off that speech processor button unless it's absolutely necessary. **ANSWER B.**

You can add a speech processor to an older ham set. The accessory unit plugs in between your mic and the transceiver microphone input

---

G2A12 What control is typically adjusted for proper ALC setting on a single sideband transceiver?

A. RF clipping level
B. Transmit audio or microphone gain
C. Antenna inductance or capacitance
D. Attenuator level

That new high frequency transceiver that you are going to reward yourself with when you pass your exam has a built in transmit safeguard called ***Automatic Level Control (ALC)***. The ALC acts as an electronic governor to throttle back ***transmit power*** in case you overdrive the input circuits with too much ***mic gain*** or too much computer drive for data. You can monitor ALC action on the rig's multi-meter. Look for a small, now-and-then jiggle of the ALC indicator, which will indicate proper drive levels. If you overdrive the ALC section of your transmitter, you'll see the ALC meter going up into the red danger area. If this happens, immediately back off mic gain or computer drive power to your transmitter. **ANSWER B.**

G4A05 Why is automatic level control (ALC) used with an RF power amplifier?

A. To balance the transmitter audio frequency response
B. To reduce harmonic radiation
C. To prevent excessive drive
D. To increase overall efficiency

The ALC output jack on your new transceiver needs to be tied into the ALC input jack on that linear amplifier. This gives your equipment a "handshake" when the drive level is correctly set. Without this simple plug-in connection between amplifier and radio, the amp could be overdriven and the ***signal distorted due to excess drive***. Further, the amplifier could go into thermal melt down from being overdriven. Be sure to hook up that needed ALC "handshake" cable between rig and amp. **ANSWER C.**

G8A08 Which of the following is an effect of overmodulation?

A. Insufficient audio
B. Insufficient bandwidth
C. Frequency drift
D. Excessive bandwidth

If you ***over-modulate*** on high frequency, you're going to spread your signal over a ***wider bandwidth*** than that of a properly modulated HF signal. If someone says you are "splattering," turn down the mic gain and turn off the speech processor. **ANSWER D.**

G4D03 What is the effect of an incorrectly adjusted speech processor?

A. Distorted speech
B. Excess intermodulation products
C. Excessive background noise
D. All these choices are correct

Most newer high frequency transceivers have a speech processor button that will turn processing on or off. Turn the speech processor off! ***Speech processing*** brings in ***excessive background pickup***, may cause your ***signal to sound distorted***, and can also cause the signal to ***cause excess intermodulation products, like splatter***. Leave your speech processor turned off as a new General Class ham! You'll learn how to use it correctly later. **ANSWER D.**

G8A10 What is meant by the term "flat-topping," when referring to an amplitude-modulated phone signal?

A. Signal distortion caused by insufficient collector current
B. The transmitter's automatic level control (ALC) is properly adjusted
C. Signal distortion caused by excessive drive or speech levels
D. The transmitter's carrier is properly suppressed

If you have excessive drive or speech levels set in an amplitude-modulated phone SSB transceiver, your signal will ***sound distorted***. The signal waveform shown on an oscilloscope has the top clipped off so it has a flat top. **ANSWER C.**

G4B08 What transmitter performance parameter does a two-tone test analyze?

A. Linearity
B. Percentage of suppression of the carrier and undesired sideband for SSB
C. Percentage of frequency modulation
D. Percentage of carrier phase shift

The faithful reproduction of your voice over single-sideband depends on equipment with excellent linearity. With new digital signal processing techniques on modulation, plus a new family of after-market, high-performance microphones, the ***2-tone test*** that enables you to view the wave forms on an oscilloscope is a great way to test for ***transmitter linearity***. But you know, even though the 2-tone test is your best answer for transmitter linearity, just ask fellow hams simply how you sound to them coming over their radio. No oscilloscope needed! **ANSWER A.**

---

ham apps

Every radio amateur needs a good audio signal generator, either for aligning equipment or merely driving the shack dog crazy. This is a great tool for tuning up a linear amplifier as well. Just place in front of your microphone and follow the detailed tune-up procedure we describe on page 111.

https://itunes.apple.com/us/app/audiosiggen/id347248794?mt=8

G4B07 What signals are used to conduct a two-tone test?

A. Two audio signals of the same frequency shifted 90 degrees
B. Two non-harmonically related audio signals
C. Two swept frequency tones
D. Two audio frequency range square wave signals of equal amplitude

If you plan to regularly service your own equipment, you can find a little "warbler" box that generates two non-harmonically related audio tones for testing. The device may either be plugged into the transmitter mike input, or the mike held up to the speaker on the device. ***The 2 tones must not be harmonically related*** in order to provide the best test. Listen to this sound on Gordo's audio CD course. **ANSWER B.**

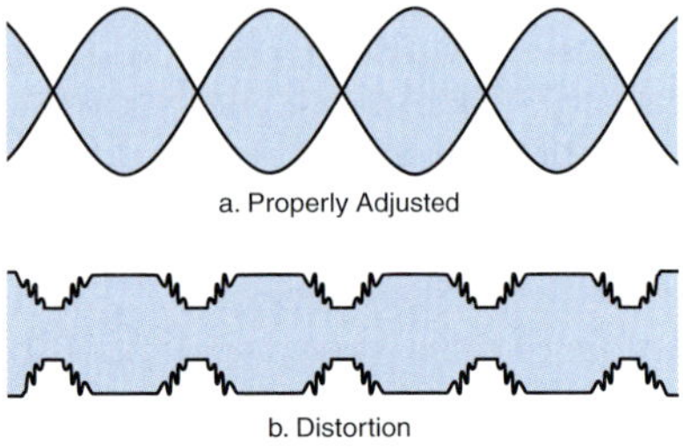

Two-Tone Test

G8A11 What is the modulation envelope of an AM signal?

A. The waveform created by connecting the peak values of the modulated signal
B. The carrier frequency that contains the signal
C. Spurious signals that envelop nearby frequencies
D. The bandwidth of the modulated signal

While Single Sideband (SSB) is the predominant "phone" mode on the HF bands, there is still a significant amount of activity on full-carrier, double-sideband Amplitude Modulation. Information is impressed on an AM carrier by altering the amplitude of the RF wave in accordance with the applied audio signal. ***The envelope of an AM signal is the "outline" or extreme outer limit of the radio frequency signal.*** 100% modulation is defined as when the envelope goes to zero (pinches off) during negative modulation peaks, or increases to twice the amplitude of the unmodulated RF carrier during positive modulation peaks. Because the human voice is quite asymmetrical, the positive and negative modulation peaks can be very different. Clever circuitry can take advantage of this asymmetry by assuring that the larger peaks are always the positive ones. This is standard practice in the AM broadcast industry, and has been adopted by many dedicated amateur AM operators. **ANSWER A.**

G4B01 What item of test equipment contains horizontal and vertical channel amplifiers?

A. An ohmmeter
B. A signal generator
C. An ammeter
D. An oscilloscope

An oscilloscope is your best piece of test equipment if you are a technical amateur operator. But it takes skill to work a "scope," so don't buy one unless you plan to do a lot in circuit design or signal calibration. The ***oscilloscope has horizontal- and vertical-channel amplifiers***. **ANSWER D.**

ham apps

Similar to the signal generator described above, this app can supply two tones simultaneously. While primarily designed for generating standard DTMF tone pairs, this can also generate the two tones you need for checking the alignment of SSB transmitters. **https://play.google.com/store/apps/details?id=net.simplyadvanced.simplytonegenerator**

G4B03 Which of the following is the best instrument to use for checking the keying waveform of a CW transmitter?

A. An oscilloscope
B. A field strength meter
C. A sidetone monitor
D. A wavemeter

The oscilloscope is your best instrument to check transmit signal quality. When magazine editors review the ***waveform of a CW signal*** or a two-tone test, they usually show photographs of the ***oscilloscope*** display. **ANSWER A.**

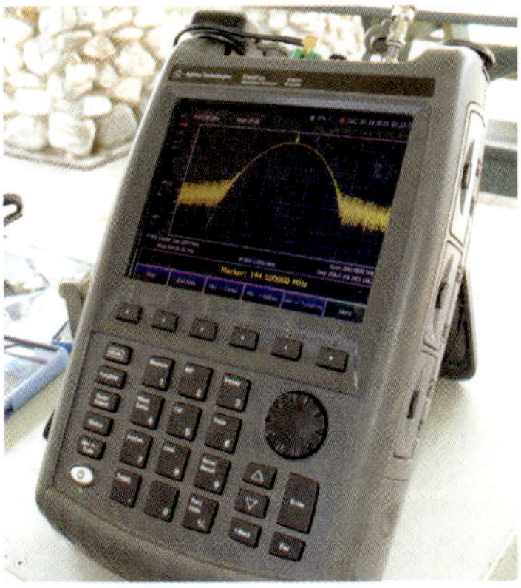

You can use a battery-powered oscilloscope to take measurements in the field, and use it on your workbench as well.

G4B04 What signal source is connected to the vertical input of an oscilloscope when checking the RF envelope pattern of a transmitted signal?

A. The local oscillator of the transmitter
B. An external RF oscillator
C. The transmitter balanced mixer output
D. The attenuated RF output of the transmitter

We take the ***attenuated RF output*** of the transmitter and couple it to the vertical input of an oscilloscope to check the quality of the transmitted signal. **ANSWER D.**

G4B02 Which of the following is an advantage of an oscilloscope versus a digital voltmeter?

A. An oscilloscope uses less power
B. Complex impedances can be easily measured
C. Greater precision
D. Complex waveforms can be measured

When you whistle into your SSB microphone and look at the resulting wave forms on an oscilloscope, you will see that only an ***oscilloscope can truly represent complex voice wave forms*** so that they can be precisely measured. **ANSWER D.**

G7B01 What is the purpose of neutralizing an amplifier?

A. To limit the modulation index
B. To eliminate self-oscillations
C. To cut off the final amplifier during standby periods
D. To keep the carrier on frequency

After new tubes have been installed in a powerful amplifier, follow the steps in the instruction manual for ***neutralization***, which ***will eliminate*** the possibility of ***self-oscillation***. **ANSWER B.**

G8A03 What is the name of the process that changes the instantaneous frequency of an RF wave to convey information?

A. Frequency convolution
B. Frequency transformation
C. Frequency conversion
D. Frequency modulation

A type of modulation that changes the frequency of an RF wave is called ***frequency modulation (FM)***. **ANSWER D.**

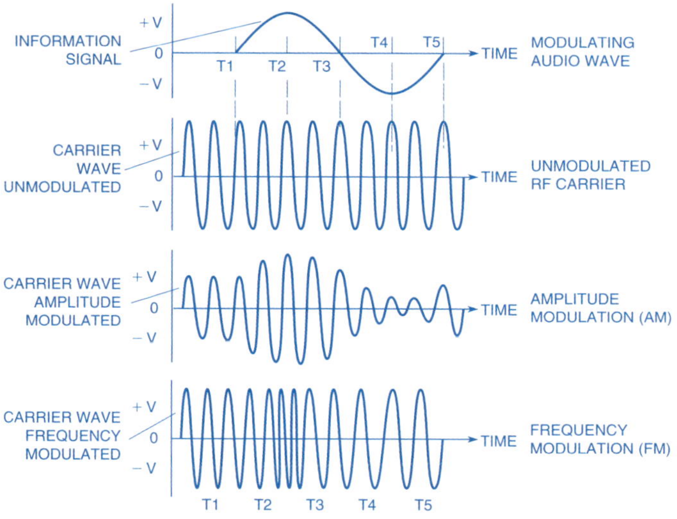

Modulation of RF Carrier

G8B04 What is the stage in a VHF FM transmitter that generates a harmonic of a lower frequency signal to reach the desired operating frequency?

A. Mixer
B. Reactance modulator
C. Balanced converter
D. Multiplier

Inside a VHF FM transmitter is a low-power oscillator that operates at HF levels. It's the job of the ***multiplier*** to select a harmonic of this signal to produce the desired operating frequency. Hint: Remember that harmonics are like octaves on a piano. Each note is 1/3rd or so higher than the last. They are mathematically related. So, it is logical that the stage of the transmitter is called a "multiplier." It's the answer choice that is mathematical! **ANSWER D.**

G8B06 What is the total bandwidth of an FM phone transmission having 5 kHz deviation and 3 kHz modulating frequency?

A. 3 kHz
B. 5 kHz
C. 8 kHz
D. 16 kHz

You can calculate this answer by multiplying 2 times the sum of the deviation and the modulating frequency. The deviation is 5 kHz plus 3 kHz of audio modulating frequency, which gives a sum of 8 kHz. Two times 8 kHz equals ***16 kHz***. This would be the ***total bandwidth*** of the FM phone transmission. **ANSWER D.**

G8B07 What is the frequency deviation for a 12.21 MHz reactance modulated oscillator in a 5 kHz deviation, 146.52 MHz FM phone transmitter?

A. 101.75 Hz
B. 416.7 Hz
C. 5 kHz
D. 60 kHz

The deviation of any Frequency Modulated transmitter is increased when you follow the oscillator with a frequency multiplier. In fact, the deviation is multiplied by exactly the same factor as the radio frequency. If we multiply the oscillator frequency by 12 to get to the final output frequency, the deviation is multiplied by the same amount. This means that if the final deviation is 5 kHz, we can divide that by 12 to come up with the required oscillator deviation. 5,000 ÷ 12 = 416.66 Hz, rounded to ***416.7 Hz***. **ANSWER B.**

G8A04 What emission is produced by a reactance modulator connected to a transmitter RF amplifier stage?

A. Multiplex modulation
B. Phase modulation
C. Amplitude modulation
D. Pulse modulation

A ***reactance modulator*** produces Frequency Modulation when applied to an oscillator, and ***Phase Modulation when applied to a subsequent amplifier stage***. **ANSWER B.**

G8A02 What is the name of the process that changes the phase angle of an RF signal to convey information?

A. Phase convolution
B. Phase modulation
C. Phase transformation
D. Phase inversion

A type of modulation that changes the phase of an RF wave is called ***phase modulation (PM).*** **ANSWER B.**

The International Space Station has a big ham station on board. The 2-meter rig in the right photo is set up in a school gym ready to make contact with the licensed ham astronauts aboard the International Space Station. Deviation levels must be accurate to insure a solid contact with the hams in space! *Photo courtesy of N.A.S.A.*

G7B08 How is the efficiency of an RF power amplifier determined?

A. Divide the DC input power by the DC output power
B. Divide the RF output power by the DC input power
C. Multiply the RF input power by the reciprocal of the RF output power
D. Add the RF input power to the DC output power

The efficiency of an RF power amplifier is calculated by ***dividing the radio frequency output power by the DC input power to that stage***. If you get 100 Watts of CW output power with 250 watts of DC input power, your efficiency is 40%, about typical. Since the RF output stage is by far the primary consumer of power in any modern HF rig, you can closely estimate the RF "final" input power by looking at the total DC current drawn by the rig, and multiplying that by the DC voltage, typically around 13.8 Volts. CAUTION! Unless you have a rather uncommon peak envelope power (PEP) meter, you cannot determine RF power output using speech, or whistling, or any such method. You must use a CW carrier (SSB transceivers have a TUNE function specifically for this). The peak power of the human voice can be over 6 times the average power. Typical peak RF output power (as well as DC input power) can be many times greater than what your slow-moving meters can indicate. **ANSWER B.**

G5B14 What is the output PEP of 500 volts peak-to-peak across a 50-ohm load?

A. 8.75 watts
B. 625 watts
C. 2500 watts
D. 5000 watts

Again, take half of the peak-to-peak voltage to obtain peak voltage. Multiply 250 × 0.707, square the result (176.75) by multiplying it by itself, and divide by 50. Here are the calculator keystrokes: Clear, Clear 250 × 0.707 = 176.75 × 176.75 = 31,240.56 ÷ 50 = 624.81, which rounds off to ***625 watts***. **ANSWER B.**

G5B11 What is the ratio of PEP to average power for an unmodulated carrier?

A. 0.707
B. 1.00
C. 1.414
D. 2.00

An unmodulated carrier is simultaneously peak and average. So the ratio of peak envelope power to average power on a steady unmodulated carrier is simply ***1.00***. **ANSWER B.**

G1C11 What measurement is specified by FCC rules that regulate maximum power?

A. RMS output from the transmitter
B. RMS input to the antenna
C. PEP input to the antenna
D. PEP output from the transmitter

In the not-too-distant past, amateur radio transmitters were limited by the DC input power to the final amplifier stage or stages, primarily because accurate means of measuring RF output power were not readily available. Nowadays, accurate peak-reading RF power meters do the job. The absolute limit on transmitter power is 1500 watts Peak Envelope Power or ***PEP output from the transmitter***, and is uniformly applicable to any mode of operation. [97.313] **ANSWER D.**

G5B13 What is the output PEP of an unmodulated carrier if the average power is 1060 watts?

A. 530 watts
B. 1060 watts
C. 1500 watts
D. 2120 watts

Remember, a steady carrier illustrates both peak power as well as average power. If your watt meter reads ***1060 watts*** average power, this is the same as PEP. **ANSWER B.**

G5B01 What dB change represents a factor of two increase or decrease in power?

A. Approximately 2 dB
B. Approximately 3 dB
C. Approximately 6 dB
D. Approximately 9 dB

The decibel is used to describe a change in power levels. It is a measure of the ratio of power output to power input. A ***two-times increase*** results in a change of ***3 dB***. **ANSWER B.**

G7B04 In a Class A amplifier, what percentage of the time does the amplifying device conduct?

A. 100%
B. More than 50% but less than 100%
C. 50%
D. Less than 50%

A Class A amplifier has the lowest distortion of any class of amplifier but also the least efficiency. The maximum efficiency of a Class A amplifier is 25% (when operating entirely within its linear range), and can be as low as 0 percent efficient, under no-signal conditions. The ***Class A amplifier is always dissipating heat whether it's putting out any useful signal power or not, because it's always "on."*** **ANSWER A.**

G7B11 For which of the following modes is a Class C power stage appropriate for amplifying a modulated signal?

A. SSB
B. FM
C. AM
D. All these choices are correct

The Class C power stage is ideal for high-efficiency, non-linear amplification of Frequency Modulation, as well as CW. A single sideband or double sideband signal will distort with Class C amplification. So use that ***Class C amplifier for*** boosting an ***FM*** transmitter's modulated signal. **ANSWER B.**

Elmer Point: Don't run out and buy a linear amplifier. The 100-watt output from your HF ham transceiver is plenty powerful enough to work the world. If you want to blast your signal out stronger, go for a directional antenna. The directional antenna also will increase incoming received signal strength – something that linear amplifier can't do. Linear amps are for those hams who have been on the air for at least a year, and who put up a 60 foot tower with a big directional beam on top. What the amplifier will do is increase their ability to bust through a pileup. Pileups occur when numerous hams are simultaneously trying to get their call signs through to a rare DX station during a contest. When you're just getting started on the General Class airwaves, steer clear of contest operation where pileups take place.

www.ameritron.com

G7B02 Which of these classes of amplifiers has the highest efficiency?

A. Class A
B. Class B
C. Class AB
D. Class C

Yes, Grandpa, I will learn the code! CW (Morse code) will always continue to be a popular mode for ham operators, even though the code test has been completely eliminated. A small CW-only transceiver operating Class C offers high efficiency with little current being consumed from the battery in between dots and dashes. ***Class C, high efficiency***. **ANSWER D.**

G7B10 Which of the following describes a linear amplifier?

A. Any RF power amplifier used in conjunction with an amateur transceiver
B. An amplifier in which the output preserves the input waveform
C. A Class C high efficiency amplifier
D. An amplifier used as a frequency multiplier

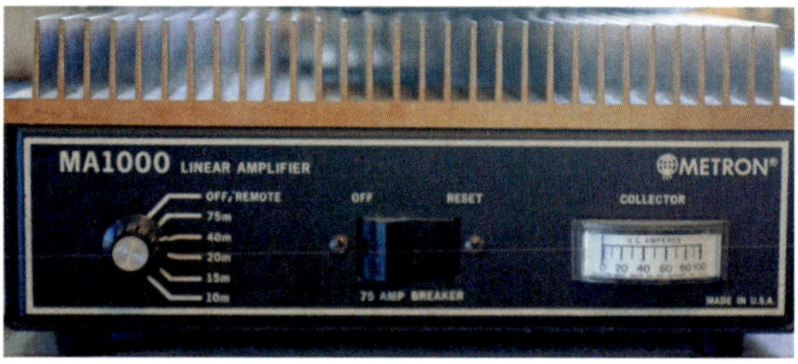

Linear amplifiers will indeed pump up your ***output waveform exactly as it appears to the amplifier input***; however, it is not wise to run any linear amplifier on high frequency mobile or on a simple home antenna until you are experienced with your equipment and discover that 100 watts can work all around the world. **ANSWER B.**

G4A08 What is the correct adjustment for the LOAD or COUPLING control of a vacuum tube RF power amplifier?

A. Minimum SWR on the antenna
B. Minimum plate current without exceeding maximum allowable grid current
C. Highest plate voltage while minimizing grid current
D. Desired power output without exceeding maximum allowable plate current

On the load control of that old power amp, seasoned hams will tell you to "tune for maximum smoke." Well, not really – but tune for ***desired power output without exceeding maximum allowable plate current,*** making sure you do not exceed 1500 watts output. **ANSWER D.**

G4A04 What is the effect on plate current of the correct setting of a vacuum-tube RF power amplifier's TUNE control?

A. A pronounced peak
B. A pronounced dip
C. No change will be observed
D. A slow, rhythmic oscillation

A vacuum tube amplifier is operating properly when the tuning is adjusted for a "dip" (minimum current), and the loading is such that the plate current at the tuning dip is at its rated value. If possible, RF output power should also be monitored while adjusting the tuning and loading. The loading should never be increased beyond the point where output power no longer increases. Whenever any adjustment is made to the loading, the tuning should once again be checked for a ***dip***, and should always be the last adjustment made. It also needs to be adjusted if you change frequency by more than a few kilohertz. **ANSWER B.**

G4A09 What is the purpose of delaying RF output after activating a transmitter's keying line to an external amplifier?

A. To prevent key clicks on CW
B. To prevent transient overmodulation
C. To allow time for the amplifier to switch the antenna between the transceiver and the amplifier output
D. To allow time for the amplifier power supply to reach operating level

The timing sequence of an amateur radio transmitter is crucial to maximizing the equipment life and signal purity of an amateur radio station. Improper timing can result in "hot keying" of relays and other components, and can cause premature failure of such components, as well as a lot of transmitted spurious signals. When pressing a microphone PTT switch (or tapping a CW key), the transmitter relays must all be fully in the transmit position before RF is applied. ***Well- designed transmitters delay the RF output until the mechanical relays in the transceiver and external power amplifier are fully activated***. **ANSWER C.**

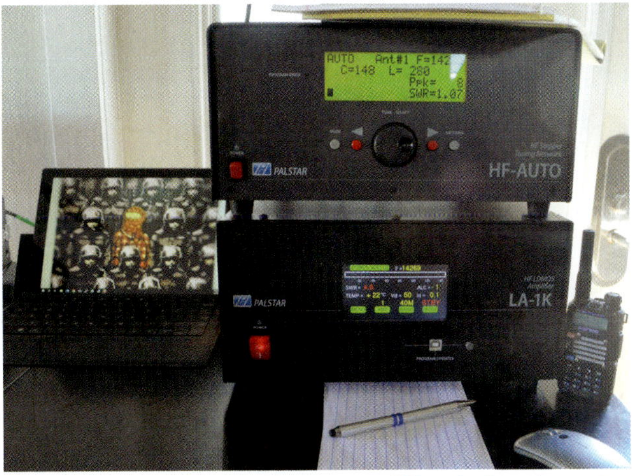

The lower unit pictured is a solid-state amplifier tied to the automatic tuner stacked above it. Because it is solid-state, the amp needs no operator tuning and works well for both base-station and portable operation.

Getting on the Air Inexpensively

If you're like most new radio amateurs, you might be horrified by the price of new rigs advertised in amateur radio magazines and catalogs. Don't be daunted! Advertisers always put their most *expensive* rigs up front and center. Remember, your first car wasn't a Maserati; it was probably a Yugo. The same situation with amateur radio prevails. Even us "well-seasoned," semi-famous hams didn't start out with "front page" rigs. Every ham radio manufacturer has entry level rigs available for a mere *fraction* of the cost of their flagship products. Start with what you can comfortably afford, and don't overlook good used equipment. It's best to have an Elmer looking over your shoulder as you consider your first HF ham radio rig… either new or used. Don't expect the advertisers to look after your best interests; their main interest is your money. Remember, amateur radio is something you learn, not something you buy!

Amplifier Tune-Up

While the FCC rules specify that amateurs should use the minimum power necessary to maintain communications, there are many instances where being able to run the full legal limit of 1500 watts is necessary, especially when conditions are poor. The typical method of achieving high power (QRO) is to use a *linear amplifier* after your transmitter, which raises the output power from 100 watts or so, to 1,000 – 1,500 watts. A linear amplifier will typically gain you about 10 dB or about 1-1/2 S-units at the distant receiver.

While you should always follow the instruction manual for your particular linear amplifier, the following procedure will allow you to operate just about any linear amplifier cleanly and safely. As with doing any on-the-air transmitter adjustments, always do this on a clear frequency, and do it quickly. Any extended tests should be done into a dummy load.

Linear amplifier tuning must be done with a steady unmodulated carrier, which can be generated by placing your transmitter or transceiver in the AM, FM, or CW mode. For initial tune-up, you want to feed your linear amplifier about 50 watts. Key your transmitter and quickly adjust the PLATE TUNING for a dip; that is, a minimum plate current reading. Next, using an RF output indicator, (an SWR meter in the FORWARD position works fine), adjust the LOADING for an increase in power. Readjust the TUNING for a plate current minimum. Continue to increase the loading in small steps while adjusting the TUNING for a dip in plate current after each step until no further increase in output power is seen. Finally, you can increase your transmitter's output power to full output, which will drive your linear amplifier to its full output power as well. If you change your transmitter frequency by more than 10 KHz or so, be sure to recheck your amplifier's TUNING for a plate current dip again.

Again, these are generic rules; be sure to consult your manual!

Your Receiver

G7C08 Which parameter affects receiver sensitivity?

A. Input amplifier gain
B. Demodulator stage bandwidth
C. Input amplifier noise figure
D. All these choices are correct

***Sensitivity is a term that is often misused in describing a receiver*.** Input amplifier gain is important to receiver sensitivity, but it is not synonymous, as a high gain input amplifier amplifies NOISE just as well as it amplifies desired signal. The "front end" of a good receiver introduces as little noise of its own as possible, has a narrow enough bandpass to reject nearby interference and noise, and enough gain to override noise accumulated in subsequent stages of the receiver. All these ingredients are necessary for a good sensitive receiver. **ANSWER D.**

G8B12 What process combines two signals in a non-linear circuit to produce unwanted spurious outputs?

A. Intermodulation
B. Heterodyning
C. Detection
D. Rolloff

Intermodulation is the mixing of two different frequencies to produce another frequency (or more). In a superheterodyne receiver, intermodulation is necessary and desirable; it's what makes the frequency conversion work. Intermodulation can also be undesirable, as when a strong station mixes with a weaker one in your receiver's front end, greatly deteriorating the performance of the receiver. Receivers that are relatively immune to undesired intermodulation products are highly prized by contesters and other high performance radio practitioners. **ANSWER A.**

G8B05 Which intermodulation products are closest to the original signal frequencies?

A. Second harmonics
B. Even-order
C. Odd-order
D. Intercept point

When applying two (or more) signals to a non-linear device, one can actually have an infinite number of sums and difference frequencies appearing at the output. (A single simple diode, while sometimes described as a "square law" device actually has a current vs voltage curve described by an exponential equation with a CONTINUALLY VARYING exponent! Needless to say, this can result in some seriously complicated math...as well as a whole lot of undesirable signals resulting. Fortunately, you don't need to know how to work out all the math; all you need to know is that with two input frequencies, ***the products with ODD exponents*** create signals CLOSEST to the original input signals. **ANSWER C.**

G8B13 Which of the following is an odd-order intermodulation product of frequencies F1 and F2?

A. 5F1-3F2
B. 3F1-F2
C. 2F1-F2
D. All these choices are correct

Despite all the complex math involved in intermodulation products (G8B05), figuring out whether an intermodulation product is even or odd is very simple. Just subtract the harmonic order of one frequency by the harmonic order of the second. If the difference is even, the order is even; if the difference is odd, the order is odd. In answer A, we have 5-3, which is 2(even). Likewise in Answer B, we have 3-1=2(also even). Answer C, we have 2-1=1(odd). **ANSWER C.**

G7C04 How is a product detector used?

A. Used in test gear to detect spurious mixing products
B. Used in transmitter to perform frequency multiplication
C. Used in an FM receiver to filter out unwanted sidebands
D. Used in a single sideband receiver to extract the modulated signal

The aforementioned double balanced mixer (G7C02) is equally useful as part of a product detector in an SSB (single sideband) receiver, which extracts intelligible audio from an SSB signal. The process is essentially the inverse of the creation of an SSB signal in an SSB transmitter. One applies the intermediate frequency to one port of the product detector, and the BFO (beat frequency oscillator) to the second port, and out of the third port comes the properly demodulated audio. **ANSWER D.**

G8B03 What is another term for the mixing of two RF signals?

A. Heterodyning
B. Synthesizing
C. Frequency inversion
D. Phase inversion

The term ***heterodyne*** comes from the Greek hetero, meaning different, and dyne, meaning "to act upon" or "to do work." When the instantaneous voltages of two different frequency signals are multiplied, the result is two new frequencies: the sum of, and the difference between, the two original frequencies. Heterodyne circuits are used in most modern transmitters and receivers to convert frequencies, to perform modulation, or to perform demodulation of combinations of RF signals consisting of what is received through your antenna and what is generated inside your radio for this function. **ANSWER A.**

G8B01 Which mixer input is varied or tuned to convert signals of different frequencies to an intermediate frequency (IF)?

A. Image frequency
B. Local oscillator
C. RF input
D. Beat frequency oscillator

More than three-quarters of a century ago, the superheterodyne receiver forever changed the way we do radio. The superheterodyne receiver uses a converter, (a mixer and a ***local oscillator***) to produce a new frequency, which can be either the sum of the local oscillator frequency and incoming RF frequency, or the difference between them. This new frequency is the intermediate frequency or IF, and this is where most of the amplification takes place in the typical superheterodyne receiver. The VFO of a typical receiver is an adjustable local oscillator. **ANSWER B.**

G7C05 Which of the following is characteristic of a direct digital synthesizer (DDS)?

A. Extremely narrow tuning range
B. Relatively high-power output
C. Pure sine wave output
D. Variable output frequency with the stability of a crystal oscillator

An HF transceiver with a ***direct digital synthesizer*** may allow you to dial in a frequency all the way down to 1 Hz! If you plan to do digital work on the air, that 1 Hz tuning and the ***variable output frequency with the stability of a crystal oscillator*** delivered by the DDS will be appreciated by other operators. The DDS circuitry keeps your signal stable on a frequency making reception of the digital signal more reliable. **ANSWER D.**

G7C11 Which of these functions is performed by software in a software-defined radio (SDR)?

A. Filtering
B. Detection
C. Modulation
D. All these choices are correct

A software defined radio (SDR) performs all the functions of a traditional "analog" receiver using digital signal processing methods. The first thing an SDR receiver does is *samples* the RF signal and converts it into a digital stream. This signal is now in the TIME domain, where filtering, detection, and modulation are performed with cheap, silicon-based number crunching. After processing, the signal is converted back to analog for either reception or transmission by "normal" means. **ANSWER D.**

The Software Defined Radio (SDR) has taken amateur radio by storm! This hybrid Ten Tec Jupiter (bottom left) can be operated the "vintage" way using its front panel knobs, or the totally modern "virtual" way by means of SDR software, shown on the laptop computer to the right.

G7C09 What is the phase difference between the I and Q RF signals that software-defined radio (SDR) equipment uses for modulation and demodulation?

A. Zero
B. 90 degrees
C. 180 degrees
D. 45 degrees

You can raise your IQ by learning how to work with I/Q modulation and demodulation methods! All modern digital receivers rely on two demodulators working in phase quadrature, or a difference of ***90 degrees***. I stands for the In Phase signal and Q stands for the Quadrature or 90 degree phase-shifted signal. **ANSWER B.**

G8B11 What combination of a mixer's Local Oscillator (LO) and RF input frequencies is found in the output?

A. The ratio
B. The average
C. The sum and difference
D. The arithmetic product

In a superheterodyne receiver, (or transmitter), there are two combinations that can result in any given IF (intermediate frequency). These are ***the sum and difference frequencies*** of the LO and the RF input frequencies. One of these combinations is the one you want; the one you don't want is called the image. The higher the IF frequency, the farther the image is removed from the desired signal. Higher performance receivers traditionally use a high IF frequency for good image rejection and a lower IF frequency for good selectivity. Such receivers are known as dual-conversion receivers. **ANSWER C.**

G8B02 What is the term for interference from a signal at twice the IF frequency from the desired signal?

A. Quadrature response
B. Image response
C. Mixer interference
D. Intermediate interference

In strong signal areas where there may be local transmissions coming in from shortwave stations outside of normal ham band limits, interference called ***"image response"*** may develop ***at the sum and difference of your VFO and intermediate frequency (IF) signal***. 13.800 MHz minus 455 kHz is 13.345 MHz, the lower image response frequency. **ANSWER B.**

G7C06 Which of the following is an advantage of a digital signal processing (DSP) filter compared to an analog filter?

A. A wide range of filter bandwidths and shapes can be created
B. Fewer digital components are required
C. Mixing products are greatly reduced
D. The DSP filter is much more effective at VHF frequencies

The new, modern high frequency transceiver usually includes digital signal processing (DSP). This allows the user to ***create multiple filter bandwidth settings***, along with ***bandwidth shape*** for "sharp cutoff" or "smooth cutoff" response. This wide range of filter combinations – all digital – really helps reduce interference under difficult conditions. Some other very useful functions of digital signal processing are noise reduction, notch filtering, and audio equalization and expansion. **ANSWER A.**

G4A07 What happens as a receiver's noise reduction control level is increased?

A. Received signals may become distorted
B. Received frequency may become unstable
C. CW signals may become severely attenuated
D. Received frequency may shift several kHz

Modern digital signal processing (DSP) methods can be wondrous things. However, they are not without their drawbacks. Digital noise reduction can greatly reduce wideband white noise and hash, but it can ***severely distort the desired signal*** if "overdone." DSP noise reduction can also generate processing "artifacts" that can be more annoying than the noise they were created to reduce in the first place! DSP is not a "silver bullet" but is a great addition to an otherwise already good receiver. **ANSWER A.**

G4A03 How does a noise blanker work?

A. By temporarily increasing received bandwidth
B. By redirecting noise pulses into a filter capacitor
C. By reducing receiver gain during a noise pulse
D. By clipping noise peaks

One of the most distracting and annoying forms of noise to be found on HF is pulse-type noise, typically generated by vehicle ignitions systems or other man-made sources. This type of noise is most audible on AM modes, including single sideband (SSB). Fortunately, pulse-type noise can be very effectively eliminated by means of a noise blanker that ***functions by reducing receiver gain during a noise pulse***. A noise blanker, however, is not effective in reducing "white noise" or "hash." These forms of noise yield better to modern digital signal processing methods. **ANSWER C.**

G4A01 What is the purpose of the notch filter found on many HF transceivers?

A. To restrict the transmitter voice bandwidth
B. To reduce interference from carriers in the receiver passband
C. To eliminate receiver interference from impulse noise sources
D. To remove interfering splatter generated by signals on adjacent frequencies

Your 40 meter privileges are shared with foreign broadcast stations. From early evening to a couple of hours after sun-up, you'll hear some mighty interesting full-carrier, double-sideband AM shortwave stations coming from the Far East. We can sometimes ***dodge the interference***, thanks to your HF transceiver's ***"notch filter."*** The notch filter may be varied to reject a specific frequency "whistle" coming from these shortwave stations. Adjust it carefully and the whistle disappears. Newer transceivers may incorporate automatic notch filters that use digital signal processing capable of notching-out several interfering frequencies. **ANSWER B.**

The automatic notch filter takes out steady tones, like shortwave broadcast carriers on 40 meters!

G4A13 What is the purpose of using a receive attenuator?

A. To prevent receiver overload from strong incoming signals
B. To reduce the transmitter power when driving a linear amplifier
C. To reduce power consumption when operating from batteries
D. To reduce excessive audio level on strong signals

On the front of your radio is a button marked ATT – attenuator. When you push it in you'll notice that the strength of the received signal drops. Why would you want to lessen reception? Easy answer – there are times you may not want to hear everything your radio is receiving. At full sensitivity, you receive interference from other stations on frequencies near that of the station you are listening to. Also, an extremely strong signal may swamp your receiver, called overload. ***The attenuator will reduce overload on a strong incoming signal***. **ANSWER A.**

G4D04 What does an S meter measure?

A. Carrier suppression
B. Impedance
C. Received signal strength
D. Transmitter power output

High frequency ham transceivers all incorporate an S meter. ***S meters measure received signal strength***. The S meter can be used to determine if your antenna system is working properly. Try this: on 40 meters, you should see an approximately S-2 indication of normal background noise. If you see a higher reading of background noise, this is an indication that your antenna is performing properly. However, if your S meter doesn't budge on 40 meter noise, something is probably wrong with your antenna system. **ANSWER C.**

Being Selective

Understanding receiver selectivity can go a long way toward increasing your amateur radio enjoyment and success.

A typical SSB radio signal, after demodulation, can pass an audio frequency range between 300 and 3000 Hz. This results in a total audio bandwidth of 2700 Hz, which is what most SSB filters are set up for by default. While many competitive hams use SSB filters as narrow as 2.1 kHz, and *voice intelligibility* can be had with even narrower filters than that, super narrow SSB signals can be annoying to listen to for long periods of time. The nice thing about modern digital signal processing (DSP) rigs is that the selectivity is continuously variable over a large range so you can adjust this periodically to greatly reduce "listener fatigue" if band conditions permit.

Somewhat ironically, super modern DSP methods show their greatest advantage on the *oldest* mode of radio communication, CW. With more conventional receivers, it was difficult to have a filter width of less than about 500 Hz without severe "ringing" occurring. Modern DSP filters can give you a bandwidth as narrow as 150 Hz with no detectable ringing. This allows you to easily separate tightly-packed CW stations jammed into a small sliver of radio spectrum. As our exclusive CW bands become gradually smaller over the years, this is a very important factor to consider.

For sound card digital modes, the actual receiver selectivity isn't as much of an issue. If you like, you can use a "wide open" receiver filter and let the decoding software do all the filtering for you. This is a great advantage because you can hear signals well outside the "waterfall" window that you might otherwise miss.

G4D07 How much must the power output of a transmitter be raised to change the S meter reading on a distant receiver from S8 to S9?

A. Approximately 1.5 times
B. Approximately 2 times
C. Approximately 4 times
D. Approximately 8 times

Seeing an S meter change from S8 to S9 is an increase of a single S unit. One S unit is 6 dB, and 6 dB is a ***4-times change***. **ANSWER C.**

G4D05 How does a signal that reads 20 dB over S9 compare to one that reads S9 on a receiver, assuming a properly calibrated S meter?

A. It is 10 times less powerful
B. It is 20 times less powerful
C. It is 20 times more powerful
D. It is 100 times more powerful

An S meter reading of ***20 dB over S-9***, compared to just an S-9 signal, illustrates the signal is ***100 times stronger.*** **ANSWER D.**

G4D06 How much change in signal strength is typically represented by one S unit?

A. 6 dB
B. 12 dB
C. 15 dB
D. 18 dB

Traditionally, the S-meter is calibrated so that every S-unit represents a doubling of antenna voltage (signal strength). For VOLTAGE, dB=20 log (V1/V2), so a 2:1 voltage ratio is 6dB. (By the way, the voltage derived dB requires that both voltage measurements are across the same impedance, which in the case of a single antenna terminal, meets this qualification). Although the "ancient" S-meter has come under a lot of fire in recent years as being obsolete, it is still extremely useful and meaningful...with the correct interpretation. It will be around for a long time to come. **ANSWER A.**

Separation Anxiety

The HF *transceiver*, which combines both transmitting and receiving functions in a single "box," is actually a relatively recent development in the big picture of amateur radio. While the typical transceiver offers simplicity and convenience, especially for single sideband operation, many experienced hams prefer the flexibility and performance offered by separate transmitters and receivers, or "separates." Transmitting and receiving are two very different functions, and there are always performance compromises made when designing one device to do it all. The same principal applies to *antennas*, by the way.

Here we have a vintage Hallicrafters SX-117 receiver sitting atop a Johnson Ranger II Transmitter. The SX-117 is a triple conversion single sideband receiver with a few advanced features for its time in the early 1960s. The Ranger II is a very popular AM transmitter, still in use by many dedicated boat anchor operators. It transmits a nearly broadcast-quality AM signal.

Many of the venerable "classic" radio manufacturers built primarily (or only) transmitters or receivers, and hams came up with some clever arrangements to make them "play nicely" with each other. The most important skill to learn when using separates of any kind is how to properly "spot" or "zero beat" the transmitter; that is to make sure that the transmitter is on exactly the same frequency as the receiver. The "spot" function transmits a very weak signal that can only be heard (in theory!) on the local receiver. To do this, adjust the transmitter to the receiver as closely as possible using the VFO (main tuning) dial, hit the spot button and carefully tune the transmitter until the carrier "note" on the receiver drops to a very low frequency. Release the spot button and you should be good to go.

Some single-manufacturer separates allow you to control both the transmitter and receiver frequencies by either the receiver or transmitter VFO. (Collins and Drake were two representative manufacturers of "matched separates" allowing this function, and there are still a ton of these on the air.) This is especially convenient when operating split (intentionally transmitting and receiving on different frequencies, an absolute must for working serious DX).

So, if you encounter a shack consisting of "separates" there's no need for anxiety. In fact, once you've used separates, you may find operation with a transceiver dull and restrictive.

Website Resources

▼ IF YOU'RE LOOKING FOR	▼ THEN VISIT
Advanced Specialties	www.advancedspecialties.net
Alltronics	www.alltronics.com
Amateur Radio Supplies	www.amateurradiosupplies.com
Asscociated Radio	www.associatedradio.com
B&H Sales	www.hamradiocenter.com
DX Engineering	www.dxengineering.com
Full-Line of Ham Accessories	www.mfjenterprises.com
Gateway Electronics	https://www.gatewayelectronics.com
GigaParts, Inc.	www.gigaparts.com
Hamcity	www.hamcity.com
Ham Equipment Reviews	www.eham.net
HamStop.com	www.hamstop.com
HamWorld	https://hamworldinc.com
HRO – Ham Radio Outlet	www.hamradio.com
JameCo Electronics	https://www.jameco.com
KJI Electronics, Inc.	www.kjielectronics.com
Main Trading Company	www.mtcradio.com
Powerwerx	https://powerwerx.com
QRZ.COM	https://www.qrz.com
R & L Electronics	www.randl.com
Universal Radio Inc	www.universal-radio.com
Wired Communications	https://www.wiredco.com

Note: This list includes many ham radio dealers where you can purchase your HF radio and accessories

Oscillators and Components

G7B07 Which of the following are basic components of a sine wave oscillator?

A. An amplifier and a divider
B. A frequency multiplier and a mixer
C. A circulator and a filter operating in a feed-forward loop
D. A filter and an amplifier operating in a feedback loop

Oscillators are crucial elements to all radio transmitters and most receivers. They are the primary signal creators in all that we do. An ***oscillator is an amplifier with positive feedback***. It usually also has a tuned circuit to set its frequency of oscillation, but may alternately employ a phase shift network or filter. In order for an oscillator to sustain oscillation, the total gain must be greater than unity at the frequency of oscillation. To keep an oscillator "in motion," a tuned circuit at one specific frequency will provide the necessary positive ***feedback loop***. Just like keeping Grandpa swinging back and forth on his brand new senior citizen swing set, a small amount of feedback in the right direction at the right time continuously keeps him in motion. **ANSWER D.**

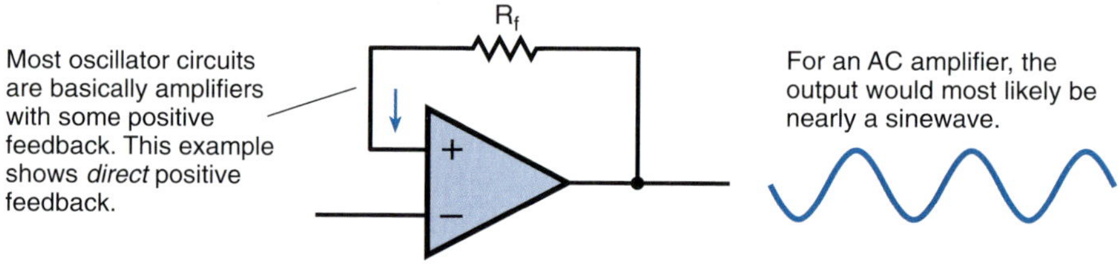

a. Amplifier with Positive Feedback – Oscillator

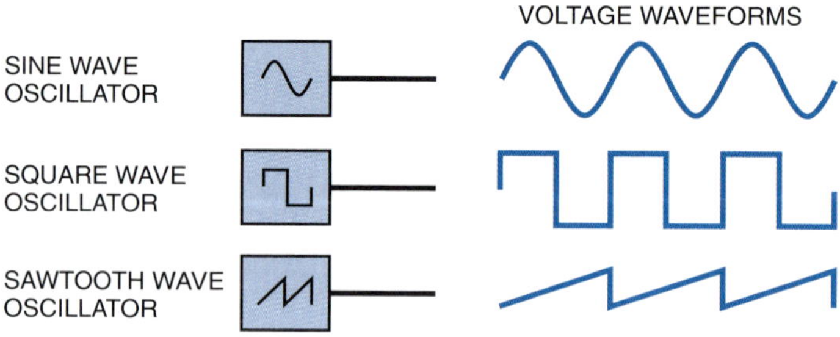

b. Oscillator Waveforms

G7B09 What determines the frequency of an LC oscillator?

A. The number of stages in the counter
B. The number of stages in the divider
C. The inductance and capacitance in the tank circuit
D. The time delay of the lag circuit

The symbol used to denote inductance is L; Capacitance is C. An LC oscillator involves inductance and capacitance. The LC oscillator is found in the radio frequency circuits of your HF transceiver. It consists of a tuned ***inductance and capacitance*** resonant circuit found in the tank circuit of the radio. **ANSWER C.**

G6A10 Which element of a vacuum tube regulates the flow of electrons between cathode and plate?

A. Control grid
B. Suppressor grid
C. Screen grid
D. Trigger electrode

In the triode vacuum tube, the ***control grid*** acts like a variable valve to regulate the flow of electrons between the cathode and plate. Hint: Regulate 5 Control. **ANSWER A.**

Yes, some amateur radio high-power amplifiers use vacuum tubes. Eric, KL7AJ, found this one at the Dayton Hamvention flea market and took home to his ham shack in North Pole, AK.

G6A12 What is the primary purpose of a screen grid in a vacuum tube?

A. To reduce grid-to-plate capacitance
B. To increase efficiency
C. To increase the control grid resistance
D. To decrease plate resistance

Yes, hams still run rigs with vacuum tubes. The tetrode tube uses an anode, cathode and a ***screen grid*** that ***reduces grid-to-plate capacitance.*** **ANSWER A.**

G6A07 What are the operating points for a bipolar transistor used as a switch?

A. Saturation and cutoff
B. The active region (between cutoff and saturation)
C. Peak and valley current points
D. Enhancement and depletion modes

When the bipolar transistor reaches saturation, collector and emitter base junctions are forward-biased. When the bipolar transistor is used as a switch in a logic circuit, an extremely small change in collector-base voltage will cause a large change in collector current, allowing the transistor to switch between cut-off and saturation within the collector current specifications to keep the transistor from self-destructing. It is in this ***saturation and cut-off region*** that the transistor will act as a switch. **ANSWER A.**

G6A08 Which of the following is characteristic of low voltage ceramic capacitors?

A. Tight tolerance
B. High stability
C. High capacitance for given volume
D. Comparatively low cost

The ceramic capacitor is the workhorse in ham radio equipment. Their reliability is very good, and their ***comparatively low cost*** helps to keep ham radio equipment reasonably priced. **ANSWER D.**

G6A09 Which of the following describes MOSFET construction?

A. The gate is formed by a back-biased junction
B. The gate is separated from the channel by a thin insulating layer
C. The source is separated from the drain by a thin insulating layer
D. The source is formed by depositing metal on silicon

Many times, we find the MOSFET transistor in the "front end" of a modern HF transceiver. The MOSFET is a Metal-Oxide Semiconductor Field-Effect Transistor in which the ***gate is separated from the channel with an extremely thin insulating layer***. Manufacturers usually install a gate-protective Zener diode, which prevents the gate insulation from being punctured by small static charges or excessive voltages from an event like a nearby lightning strike. **ANSWER B.**

G6A03 What is the approximate forward threshold voltage of a germanium diode?

A. 0.1 volt
B. 0.3 volts
C. 0.7 volts
D. 1.0 volts

The ***Germanium diode*** is sometimes found in the detector stage of a receiver. Their low forward voltage drop is minimal and the approximate ***junction threshold voltage*** of this diode is ***0.3 volts***. These signal diodes are sensitive and can burn out if you accidentally overheat them while soldering in a replacement. **ANSWER B.**

G6A05 What is the approximate forward threshold voltage of a silicon junction diode?

A. 0.1 volt
B. 0.3 volts
C. 0.7 volts
D. 1.0 volts

We find ***silicon diodes*** in the rectifier section of your transceiver's power supply. The silicon diode offers stable operation at high temperatures, a ***junction threshold voltage*** of about ***0.7 volts***, high reverse resistance, and long-term reliability. **ANSWER C.**

You can bet that when you see a quartet of large silicon diodes in close proximity that they are the main ingredients of a full-wave rectifier.

G7B06 What is a shift register?

A. A clocked array of circuits that passes data in steps along the array
B. An array of operational amplifiers used for tri-state arithmetic operations
C. A digital mixer
D. An analog mixer

A ***shift register passes*** flip-flop ***data up or down*** to each other, rather than just an output. Parallel data may be converted to serial data, or the reverse, through a shift register. **ANSWER A.**

G6B08 How is an LED biased when emitting light?

A. In the tunnel-effect region
B. At the Zener voltage
C. Reverse biased
D. Forward biased

Not all semiconductors are based on silicon. While a light emitting diode (LED) has two terminals and conducts better in one direction than the other, its similarity to a "normal" diode ends there. LEDs use exotic materials that function as semiconductors. One of the first light-emitting materials was Gallium Arsenide Phosphide, GaAsp (GASP!). Many more exotic materials have been discovered and exploited to manufacture LEDs of various colors. Change the exotic material and you change the LED color. The ***light emitting diode*** is always ***forward biased*** when emitting light. **ANSWER D.**

G6B09 How does a liquid crystal display compare to an LED display?

A. Higher contrast in high ambient lighting
B. Wider dynamic range
C. Higher power consumption
D. Shorter lifetime

There are a lot of great display types available nowadays for radio amateurs, but the most common ones are still liquid crystal and LED displays. ***Although LEDs create their own light, this often has to "compete" with external light***. There's only so much light an LED can generate. Liquid crystal displays, while the don't create their own light, can use the ambient light to their advantage, using the black as a contrast, regardless of the external light source. **ANSWER A.**

The black on amber LCD can easily be seen under any lighting condition!

Elmer Point: If you plan to operate your radio in the field, make sure it offers a liquid crystal display. An amber background with black numbers is best for reading the display in bright sunlight. Color LCD displays are great at night, but they may require some shade during the day. Older HF transceivers may use LED or vacuum florescent display, and these are next to impossible to see when operating Field Day in a tent out in the sunshine. Go for amber LCD with black numbers for best viewing.

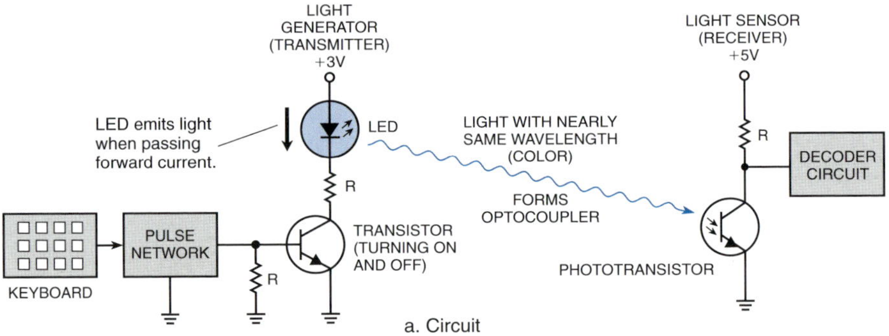

a. Circuit

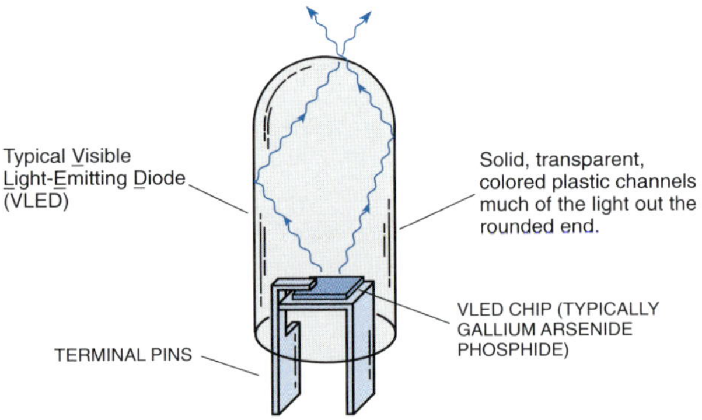

b. Physical Unit for Visible LED

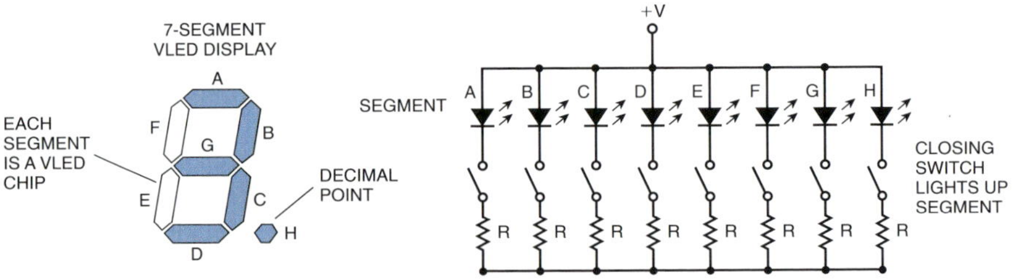

c. VLED Array

An array of LEDs and resistors mounted on a printed circuit board.

G6B02 What is meant by the term MMIC?

A. Multi-Mode Integrated Circuit
B. Monolithic Microwave Integrated Circuit
C. Metal Monolayer Integrated Circuit
D. Mode Modulated Integrated Circuit

The ***monolithic microwave integrated circuit (MMIC)*** is a favorite among microwave operators, up on 10 GHz. On the "X" band, we use MMICs in the microwave equipment as fixed-gain amplifiers with excellent signal to noise ratios. **ANSWER B.**

Monolithic Microwave Integrated Circuit
Photo Courtesy of Hewlett Packard Co.

G6B06 What kind of device is an integrated circuit operational amplifier?

A. Digital
B. MMIC
C. Programmable Logic
D. Analog

We nickname the operational amplifier an ***"op amp"***. It is an ***analog integrated circuit device***. The op amp offers high gain over a large range of input frequencies and is a direct-coupled differential amplifier whose characteristics are determined by components external to the amplifier unit. **ANSWER D.**

G6B03 Which of the following is an advantage of CMOS integrated circuits compared to TTL integrated circuits?

A. Low power consumption
B. High power handling capability
C. Better suited for RF amplification
D. Better suited for power supply regulation

Two different kinds of transistors are commonly used in the digital world, the bipolar junction transistor, BJT, and the Field Effect Transistor, FET. Standard TTL logic is based on BJTs, while CMOS logic is based on FETs, specifically MOSFETS. The truth tables for TTL and CMOS are identical. However, there are some practical, physical differences. TTL is very fast, but is subject to noise, which can result in "false triggering." In addition, it can use considerable power in high density circuits. CMOS is more immune to noise, and uses considerably less power, but at the cost of speed. While most commercial amateur equipment uses digital logic in the form of large scale or Very Large Scale integrated circuits, such as microprocessors, many homebrew projects still use individual TTL or CMOS gates. Many inveterate home-brewers have drawers full of these small-scale devices. The big advantage of CMOS Logic over TTL is that ***CMOS*** offers ***low power consumption***. **ANSWER A.**

Elmer Point: The NAND and NOR gates, (negative AND and negative OR, respectively), have the same characteristics as their positive equivalents, followed by an inverter sometimes called a NOT gate. The truth table for all 5 basic gates is shown below. While gates do exist that have more than two input terminals, these are relatively rare. Any multiple-input gate can be built up from a combination of two-input gates.

AND

Input A	Input B	Output
0	0	0
1	0	0
0	1	0
1	1	1

OR

Input A	Input B	Output
0	0	0
1	0	1
0	1	1
1	1	1

NAND

Input A	Input B	Output
0	0	1
1	0	1
0	1	1
1	1	0

NOR

Input A	Input B	Output
0	0	1
1	0	0
0	1	0
1	1	0

XOR

Input A	Input B	Output
0	0	0
1	0	1
0	1	1
1	1	0

When logic gates are *cascaded*, the output state of one gate becomes the input state of the following gate terminal. It is easy to follow complex combinational logic if you simply write down the state of each terminal as you move from left to right through the schematic. With a little practice, you should be able to follow some pretty complicated logic circuits in your head!

G7B03 Which of the following describes the function of a two-input AND gate?

A. Output is high when either or both inputs are low
B. Output is high only when both inputs are high
C. Output is low when either or both inputs are high
D. Output is low only when both inputs are high

Digital logic circuits are, well, logical. Their functions can be explained by some simple grammatical statements. The basic decision-making element of a digital logic circuit is the gate. An AND gate, as the name suggest, gives an answer "C" if "A" and "B" are true. If we use a 1 to represent a TRUE condition, and a 0 to represent a FALSE condition, we can easily describe the behavior of the gate. C will only be TRUE if A and B are TRUE. Or C is a 1 if and only if A and B are 1. The behavior of any type of gate is defined by a Truth Table. There are five basic types of combinational logic gates: AND, OR, NAND, NOR, and exclusive OR, (XOR). If an input or output is "high," we represent it with the binary number 1. If we look at a truth table, an ***AND gate*** will only give us a ***high output when BOTH inputs are high***. **ANSWER B.**

G7B05 How many states does a 3-bit binary counter have?

A. 3
B. 6
C. 8
D. 16

Each flip-flop requires two input pulses to generate one output pulse. Each time you add another flip-flop in series, you multiply the number of inputs required to generate one output by a factor of two. 2 x 2 x 2 = ***8***. In short, being Base 2, 3-bit is $2^3 = 8$. **ANSWER C.**

Elmer Point: Here is a very important point for your understanding of digital electronics: To write and keep track of the many possible combinations of high or low signals in digital information, the combinations are treated as binary numbers. Binary numbers are also called base two numbers. An example is shown below.

These days, most children learn about decimal numbers in elementary school. When written in ordinary decimal form, integers (whole numbers) are expressed as so many ones, so many tens, so many hundreds, and so forth. Each place in the number has a value ten times the place to the right. This requires using ten (for decimal) different symbols called decimal numerals or digits: 0, 1, 2, 3, 4, 5, 6, 7, 8, and 9. But in binary form, whole numbers are expressed as so many ones, so many twos, so many fours, and so forth. Each place in the number has twice the value of the next place to the right. Binary numbers use only two digits instead of ten: just 0 and 1.

So, in binary form, a number is written as a string of ones and zeroes. For instance, the integer one is written as 1. Two would be 10, which we read as "one-zero". It means a two and no one. Three would be 11 ("one-one", not eleven), meaning a two and a one. Four would be 100, called "one-zero-zero", meaning a four, no two, and no one. Five would be 101, meaning a four, no two, and a one. One hundred would be 1100100. That means a sixty-four, a thirty-two, no sixteen, no eight, a four, no two, and no one.

Each zero or one in a binary number is called a ***bi****nary digi****t***, or bit for short. Bit also means a little piece of information. In fact, a bit is the smallest possible piece of information in a digital system. It expresses a choice between only two possibilities. In a binary number, for instance, a particular bit can say either, "Yes, there is a 64 in this number," or, "No, there is not a 64 in this number."

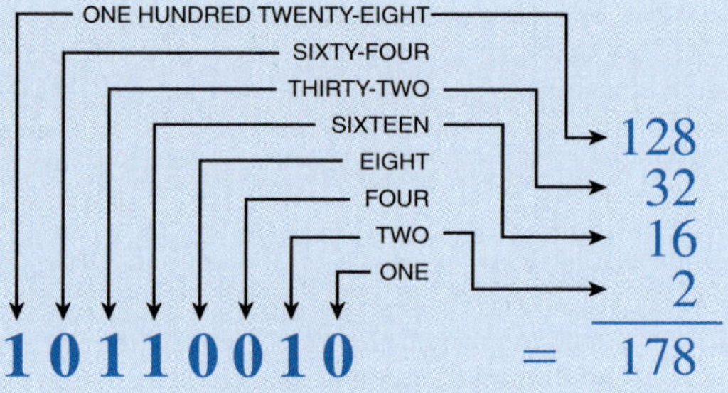

Binary Number:

Each place has a value **twice as great** as the next place to the right. **Two numerals or digits** are used:

0 (Zero = "No")
1 (One = "Yes")

These digits are called bits.

Binary System

In digital systems, binary numbers are used to write and keep track of the many possible combinations of the two electrical states.

Source: *Basic Electronics* © 1994, Master Publishing, Inc., Niles, Illinois

Rolling Your Own Equipment

A great many radio amateurs derive a thrill from designing and building their own equipment from scratch. Remember, Amateur Radio is something you learn, not just the things you buy!

Regardless of your technical aptitude, you can always participate to some degree in "homebrewing" amateur radio gear. You don't have to build an all-mode DC-to-Daylight transceiver from scratch to be considered a homebrewer! There are countless simple accessories you can put together in an evening. Antenna switches, dummy loads, test oscillators and such are useful projects. Building a dipole antenna is a simple homebrew project that nearly every ham has participated in at one time or another. At the very least, every radio amateur should know how to handle a soldering iron.

There was a time in the not-too-distant past when every town had a radio store or TV repair shop. These were treasure troves full of inexpensive electronics components where the eager young ham could find anything he needed to build whatever ham radio widget he could imagine. For the most part, the corner parts stores have gone away. While components are still readily available online and through mail order electronics retail stores, it can be inconvenient to find all the parts necessary to complete a project.

This is where it helps to know who the hams are in your neighborhood. There is an untold wealth of electronic parts languishing in ham shacks all over the country. This collection would put the "big" electronics stores to shame if it were all in one place. The big problem is, this vast storehouse of components is rarely in any kind or order! On-line ham radio forums, local ham flea markets, and military surplus (DRMO/DLA) sales and auctions are also great sources of radio parts.

The best way to learn is by doing. It never hurts to sit at the feet of an experienced Elmer for learning the finer points. The ***ARRL Handbook*** is full of great projects, as are any of the popular Amateur Radio periodicals.

Where there's a project, there's a way to find the parts! Happy Homebrewing!

ham apps

Speaking of the more homebrew inclined ham, we have a neat interface between Arduino and your smart phone: This hybrid between Arduino and smart phone technology lets you develop your very own ham radio app. Many modern hams consider software "The New Homebrew."

http://www.amarino-toolkit.net/

Elmer Point: Your Granddad ham likely knew that a chap named Georg Simon Ohm (1789-1854) experimented with electricity and discovered that the resistance (R) of a conductor depends on its length in feet, cross-sectional area in circular mils, and the resistivity, which is a parameter that depends on the molecular structure of the conductor and its temperature. Ohm's Law states:

The current in an electrical circuit is directly proportional to the voltage and inversely proportional to the resistance.

The Ohm's Law and Power Circle shown here includes 12 equations that allow us to solve for voltage (E), current (I), resistance (R), and power (P), if we know the other values. There isn't much tough math in this section, but keep this page bookmarked to help you solve common electrical formulas.

To solve for Voltage (E):

E = I (current) × R (resistance)

$E = \sqrt{P \text{ (power)} \times R \text{ (resistance)}}$

E = P (power) ÷ I (current)

To solve for Current (I):

I = P (power) ÷ E (voltage)

$I = \sqrt{P \text{ (power)} \div R \text{ (resistance)}}$

I = E (voltage) ÷ R (resistance)

To solve for Resistance (R):

R = E^2 (voltage squared) ÷ P (power)

R = P (power) ÷ I^2 (current squared)

R = E (voltage) ÷ I (current)

To solve for Power (P):

P = E (voltage) × I (current)

P = I^2 (current squared) × R (resistance)

P = E^2 (voltage squared) ÷ R (resistance)

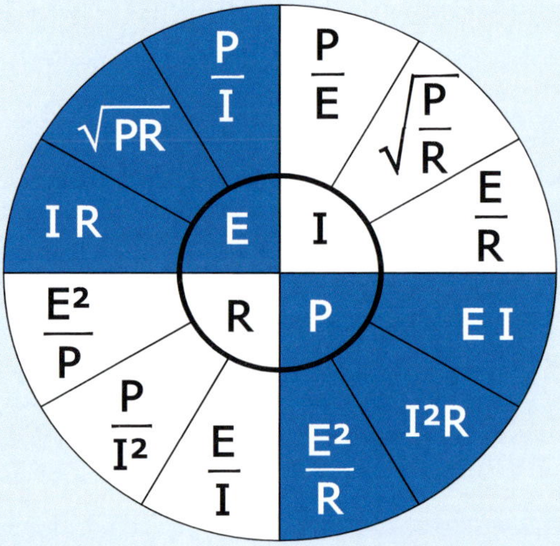

Source: The ARRL Handbook, 2207, © 2006, American Radio Relay League

Electrical Principles

G5B12 What is the RMS voltage across a 50-ohm dummy load dissipating 1200 watts?

A. 173 volts
B. 245 volts
C. 346 volts
D. 692 volts

When you work with high-frequency mobile antennas or, in this question, a high-frequency dummy load, you may wish to calculate the voltage across it to make sure things won't arc over or to determine the maximum voltage that can be applied without exceeding the power rating. In this question we are looking for Voltage (E). We have Resistance (R) in ohms and Power (P) in watts. Hint: resistance is always in ohms and power is always in watts. Consulting the magic circle we find the relationship for voltage when we have resistance and power to be:

$$E = \text{Square root of } P \times R = \sqrt{P \times R}$$

$$E = \text{Square root of } 50 \times 1200 = \sqrt{50 \times 1200}$$

$$E = \text{Square root of } 60{,}000 = \sqrt{60{,}000}$$

$$E = 244.948$$

This is an easy one to work out on a calculator – and yes, calculators are allowed in the exam room. We strongly recommend that you have one. Here are the keystrokes: Clear, Clear, 50 x 1200 = 60,000. Now simply tap the square root sign and, voila, the correct answer pops out at (approximately) 245 volts, which shows up as Answer B on your exam. Don't forget, examiners are allowed to scramble the A, B, C, D order, so look for ***245 volts*** as the correct answer. **ANSWER B.**

G5B03 How many watts of electrical power are consumed if 400 VDC is supplied to an 800-ohm load?

A. 0.5 watts
B. 200 watts
C. 400 watts
D. 3200 watts

Look at the magic circle on page 132. The equation for this problem is $P = E^2 \div R$. E^2 (400^2) is 160,000 divided by R (800) is 200, so the answer is ***200 watts***. Calculator keystrokes are: Clear, 400 × 400 ÷ 800 = 200. **ANSWER B.**

G5B04 How many watts of electrical power are consumed by a 12 VDC light bulb that draws 0.2 amperes?

A. 2.4 watts
B. 24 watts
C. 6 watts
D. 60 watts

Using the magic circle for power, you see that power (P) is equal to voltage (E) times current (I). Multiply volts times amps and you end up with ***2.4 watts***. Calculator keystrokes are: Clear, 12 × 0.2 = 2.4 (in watts). **ANSWER A.**

G5B05 How many watts are consumed when a current of 7.0 milliamperes flows through a 1,250-ohm resistance?

A. Approximately 61 milliwatts
B. Approximately 61 watts
C. Approximately 11 milliwatts
D. Approximately 11 watts

Unless metric prefixes are second nature to you, we always recommend converting everything to the fundamental units before doing any further calculations. It can be very confusing, especially in the heat of an exam, to work with "mixed" units such as "millis," "micros," and "kilos" all in the same formula. In this case 7.0 milliamperes is 0.007 amperes. Now use the current and resistance version of the magic circle for the equation $P = I^2 \div R$. $P = 0.007^2 \div 1250$. This gives the answer in WATTS – 0.06125 watts. Now you may convert the unit into milliwatts by multiplying by 1000 for the correct answer of ***61 milliwatts***. Calculator key strokes are: Clear, 0.007 × 0.007 × 1250 = 0.06125 (in watts). **ANSWER A.**

G5B06 What is the PEP produced by 200 volts peak-to-peak across a 50-ohm dummy load?

A. 1.4 watts
B. 100 watts
C. 353.5 watts
D. 400 watts

This particular question has you looking at an oscilloscope that indicates 200 volts peak-to-peak across a 50-ohm dummy load. We are looking for Power (P). We have Resistance (R) in ohms and Voltage (E) in volts. Consulting the magic circle on page 132 we find the relationship for power when we have resistance and voltage to be:

$$\text{Power} = \text{Voltage}^2 \div \text{Resistance} \quad - \quad P = E^2 \div R$$

But we don't have the pieces we need quite yet for this formula. We have 200 volts peak-to-peak (V_{pp}). We need peak voltage for the calculations. 200 volts peak to peak ÷ 2 = 100 volts peak. The question is asking for PEP (Peak Envelope Power) which is calculated as the root mean square (RMS) of the output power, according to the FCC.

$$V_{rms} = 0.707 \times V_{pk}$$

$$V_{rms} = 0.707 \times 100 = 70.7$$

Now we can find power using the formula:

$P = 70.7^2 \div 50 = 4998.49 \div 50 = 99.96$ or about 100 watts.

This is an easy one to work out on a calculator – and yes, calculators are allowed in the exam room and we strongly recommend that you have one with you. Here are the keystrokes: Clear, Clear, $200 \div 2 = 100 \times 0.707 = 70.7 \times 70.7 = 4998.49 \div 50 = 99.96$ rounded to 100 watts. It was only a little hard because the numbers given were not quite as we needed them. Most high frequency ham rigs put out 100 watts. **ANSWER B.**

G5B07 What value of an AC signal produces the same power dissipation in a resistor as a DC voltage of the same value?

A. The peak-to-peak value
B. The peak value
C. The RMS value
D. The reciprocal of the RMS value

Root Mean Square (RMS) measurement of an AC signal (also called the effective value of an AC voltage) is the same as a DC voltage of the same value. **ANSWER C.**

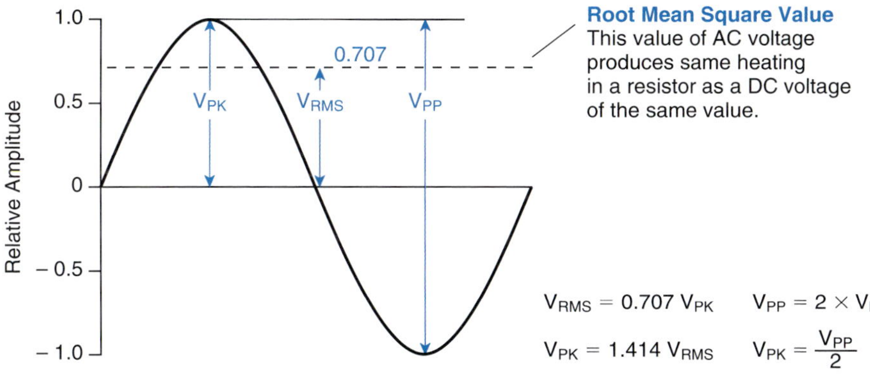

RMS (V_{RMS}), Peak, (V_{PK}), and Peak-to-Peak (V_{PP}) Voltage

---

G5B08 What is the peak-to-peak voltage of a sine wave with an RMS voltage of 120 volts?

A. 84.8 volts
B. 169.7 volts
C. 240.0 volts
D. 339.4 volts

To convert from RMS voltage to peak voltage, multiply the RMS voltage by the square root of 2, or 1.414. $120 \times 1.414 = 169.7$ volts. To get peak-to-peak voltage, simply double the peak voltage. 2×169.7 gives us ***339.4 volts***. Keep in mind that this procedure only works for a pure sine wave. **ANSWER D.**

G5B09 What is the RMS voltage of a sine wave with a value of 17 volts peak?

A. 8.5 volts
B. 12 volts
C. 24 volts
D. 34 volts

This question simply works the formula backwards. From the formulas shown in the figure for Root Mean Square Value we see that peak voltage (the value we have in the question) is equal to 1.414 × RMS voltage (the value the question is asking for):

$V_{pk} = 1.414 \times V_{rms}$

$17 = 1.414 \times V_{rms}$

$V_{rms} = 17 \div 1.414 = 12.0226$ or about ***12 volts***. **ANSWER B.**

G7A08 Which of the following is characteristic of a switchmode power supply as compared to a linear power supply?

A. Faster switching time makes higher output voltage possible
B. Fewer circuit components are required
C. High-frequency operation allows the use of smaller components
D. Inherently more stable

The switching power supply uses a relatively ***high-frequency*** oscillator at a frequency where ***small, light-weight, low-cost miniature transformers*** create relatively smooth DC power output. These units are smaller and lighter than older units that use large, heavy traditional transformers. One concern of the switching power supply is its proximity to your high-frequency antenna system. The antenna system must be 10 feet or more away from the switching power supply so that broad-band noise from the unit is not picked up by the antenna. **ANSWER C.**

Modern switching power supplies incorporate "crowbar protection" to provide overvoltage protection.

G7A04 What is characteristic of a half-wave rectifier in a power supply?

A. Only one diode is required
B. The ripple frequency is twice that of a full-wave rectifier
C. More current can be drawn from the half-wave rectifier
D. The output voltage is two times the peak input voltage

Half-wave rectifiers are generally used when cost is of primary consideration, as only one diode is required. Compared to a full-wave rectifier or bridge circuit, the half-wave rectifier has more ripple, and so is used when the load requirements are very light or where ripple is not a consideration. Two half-wave rectifiers can be wired "back to back" to create an inexpensive bipolar power supply, which can provide, for example, +/- 15 volts for powering op-amps at very low cost and parts count. **ANSWER A.**

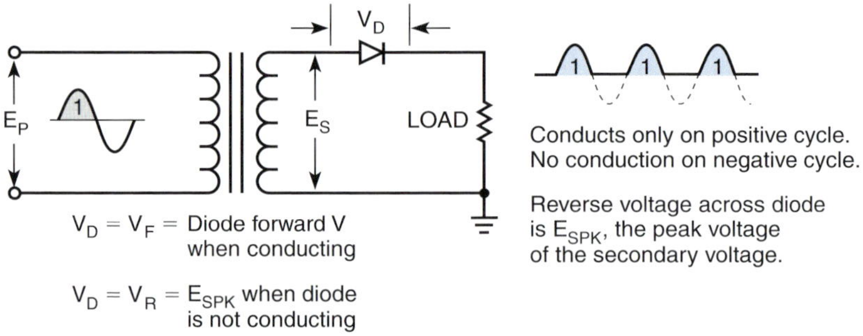

Half-Wave Rectifier

G7A05 What portion of the AC cycle is converted to DC by a half-wave rectifier?

A. 90 degrees
B. 180 degrees
C. 270 degrees
D. 360 degrees

The half-wave rectifier uses only half of the cycle, which is ***180 degrees.*** **ANSWER B.**

G7A06 What portion of the AC cycle is converted to DC by a full-wave rectifier?

A. 90 degrees
B. 180 degrees
C. 270 degrees
D. 360 degrees

A full-wave rectifier is much more efficient because it uses all ***360 degrees*** of the AC cycle. The output of a full-wave rectifier is much easier to filter to provide pure DC voltage. **ANSWER D.**

G7A03 Which type of rectifier circuit uses two diodes and a center-tapped transformer?

A. Full-wave
B. Full-wave bridge
C. Half-wave
D. Synchronous

The oldest type of ***full-wave*** rectifier consists of a center-tapped transformer and a pair of diodes. The output voltage is only half that of a full wave bridge, since at any instant in time only one half of the transformer is in use. As with any other type of rectifier, it is usually necessary to follow it with a filter to eliminate ripple. **ANSWER A.**

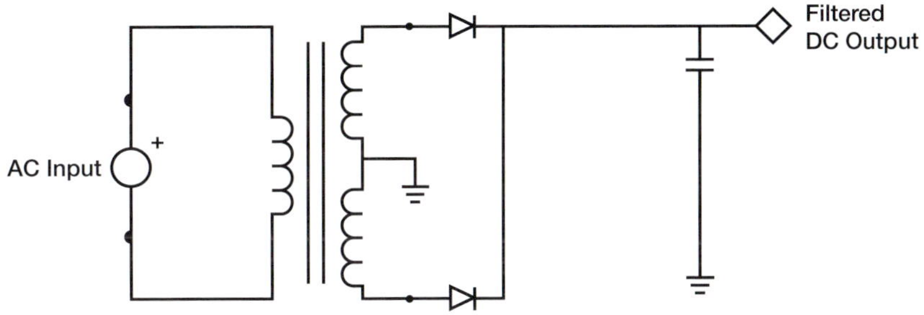

Full-Wave Rectifier

G7A07 What is the output waveform of an unfiltered full-wave rectifier connected to a resistive load?

A. A series of DC pulses at twice the frequency of the AC input
B. A series of DC pulses at the same frequency as the AC input
C. A sine wave at half the frequency of the AC input
D. A steady DC voltage

A full-wave rectifier gives a much smoother ***pulsating DC*** than a half-wave rectifier because the full-wave rectified half sine waves are ***double the frequency of the AC line input***. **ANSWER A.**

G7A02 Which of the following components are used in a power supply filter network?

A. Diodes
B. Transformers and transducers
C. Capacitors and inductors
D. All these choices are correct

In power supplies, transformers supply the voltage and current, diodes rectify, ***capacitors and inductors filter***, and a bleeder resistor protects. So, your best answer for filtering are capacitors and inductors.
ANSWER C.

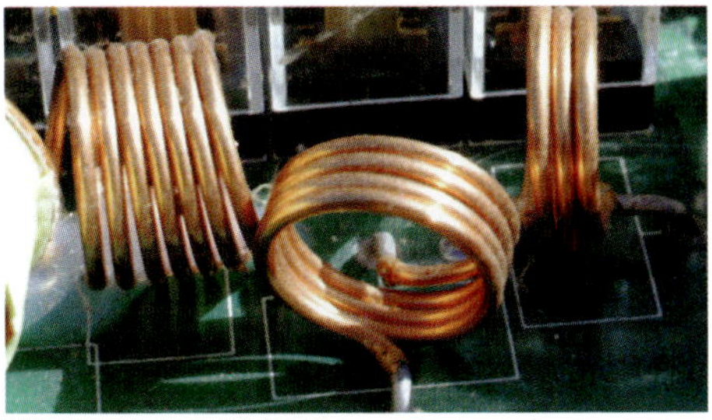
An inductor is a coil of wire that opposes AC current trapped in its magnetic field. Your new radio is loaded with many types of inductor coils used in different stages throughout the radio.

G6A04 Which of the following is characteristic of an electrolytic capacitor?

A. Tight tolerance
B. Much less leakage than any other type
C. High capacitance for a given volume
D. Inexpensive RF capacitor

We usually find the electrolytic capacitor in the power supply section of our new rig. The electrolytic capacitor is polarized with a positive and negative connection point and offers ***high capacitance for given volume*** (volume 5 size). **ANSWER C.**

Electrolytic capacitors are used in just about every power supply as they can contain a lot of capacitance in a small space.

G7A01 What is the function of a power supply bleeder resistor?

A. It acts as a fuse for excess voltage
B. It discharges the filter capacitors when power is removed
C. It removes shock hazards from the induction coils
D. It eliminates ground loop current

When you turn off your big rig, it dims down and then cycles off completely. This slow decay of voltage is from the ***filter capacitors*** that are slowly ***being discharged by the bleeder resistors.*** This is a safety feature that also helps provide voltage regulation. **ANSWER B.**

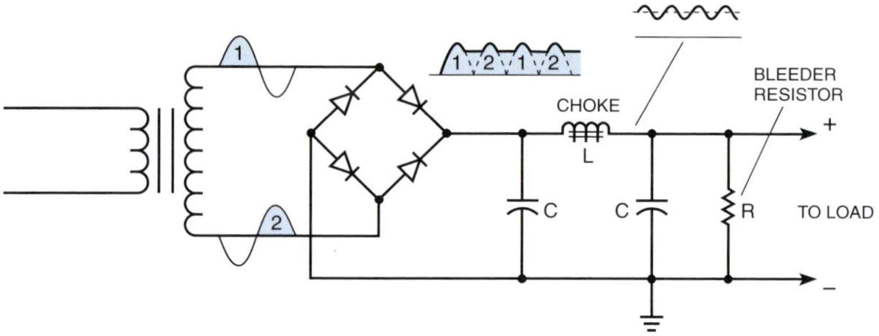

Full-Wave Bridge Power Supply with Bleeder Resistor

G4B06 What is an advantage of a digital multimeter as compared to an analog multimeter?

A. Better for measuring computer circuits
B. Less prone to overload
C. Higher precision
D. Faster response

Your buddy discovers you are a brand new General and gives you several gel-cell 12 volt batteries. To see which one has the absolute best charge, use a digital volt meter to get a ***higher precision digital readout*** of the battery voltage. An analog volt meter might not show you subtle changes in battery terminal voltage. **ANSWER C.**

G4B09 When is an analog multimeter preferred to a digital multimeter?

A. When testing logic circuits
B. When high precision is desired
C. When measuring the frequency of an oscillator
D. When adjusting circuits for maximum or minimum values

Don't throw away that old Simpson model 260 needle meter. The analog needle movement can give you the "feel," visually, ***when adjusting circuits for maximum and minimum values,*** as long as that particular tuned circuit does not call for specialized, non-loading measurements. That old needle readout may be less affected by strong nearby signals up at the repeater site, too! **ANSWER D.**

G4B05 Why do voltmeters have high input impedance?

A. It improves the frequency response
B. It allows for higher voltages to be safely measured
C. It improves the resolution of the readings
D. It decreases the loading on circuits being measured

New digital volt meters have a relatively ***high input impedance to avoid loading*** down ***the circuit being measured***. If you are measuring a fraction of a volt, you don't want to use an older volt meter that might significantly add load to the circuit and result in a bogus reading. **ANSWER D.**

G6A02 What is an advantage of batteries with low internal resistance?

A. Long life
B. High discharge current
C. High voltage
D. Rapid recharge

The Nickel Cadmium battery is a low-cost, rechargeable voltage source for handheld radios as well as for some QRP (low power output) high frequency transceivers. The low internal resistance of the nickel cadmium battery allows for ***high discharge current*** when transmitting. The disadvantage of low internal resistance is the slight self-discharge between uses of your radio equipment. So before going out on Field Day, be sure to cycle your nickel cadmium battery pack several times, and end the cycle with a good charge. **ANSWER B.**

Always check the polarity of your batteries. Many "dead" radios are simply the result of one or more batteries being installed backwards!

G6A01 What is the minimum allowable discharge voltage for maximum life of a standard 12-volt lead-acid battery?

A. 6 volts
B. 8.5 volts
C. 10.5 volts
D. 12 volts

When operating your equipment with a 12 volt lead acid automobile battery during Field Day, make sure you never pull your battery below ***10.5 volts***. If you do, you will shorten the maximum life of that battery. An indication that you are reaching that minimum is that any transmitter running at 10.5 volts (instead of 12 volts) usually sounds distorted on high frequencies. **ANSWER C.**

G4E09 What is the approximate open-circuit voltage from a fully illuminated silicon photovoltaic cell?

A. 0.02 VDC
B. 0.5 VDC
C. 0.2 VDC
D. 1.38 VDC

A complete photovoltaic cell will yield ***0.5 volts*** direct current. A solar panel is made up of a series-parallel connection of these cells in order to charge your storage battery system. **ANSWER B.**

These solar panels will easily keep the field-day station inside the tent running all day!

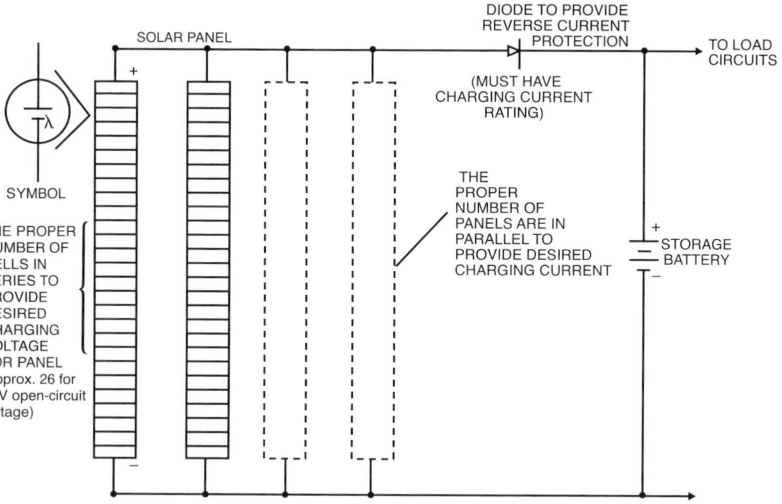

Schematic of Solar Panel for Charging Storage Battery

G4E08 In what configuration are the individual cells in a solar panel connected together?

A. Series-parallel
B. Shunt
C. Bypass
D. Full-wave bridge

A single solar cell has insufficient voltage or current to power most practical electrical devices or appliances. Wiring solar cells in series increases the voltage, and wiring them in parallel increases the current. ***Wiring them in series AND parallel increases both, logically enough***. **ANSWER A.**

G4E10 Why should a series diode be connected between a solar panel and a storage battery that is being charged by the panel?

A. To prevent overload by regulating the charging voltage
B. To prevent discharge of the battery through the panel during times of low or no illumination
C. To limit the current flowing from the panel to a safe value
D. To prevent damage to the battery due to excessive voltage at high illumination levels

Always monitor solar power charging with a small amp meter in series with the red lead. You can really see how a single shadow will decrease output. Then one night you check the panel and its actually showing a discharge on your battery. There probably was no series diode to prevent the panel from slightly discharging your battery. Newer panels usually have the diodes built in. But some older panels, or scavenged panels without a controller, could really use that ***reverse current diode to prevent battery discharge***. **ANSWER B.**

G4E11 What precaution should be taken when connecting a solar panel to a lithium iron phosphate battery?

A. Ground the solar panel outer metal framework
B. Ensure the battery is placed terminals-up
C. A series resistor must be in place
D. The solar panel must have a charge controller

ANY battery charging system requires providing more voltage than the battery has "at rest." A discharged battery of any type has a lower impedance than a fully charged battery. In fact, most high-capacity batteries, not just lithium iron phosphate batteries, can look like a dead short in their discharged state. ***Some means of limiting the charging current must be provided, and an "official" charge controller is the standard, modern way of doing this***. Modern charge controllers have other sophisticated monitoring functions as well. **ANSWER D.**

G4E03 Which of the following direct, fused power connections would be the best for a 100-watt HF mobile installation?

A. To the battery using heavy-gauge wire
B. To the alternator or generator using heavy-gauge wire
C. To the battery using insulated heavy duty balanced transmission line
D. To the alternator or generator using insulated heavy duty balanced transmission line

As a General Class operator, you'll probably be running a 100-watt, HF mobile transceiver in your car. You cannot rely on the car's 12-volt accessory or "power port" socket wiring to support the necessary 20-amp (minimum) power demands from your HF radio. Wire your red and black power leads ***directly to the battery using heavy-gauge wire***. Fuse both the red and the black power leads close to the battery connection point. **ANSWER A.**

G4E04 Why should DC power for a 100-watt HF transceiver not be supplied by a vehicle's auxiliary power socket?

A. The socket is not wired with an RF-shielded power cable
B. The socket's wiring may be inadequate for the current drawn by the transceiver
C. The DC polarity of the socket is reversed from the polarity of modern HF transceivers
D. Drawing more than 50 watts from this socket could cause the engine to overheat

While you might be tempted to grab 12 volts from an automobile auxiliary power socket, don't! Sure, the radio will work for a few minutes, but after a little bit of transmitting the auxiliary power receptacle wiring will get red hot from ***over-drawing the current***, and quite possibly cause a fire in your dashboard! **ANSWER B.**

Elmer Point: To go mobile with your 100-watt HF ham transceiver, you'll need to run the red and black power wires directly to the positive and negative terminals on your car or truck battery. You should have separate fuses right next to the battery terminal connections for safety. While automotive sound systems sometimes use the vehicle chassis as the negative black wire return, commercial two-way radio installers always say it's best to run directly to the positive and negative terminals on the battery. The chassis of your HF radio also should be well grounded to your vehicle frame.

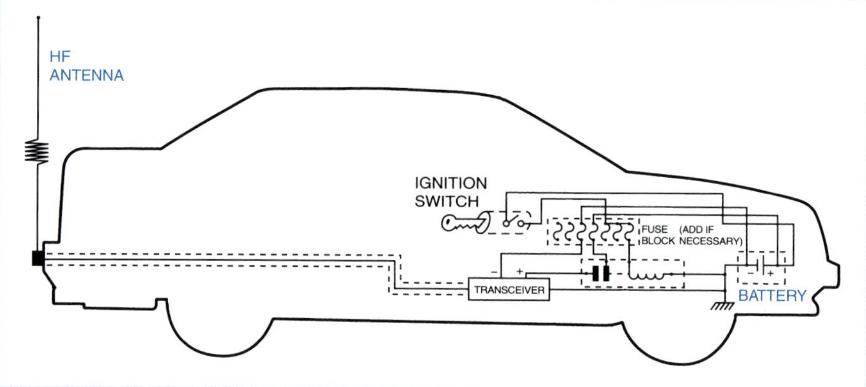

Wire Your Mobile Transceiver Directly to the Car Battery and Fuse Both Power Leads

YouTube Resources

You Tube is a wonderful resource for videos showing how electronics work, and teach how to make electronic homebrew gear. Here are some of Eric's favorite You Tube sites for learning more about electronics:

ElectroBOOM is a wonderful general electronics and science site with great humor:
https://www.youtube.com/channel/UCJ0-OtVpF0wOKEqT2Z1HEtA

Mr. Carlson's Lab is an excellent instructional channel:
https://www.youtube.com/channel/UCU9SoQxJewrWb_3GxeteQPA

All About Circuits is his favorite overall electronics site – probably the best electronics forum anywhere on the web:
https://www.allaboutcircuits.com/

A first-rate YouTube channel for learning all about test instruments and their uses:
https://www.youtube.com/user/tektronix

Jeri Ellsworth makes regular appearances at Dayton Hamvention. This site is for the geekiest of radio geeks:
https://www.jeriellsworth.com/

Another set of instructional YouTube videos from a giant in the test equipment business:
https://www.youtube.com/channel/UCsUQ4q-woGsK3VaAQynptbg

FlexRadio is the world leader in Software Defined Radios (SDR):
https://www.youtube.com/user/FlexRadioSystems

Join Gordo and his Ham friends on YouTube! Just type the following into your browser: HAMRADIOCRASHCOURSEYOUTUBE

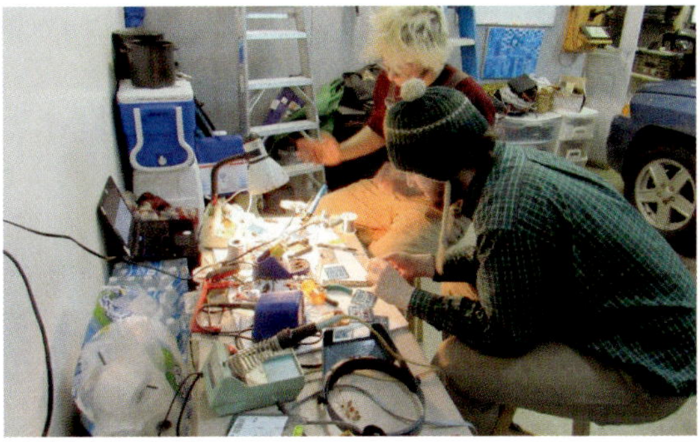

Ham radio homebrewing can lead to a career in electronics! Here, Roger and Joshua assemble circuit boards for the eXOgon circularly polarized HF receiving antennas made by AlasKit. AlasKit Educational and Scientific Resources builds special instrumentation for ionosphere research and other "outside-the-box" applications.

Website Resources

IF YOU'RE LOOKING FOR	THEN VISIT
equipment reviews	www.hamoperator.com
call sign lookups and more	www.qrz.com
ham radio gear, call sign look-ups	www.hamcall.net
QSO's and more	www.hamgallery.com
ham radio resources	www.dxzone.com
articles, reviews, etc.	www.eham.net
used equipment ads and more	www.qth.com
directional antennas	www.arrowantennas.com
direction finding tips and more	www.homingin.com
free e-mail service for hams	www.qsl.net
ham radio for people with disabilities	www.handiham.org
Canada's amateur radio society	www.rac.ca
California club with good tech articles	www.cvarc.org/faq.htm
antennas and related gear	www.natcommgroup.com
every ham accessory known to man	www.mfjenterprises.com
CQ Magazine's website	www.cq-amateur-radio.com
radio propagation reports	www.dxworld.com/50prop.html
news & science reports about space	www.spacetoday.org
mobile antennas and accessories	www.hiqantennas.com
educational resources and links	www.ecjones.org
linking ham radio via the internet	www.winlink.org
inductive components for RFI	www.amidoncorp.com
HF amplifiers, antennas, and more	www.ameritron.com
feedlines, connectors, & wire galore	www.cablexperts.com
all kinds of antennas & accessories	www.antennaworld.com
old instruction manuals	http://bama.edebris.com/manuals/
RF safety calculator	http://hintlink.com/power_density.htm

Elmer Point: *Want to learn more about electricity and how electronics work? Here are two books we recommend highly for your self-education!*

Getting Started in Electronics by Forrest M. Mims III is a true classic. It is used by a wide range of people – from junior-high teachers to the U.S. Army to teach the fundamentals of electricity and electronics.

Basic Electronics by Alvis J. Evans and Gene McWhorter goes a little deeper into the topic, and includes end of chapter quizzes and worked-out problems to teach you in detail the various aspects of electronics.

Either book – or both – will give you a solid grounding in the theory, science, and practical applications of electronics. You can get your copies of the books at your local ham radio store, on line at www.w5yi.org, or by calling The W5YI Group at 800-669-9594.

Elmer Point: Want to learn more about how radios work? We suggest you read and study **Basic Communications Electronics** by Jack Hudson, W9MU, and Jerry Luecke, KB5TZY. It explains how transmitters and receivers work, the science behind antennas, integrated circuits, and more. You can pick up a copy at your ham radio store, online at www.w5yi.org, or by calling W5YI Group at 800-669-9594. Understanding how radios work will add to your enjoyment of your General Class privileges!

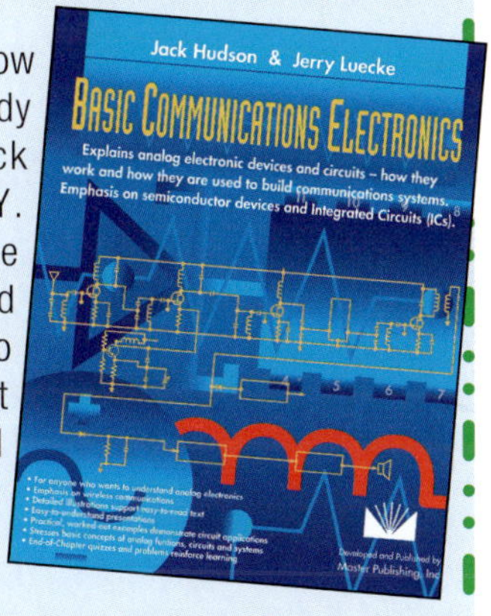

www.W5YI.org

CD 4 TRACK 1

Circuits

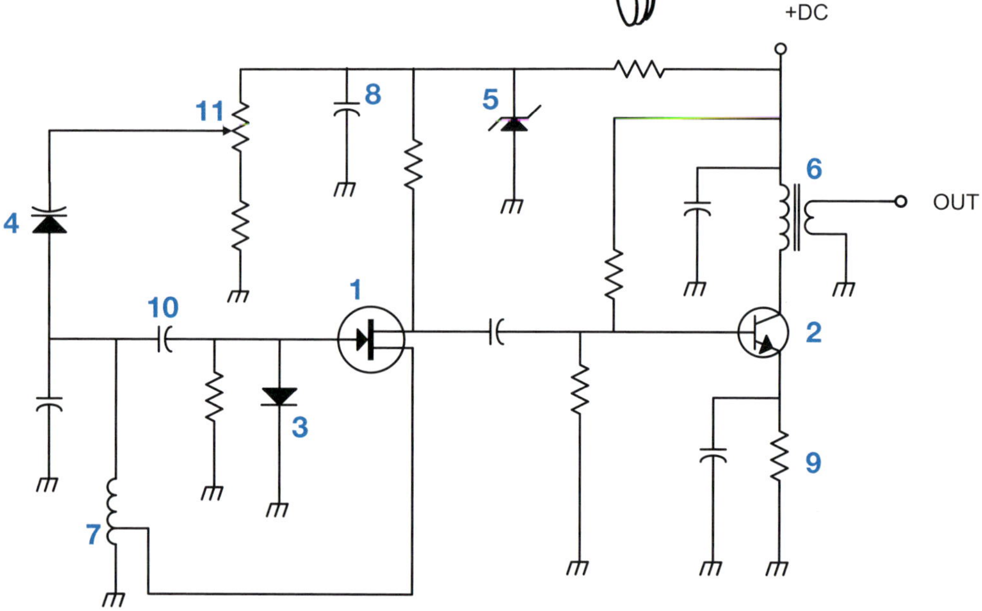

Look at Figure G7-1. On your exam, it may appear on the last page of the examination sheets or may appear for a single question about the components. We can identify this circuit as a Hartley oscillator, with symbol 7 as the telltale tapped coil. This is a voltage-controlled Hartley oscillator, seen by the varactor, symbol 4. Symbol 11 is a variable potentiometer, and symbol 8 is a bypass capacitor. Symbol 10 is a blocking capacitor, isolating out DC. Symbol 1 is a field effect transistor (JFET) with symbol 5 being a Zener diode for voltage regulation. Symbol 6 is the oscillator's companion amplifier output transformer, and symbol 2 is an NPN transistor. Symbol 9 is a fixed resistor, and symbol 3 is a diode. Now, let's see what they're going to ask on the exam.

G7A09 Which symbol in figure G7-1 represents a field effect transistor?

A. Symbol 2
B. Symbol 5
C. Symbol 1
D. Symbol 4

Symbol 1 is the Field Effect Transistor. The schematic symbol in the diagram is an N channel FET. We know it's an N Channel, because the arrow is pointing "Nwards." (Bad puns are always a great way to remember electronic principles!) **ANSWER C.**

Symbol 1

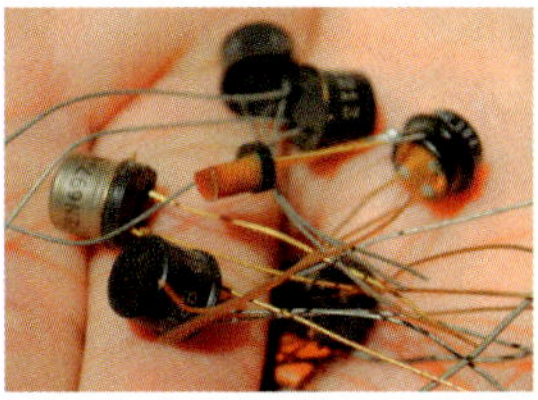

G7A10 Which symbol in figure G7-1 represents a Zener diode?

A. Symbol 4
B. Symbol 1
C. Symbol 11
D. Symbol 5

Symbol 5 is the Zener diode, used for voltage regulation. The cathode end of a Zener symbol is somewhat Z shaped. And always remember, in nearly every case the Zener diode is in the circuit backwards from a normal diode. **ANSWER D.**

Symbol 5

G7A11 Which symbol in figure G7-1 represents an NPN junction transistor?

A. Symbol 1
B. Symbol 2
C. Symbol 7
D. Symbol 11

See the transistor all the way to the right, ***symbol 2***? The arrow is Not Pointing In so it is an NPN junction transistor. **ANSWER B.**

Symbol 2

G7A12 Which symbol in Figure G7-1 represents a solid core transformer?

A. Symbol 4
B. Symbol 7
C. Symbol 6
D. Symbol 1

It's easy to spot the transformer – we find it at ***symbol 6***. The 2 vertical lines indicate an iron core. Sometimes you'll see a dot near the ends of the windings. The dots indicate the relative phasing of the transformer. This is more common in radio frequency transformers such as baluns and transmission line transformers. **ANSWER C.**

Symbol 6

G7A13 Which symbol in Figure G7-1 represents a tapped inductor?

A. Symbol 7
B. Symbol 11
C. Symbol 6
D. Symbol 1

This is what gives away the Hartley oscillator; ***symbol 7***, the tapped inductor. This provides us with the feedback necessary to keep the oscillator oscillating! The tapped inductor actually functions as a step up autotransformer. **ANSWER A.**

Symbol 7

Elmer Point: Electrical circuits are represented graphically in schematic diagrams using symbols to indicate the various components. Here's a table of schematic symbols that will help you read the diagram used for questions G7A09 through G7A13. If you really get into experimental electronics or kit building, you might want to buy a copy of Forrest Mims's **Engineer's Mini Notebook #4, Electronic Formulas, Symbols, & Circuits** available at your local ham radio store, on-line at www.w5yi.org or by calling the W5YI Group at 800-669-9594.

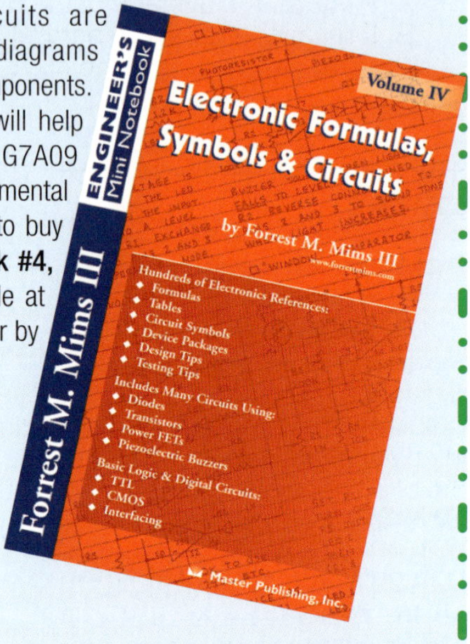

SCHEMATIC SYMBOLS

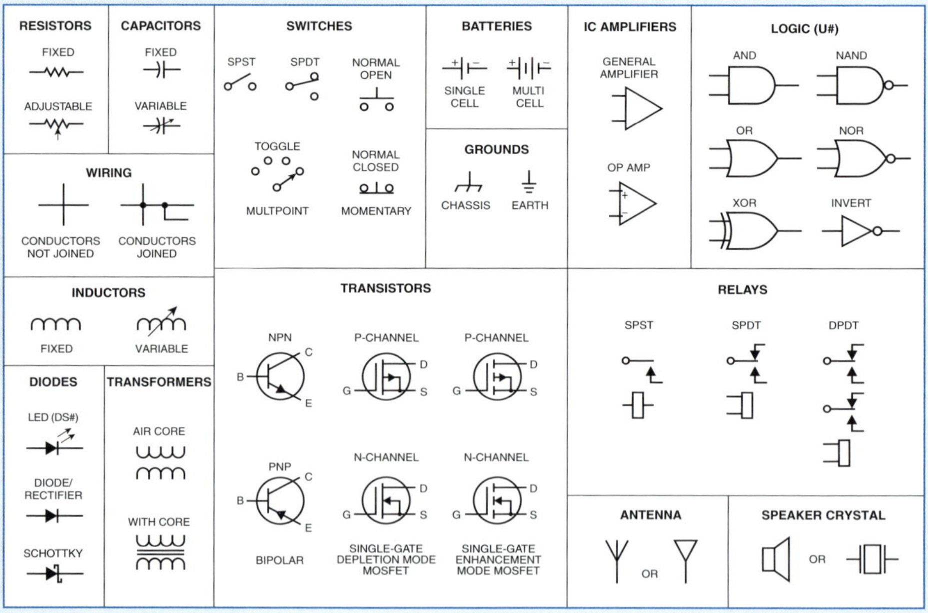

G5B02 How does the total current relate to the individual currents in a circuit of parallel resistors?

A. It equals the average of the branch currents
B. It decreases as more parallel branches are added to the circuit
C. It equals the sum of the currents through each branch
D. It is the sum of the reciprocal of each individual voltage drop

If you ***add up the current*** in each branch of a parallel circuit, you will come up with the total current in the circuit. **ANSWER C.**

G5C05 Why is the primary winding wire of a voltage step-up transformer usually a larger size than that of the secondary winding?

A. To improve the coupling between the primary and secondary
B. To accommodate the higher current of the primary
C. To prevent parasitic oscillations due to resistive losses in the primary
D. To ensure that the volume of the primary winding is equal to the volume of the secondary winding

On any ideal transformer, the product of the primary voltage and current has to equal the product of the secondary voltage and current. This is the "no free lunch" principle of transformers. You can never get any more power out than you put in. A step up transformer will have low voltage/high current on the primary side and high voltage/low current on the secondary side. ***The primary winding needs to have larger wire to handle the higher current.*** **ANSWER B.**

G5C03 What is the total resistance of a 10-, a 20-, and a 50-ohm resistor connected in parallel?

A. 5.9 ohms
B. 0.17 ohms
C. 17 ohms
D. 80 ohms

While you can solve this problem with a big formula, always remember that with unlike resistors in parallel, just like unlike capacitors in series, the resulting answer will always be less than the smallest value component. ***5.9 ohms*** is a logical answer to solve for when you work the big long formula all the way out. **ANSWER A.**

G5C04 What is the approximate total resistance of a 100- and a 200-ohm resistor in parallel?

A. 300 ohms
B. 150 ohms
C. 75 ohms
D. 67 ohms

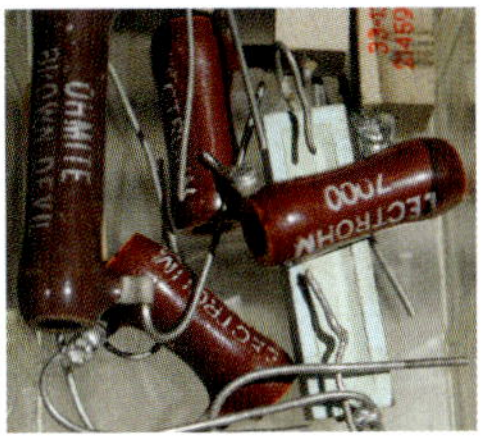

When working with just TWO parallel resistances, the total resistance is the PRODUCTS divided by the SUMS. ***In this case we have 100x200/100+200 = 20,000/300 =66.666 ohms***. (About 67 ohms). As a sanity check, in any parallel resistance circuit, the total resistance MUST be less than the smallest value of resistance. This immediately eliminates Answers A and B. This, of course, leaves only two possibilities, before doing any calculations at all. **ANSWER D.**

ham apps

Resistor Color Codes allows you to identify standard resistors, something us old timers were expected to memorize. These apps make it so easy it should be illegal! **https://itunes.apple.com/us/app/resistor-color-code/id322001850?mt=8**
https://play.google.com/store/apps/details?id=com.blogspot.karabut.rescal&hl=en

Elmer Point: Here is a set of questions that asks about the total value of resistors, capacitors, and inductors connected in SERIES and in PARALLEL. Resistors (R) and Inductors (L) act the same way. Capacitors (C) act in the opposite way. Here are the formulas to calculate the total value of these components:

Resistors in SERIES simply add up: $R_{total} = R_1 + R_2 + R_3$

Inductors in SERIES simply add up: $L_{total} = L_1 + L_2 + L_3$

Resistors and Inductors in PARALLEL combine with a resulting total value that is always LESS than the value of the lowest value resistor in parallel, for easy problem solving! Here are the formulas:

when there are 2 resistors or inductors: $R_{total} = \dfrac{R_1 \times R_2}{R_1 + R_2}$ or $L_{total} = \dfrac{L_1 \times L_2}{L_1 + L_2}$

when there are 3 or more resistors: $R_{total} = \dfrac{1}{\frac{1}{R_1} + \frac{1}{R_2} + \frac{1}{R_3}}$ or $L_{total} = \dfrac{1}{\frac{1}{L_1} + \frac{1}{L_2} + \frac{1}{L_3}}$

Capacitors in PARALLEL simply add up: $C_{total} = C_1 + C_2 + C_3$

Capacitors in SERIES combine with a resulting total value that is always LESS than the value of the lowest value capacitor in series, for easy problem solving! Here is the formula:

when there are 2 capacitors: $C_{total} = \dfrac{C_1 \times C_2}{C_1 + C_2}$

when there are 3 or more capacitors: $C_{total} = \dfrac{1}{\frac{1}{C_1} + \frac{1}{C_2} + \frac{1}{C_3}}$

G5C08 What is the equivalent capacitance of two 5.0-nanofarad capacitors and one 750-picofarad capacitor connected in parallel?

A. 576.9 nanofarads
B. 1,733 picofarads
C. 3,583 picofarads
D. 10.750 nanofarads

Capacitors in parallel add up, similar to resistors in series: C1 + C2 + C3 = C total. But hold on, they have mixed in one picofarad capacitor with two same-size nanofarad capacitors! This is easy. Let's take the 750 picofard capacitor, and determine what its value is as a matching nanofarad capacitor!

One nanofarad = 10^{-9} of a farad.

One picofarad = 10^{-12} of a farad.

So to convert the picofarad to the equivalent nanofarad value, we move the decimal point three places to the left. The 750 picofarad capacitor equals 0.750 nanofarads. Now we can do the easy math for the 3 capacitors in parallel: *5.0 + 5.0 + 0.750 = 10.750 nanofarads*. **ANSWER D.**

G5C09 What is the capacitance of three 100-microfarad capacitors connected in series?

A. 0.33 microfarads
B. 3.0 microfarads
C. 33.3 microfarads
D. 300 microfarads

We have three like capacitors in series – since they are in series, just like resistors in parallel, total capacitance will be 1/3 of each of the 100 microfarad capacitors. ***33.3 microfarads*** is an answer you can do in your head! The formula is:

$C_T = 1 \div (1/C_1 + 1/C_2 + 1/C_3.)$ **ANSWER C.**

G5C12 What is the capacitance of a 20-microfarad capacitor connected in series with a 50-microfarad capacitor?

A. 0.07 microfarads
B. 14.3 microfarads
C. 70 microfarads
D. 1,000 microfarads

Calculating for total capacitance of unlike capacitors in series is much like the formula for calculating unlike resistors in parallel: $(C_1 \times C_2) \div (C_1 + C_2)$. In this equation, the total capacitance will always be less than the smaller capacitor, so 14.3 microfarads can be confirmed as the correct answer by working through the formula. **ANSWER B.**

Capacitors on a circuit board, mounted on-end to conserve space.

G5C13 Which of the following components should be added to a capacitor to increase the capacitance?

A. An inductor in series
B. An inductor in parallel
C. A capacitor in parallel
D. A capacitor in series

If we need to add some additional capacitance to a circuit which already has a fixed capacitor, we would add a second ***capacitor in PARALLEL***. **ANSWER C.**

G5C14 Which of the following components should be added to an inductor to increase the inductance?

A. A capacitor in series
B. A capacitor in parallel
C. An inductor in parallel
D. An inductor in series

If we need to increase the inductance (L) of a circuit, we would simply add another ***inductor in series.*** **ANSWER D.**

Handy Hint: In a test you can encounter mixed units as in this question, such as milliwatts and microwatts. If working with metric prefixes isn't second nature, always convert the values to their fundamental units first! In other words, rewrite the numbers as watts or ohms or farads, not nanofarads or picofarads. Then when you're all done with the calculations, go back and give the answer in the units they want! You'll save yourself a lot of heartburn.

G5C10 What is the inductance of three 10-millihenry inductors connected in parallel?

A. 0.30 henries
B. 3.3 henries
C. 3.3 millihenries
D. 30 millihenries

Treat inductors like resistors when working either a series or parallel problem. This one you can do in your head. Three 10 millihenry inductors in parallel, total inductance will be 1/3 or ***3.3 millihenrys*** when connected in parallel. **ANSWER C.**

These open air coils mounted on a circuit board are held in place with some blobs of hot glue to retain their precise inductance.

G5C11 What is the inductance of a circuit with a 20-millihenry inductor connected in series with a 50-millihenry inductor?

A. 7 millihenries
B. 14.3 millihenries
C. 70 millihenries
D. 1,000 millihenries

Easy one. Just like resistors add up in series, inductors add up in series. 20 + 50 = ***70 millihenrys***. **ANSWER C.**

G6A11 What happens when an inductor is operated above its self-resonant frequency?

A. Its reactance increases
B. Harmonics are generated
C. It becomes capacitive
D. Catastrophic failure is likely

All real-world inductors have a certain amount of parasitic capacitance as well as inductance. In general, this capacitance causes the inductor to have a sharply-tuned PARALLEL self-resonant frequency. As in any parallel resonant circuit, as you move higher in frequency the capacitive REACTANCE decreases. But remember: capacitive REACTANCE is the reciprocal of frequency, so the overall effect is to INCREASE the apparent parallel capacitance. In other words, it appears as if there is a larger capacitor in parallel with the inductor. We say ***the circuit becomes capacitive***. **ANSWER C.**

G5A02 What is reactance?

A. Opposition to the flow of direct current caused by resistance
B. Opposition to the flow of alternating current caused by capacitance or inductance
C. Reinforcement of the flow of direct current caused by resistance
D. Reinforcement of the flow of alternating current caused by capacitance or inductance

Inductive ***reactance is the opposition to AC*** caused by inductors. Capacitive reactance is the opposition to AC caused by capacitors. Both reactances vary with frequency. When there are an inductor and a capacitor in the same circuit, there is a special frequency, called the resonant frequency, where the inductive reactance equals the capacitive reactance. **ANSWER B.**

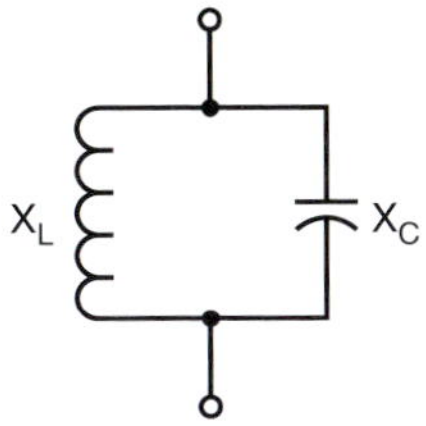

$$X_L = 2\pi fL$$

$$X_C = \frac{1}{2\pi fC}$$

The resonant frequency of a circuit is:

$$f_r = \frac{1}{2\pi\sqrt{LC}}$$

The resonant frequency is the frequency where $X_L = X_C$.

$$\therefore 2\pi fL = \frac{1}{2\pi fC}$$

$$f^2 = \frac{1}{(2\pi L)(2\pi C)}$$

$$f^2 = \frac{1}{(2\pi)^2 LC}$$

$$\therefore f_r = \frac{1}{2\pi\sqrt{LC}}$$

Resonant Frequency

G5A12 What occurs in an LC circuit at resonance?

A. Current and voltage are equal
B. Resistance is cancelled
C. The circuit radiates all its energy in the form of radio waves
D. Inductive reactance and capacitive reactance cancel

Resonance is one of the most useful phenomenon in all of radio; it is what allows us to tune radios to different frequencies, among countless other functions. ***By definition, resonance is when inductive reactance (XL) is equal to capacitive reactance (XC), and thus cancel out***. **ANSWER D.**

G5A01 What happens when inductive and capacitive reactance are equal in a series LC circuit?

A. Resonance causes impedance to be very high
B. Impedance is equal to the geometric mean of the inductance and capacitance
C. Resonance causes impedance to be very low
D. Impedance is equal to the arithmetic mean of the inductance and capacitance

In a series LC circuit, the inductive and capacitive reactances are equal and opposite, and cancel out, resulting in no net impedance. ***In reality, any practical capacitor or inductor has some small internal resistance, so the net impedance is not zero, but very very low***. The ratio of reactance to "parasitic" resistance in a series circuit is the Q, a very important factor in circuit performance. **ANSWER C.**

These coils were in place to test a mobile antenna's feed point impedance on different bands.

G5A03 Which of the following is opposition to the flow of alternating current in an inductor?

A. Conductance
B. Reluctance
C. Admittance
D. Reactance

Think of an inductor as a coil of wire. Its opposition to AC is called inductive ***reactance***, which is calculated as $X_L = 2\pi fL$ where f is the frequency in hertz and L is the inductance in henries. X_L increases as frequency increases. **ANSWER D.**

G5A09 What unit is used to measure reactance?

A. Farad
B. Ohm
C. Ampere
D. Siemens

The ***ohm*** is the unit of measurement for reactance as well as resistance. **ANSWER B.**

G5A04 Which of the following is opposition to the flow of alternating current in a capacitor?

A. Conductance
B. Reluctance
C. Reactance
D. Admittance

A capacitor has plates separated by an insulating dielectric. Its opposition to AC is called capacitive ***reactance***, which is calculated as $X_C = 1 \div 2\pi fC$ where f is the frequency in hertz and C is the capacitance in farads. X_C decreases as frequency increases. **ANSWER C.**

G5A05 How does an inductor react to AC?

A. As the frequency of the applied AC increases, the reactance decreases
B. As the amplitude of the applied AC increases, the reactance increases
C. As the amplitude of the applied AC increases, the reactance decreases
D. As the frequency of the applied AC increases, the reactance increases

Inductors (coils) are effective in reducing alternator whine in high-frequency mobile installations. The ***higher*** the alternator whine ***frequency***, the ***greater*** the ***reactance*** from the inductor. Remember, as f increases, X_L increases ($X_L = 2\pi fL$). **ANSWER D.**

G5A06 How does a capacitor react to AC?

A. As the frequency of the applied AC increases, the reactance decreases
B. As the frequency of the applied AC increases, the reactance increases
C. As the amplitude of the applied AC increases, the reactance increases
D. As the amplitude of the applied AC increases, the reactance decreases

Capacitors offer reactance to AC inversely proportional to the frequency. Capacitors have high reactance at ***low frequencies and low reactance at high frequencies***. Remember, as f increases, X_C decreases ($X_C = 1 \div 2\pi fC$). **ANSWER A.**

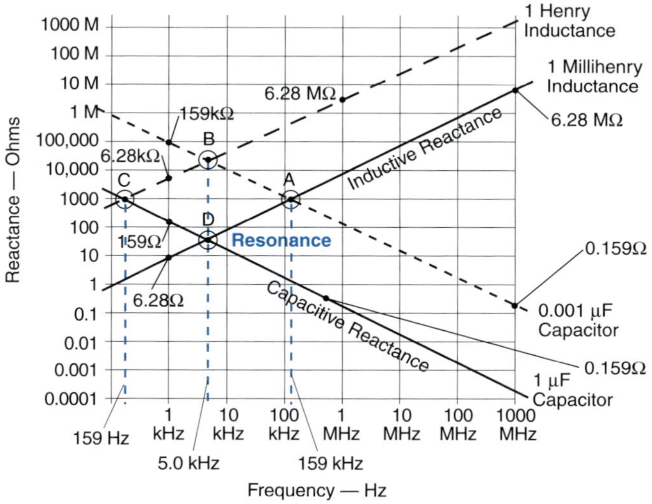

Variation of inductance and capacitive reactance with frequency (illustration not to exact log-log scale).
Source: *Basic Communications Electronics,* © 1999 Master Publishing, Inc., Niles, IL

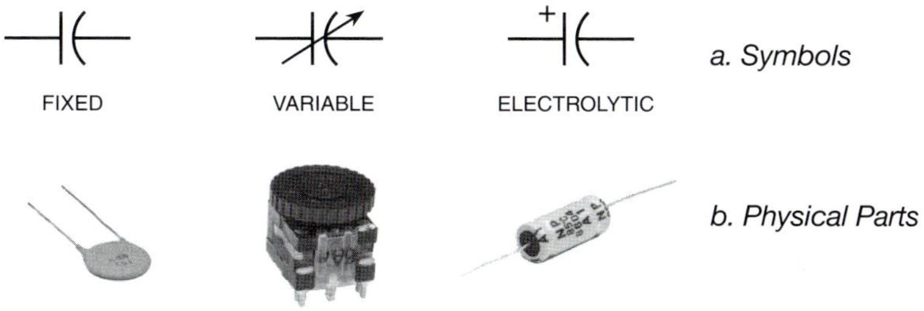

Capacitors

G5A11 What letter is used to represent reactance?

A. Z
B. X
C. B
D. Y

Every electrical value has both a SYMBOL and a UNIT. It is important to learn very early in your electronics career not to confuse symbols with units! ***The SYMBOL for reactance is X***, but the UNIT of reactance is the OHM. **ANSWER B.**

G5A08 What is impedance?

A. The ratio of current to voltage
B. The product of current and voltage
C. The ratio of voltage to current
D. The product of current and reactance

Most electrical values have logical grammatical names. Like resistance, impedance implies that we're impeding something; in this case, it's current flow. For a given applied voltage, the greater the impedance, the less the current flow. ***The term impedance means the ratio of voltage to current in an AC circuit***. Pretty simple! **ANSWER C.**

G5A07 What is the term for the inverse of impedance?

A. Conductance
B. Susceptance
C. Reluctance
D. Admittance

All electronic values have inverse, or reciprocal values. These are very useful values, though you may not encounter them much in amateur radio. The reciprocal of resistance is conductance; the reciprocal of reactance is susceptance, ***and the reciprocal of impedance is admittance***. These three values, conductance, susceptance, and admittance all have the same unit, the siemens. The symbol for the siemens is the ℧, or upside down ohm. In fact, the former name for the siemens was the MHO, which is ohm spelled backwards! I actually like the mho better, because it's easy to remember that with mo' mho, you have mo' current flow. But siemens is now the proper term. We old timers can't always have our way. **ANSWER D.**

G5A10 Which of the following devices can be used for impedance matching at radio frequencies?

A. A transformer
B. A Pi-network
C. A length of transmission line
D. All these choices are correct

There are plenty of ways we can match impedances at radio frequencies. Up at the antenna, we sometimes will use fractional wavelength impedance-matching transmission lines. In a radio RF output stage, we might use an impedance-matching Pi-network. And within the radio, small transformers will allow us to impedance match. ***All of these*** are great ways for providing the maximum transfer of radio frequency energy. **ANSWER D.**

G7C12 What is the frequency above which a low-pass filter's output power is less than half the input power?

A. Notch frequency
B. Neper frequency
C. Cutoff frequency
D. Rolloff frequency

No filter is perfect. It would be nice if you could design a high pass filter, for instance, that passes all frequencies above some frequency with no loss, while totally blocking all frequencies below that frequency. Filters with sharper cutoff frequencies can be built with multiple sections, but still there is no perfect filter. Filter "shapes" are specified by how quickly the filter transitions from its pass band to its stop band, using the half power or 3 dB point to define the ***cutoff frequency***. **ANSWER C.**

G7C13 What term specifies a filter's maximum ability to reject signals outside its passband?

A. Notch depth
B. Rolloff
C. Insertion loss
D. Ultimate rejection

More complex filters are defined by two or more parameters, the first being the 3 dB cutoff frequency, and an "outer" ***ultimate rejection*** frequency, generally specified by the -60 dB point. The ratio of the cutoff frequency to the ultimate rejection frequency is the "shape factor" and is an indication of how sharply the filter transits from its passband to its band-stop properties. **ANSWER D.**

G7C14 The bandwidth of a band-pass filter is measured between what two frequencies?

A. Upper and lower half-power
B. Cutoff and rolloff
C. Pole and zero
D. Image and harmonic

A band-pass filter can be synthesized by putting a high-pass filter and a low-pass filter "back to back." When viewed in this manner, we can use ***the upper half-power cutoff frequency and the lower half-power cutoff frequency*** to fully define this filter. This now is standard practice and is less awkward than the older method of having different specifications for high-pass, low-pass, band-pass, and band-stop filters. **ANSWER A.**

G7C07 What term specifies a filter's attenuation inside its passband?

A. Insertion loss
B. Return loss
C. Q
D. Ultimate rejection

As mentioned earlier, no filter is perfect. However, we can approach the ideal filter by using the highest Q (low loss) filter components available (or practical). It is desirable for a bandpass filter, for instance, to have the minimum loss possible inside the passband. ***Insertion loss*** is the loss in dB in the center of the desired passband, and almost without exception, the lower the better. Less frequently, insertion loss is used for high-pass or low-pass filters as well. **ANSWER A.**

G6A06 Why should wire-wound resistors not be used in RF circuits?

A. The resistor's tolerance value would not be adequate
B. The resistor's inductance could make circuit performance unpredictable
C. The resistor could overheat
D. The resistor's internal capacitance would detune the circuit

If you were able to scrape off the brown glaze coating on a ***wire-wound resistor***, you would quickly see it looks exactly like a coil with evenly spaced turns. Actually, it IS an inductor and would not be suitable in any circuit that ***could accidentally make the circuit performance unpredictable*** through the use of the wrong component. Normally, we find wire-wound resistors in simple DC applications where we need to drop a small amount of voltage with relatively high current being passed. **ANSWER B.**

Here we see the inner workings of a wire-wound resistor. Most resistors of this sort are wound with nichrome wire or other resistance wire, which has much more resistance than copper. It's the same stuff used for the heating elements in your toaster.

G6B05 What is an advantage of using a ferrite core toroidal inductor?

A. Large values of inductance may be obtained
B. The magnetic properties of the core may be optimized for a specific range of frequencies
C. Most of the magnetic field is contained in the core
D. All these choices are correct

When you pass this exam and earn General Class privileges, you may begin to operate HF. A couple of rigs actually have their batteries on the inside! With any portable transceiver, including VHF/UHF handhelds, make sure they never get dropped! Dropping radio equipment can fracture the brittle iron cores within a toroidal inductor. The ferrite core within a toroidal inductor offers large values of inductance, with most of the magnetic field contained within the core so it does not affect other nearby components. The toroidal inductor may be used in applications where core saturation is desirable, so ***all of the answer choices are correct***. **ANSWER D.**

G6B01 What determines the performance of a ferrite core at different frequencies?

A. Its conductivity
B. Its thickness
C. The composition, or "mix," of materials used
D. The ratio of outer diameter to inner diameter

Ferrites are extremely useful and sometimes strange materials. A ferrite is an iron-based ceramic material which greatly increases the permeability of an inductor when used as a core. However, one must be careful to use the right ***composition, or "mix," of materials used in the core***, based on the frequency and power levels of the inductor in question. Winding ferrite core inductors and transformers is quite an art form, and highly educational. **ANSWER C.**

A transformer wound around a ferrite toroid core is a common component in modern radio gear. Such cores allow a lot of inductance to be provided in a small space.

G5C01 What causes a voltage to appear across the secondary winding of a transformer when an AC voltage source is connected across its primary winding?

A. Capacitive coupling
B. Displacement current coupling
C. Mutual inductance
D. Mutual capacitance

Think of a transformer with interlaced coils. Through mutual inductance within the transformer, voltage applied to the primary will also appear across the secondary. ***Mutual inductance***. **ANSWER C.**

G5C06 What is the voltage output of a transformer with a 500-turn primary and a 1500-turn secondary when 120 VAC is applied to the primary?

A. 360 volts
B. 120 volts
C. 40 volts
D. 25.5 volts

In an ideal transformer, the voltage ratio is equal to the turns ratio. In this example, the turns ratio is 3:1. So the input voltage has to also be multiplied by 3 to come out with 360 volts, our final answer. Keep in mind that this assumes an ideal transformer. We need to always explore the ideal before we consider the "real world" components with all their warts and wrinkles! **ANSWER A.**

G5C02 What is the output voltage if an input signal is applied to the secondary winding of a 4:1 voltage step-down transformer instead of the primary winding?

A. The input voltage is multiplied by 4
B. The input voltage is divided by 4
C. Additional resistance must be added in series with the primary to prevent overload
D. Additional resistance must be added in parallel with the secondary to prevent overload

A transformer consists of two or more windings of wire that are magnetically coupled. The ratio of voltages of any transformer is proportional to the turns ratio. A transformer with 10 turns on the primary side and 100 turns on the secondary side is a 10:1 step up transformer. Likewise, a transformer in this question with 400 turns on the primary side and 100 turns on the secondary side is a 4:1 step- down transformer. Whatever voltage you put across the primary winding will be divided by 4 on the secondary. Going back through the transformer the other way, ***the input voltage is multiplied by 4***. Important note: While a transformer can have a tremendous amount of voltage step up, there is no free lunch! The power out of any transformer is only equal to the power going into the transformer (minus some losses). A 4:1 voltage step down transformer will have a 4:1 CURRENT step UP. The product of the input voltage and current must always equal the product of the output voltage and current. **ANSWER A.**

G5C07 What transformer turns ratio matches an antenna's 600-ohm feed point impedance to a 50-ohm coaxial cable?

A. 3.5 to 1
B. 12 to 1
C. 24 to 1
D. 144 to 1

The voltage ratio of a transformer is proportional to the turns ratio, but the IMPEDANCE ratio of a transformer is equal to the SQUARE of the turns ratio. Or, working backwards, as in this example, the turns ratio is the SQUARE ROOT of the impedance ratio. In this case ***600 ohms/50 ohms gives us an impedance ratio*** of 12. We now take the square root of 12 is 3.46, our turns ratio, rounded up to 3.5. Note: Alternatively, we could put this transformer in "backwards" to match a 600 ohm open wire transmission line to a 50 ohm antenna, a much more common situation. **ANSWER A.**

Advancing the Radio Art

One of the primary reasons radio amateurs have retained valuable frequency allocations is so that we may "advance the state of the radio art." Countless advances in science and technology – not all of them directly related to communications – have come about by amateur radio experimentation.

If you're a new radio amateur, you might feel the need to be a rocket scientist to contribute anything new to the radio art. Not so! There is still a great deal to be learned about such matters as radio propagation, which can easily be investigated by anyone with an amateur radio license. All that is required is insatiable curiosity, an observant eye and ear, and systematic record keeping. Your amateur radio log book can be a valuable scientific instrument! Give honest signal reports and keep good station notes. Experiment with odd radio modes. Explore some of our unused bands. Do some homebrewing. Write some technical articles. Spend a lot of time on the air. You are quite likely to stumble across something nobody has seen or heard before!

One area where the opportunity to explore is wide open are our 12 microwave bands! For the most part, these bands are unused by radio amateurs. Granted, there may not be a lot of "ready-made" amateur gear for some of these bands, but that lack provides a great opportunity to exercise your home brewing skills. These are prime bands for experimenting. Remember, one of the reasons we exist as amateur operators is to "advance the state of the radio art," and that advancement comes through our experimentation.

If you want some more encouragement, read Eric's book ***Radio Science for the Radio Amateur***. You can get a copy from The W5YI Group by calling 800-669-9594 or visit www.w5yi.org.

Good Grounds

G4C05 What is a possible cause of high voltages that produce RF burns?

A. Flat braid rather than round wire has been used for the ground wire
B. Insulated wire has been used for the ground wire
C. The ground rod is resonant
D. The ground wire has high impedance on that frequency

Nothing worse than petting Fido while going on the air with your new high frequency installation and seeing a blue arc from your D-104 microphone to his metal nametag, accompanied by a yelp! Welcome to RF floating along the chassis ground of your equipment. Using wire to ground HF equipment may create an antenna-like circuit that looks like an open circuit to earth ground. Round ground wires may also behave like wire coils, developing a reactance at specific frequencies, thus blocking the ground connection to that cold water pipe. This blocking action is called ***impedance***. Always ground your equipment with flat braid or copper foil, using the shortest run possible to an actual earth ground. In some cases, this may not be possible. In such a situation you might try a device called an artificial ground, which makes a low impedance, series resonant circuit out of any ground wire you do have. Sometimes acquiring a good RF ground is an art form and may require patience and persistence. **ANSWER D.**

G4C09 How can the effects of ground loops be minimized?

A. Connect all ground conductors in series
B. Connect the AC neutral conductor to the ground wire
C. Avoid using lock washers and star washers when making ground connections
D. Bond equipment enclosures together

Gordo has several HF transceivers at the shack, and all copper foil ground connections go to a single ground point. From that point, the flattened copper pipe goes through the wall and into the earth. ***Bonding equipment enclosures together*** will minimize ground loops. **ANSWER D.**

Copper foil ground strap provides a good surface area ground. Flat copper foil attached to the rear of an HF transceiver. Never use wire for RF grounding.

G4C10 What could be a symptom caused by a ground loop in your station's audio connections?

A. You receive reports of "hum" on your station's transmitted signal
B. The SWR reading for one or more antennas is suddenly very high
C. An item of station equipment starts to draw excessive amounts of current
D. You receive reports of harmonic interference from your station

You are on the air for the first time and everyone reports you sound loud and sort of clear, but with a ***hum behind your signal***. Sounds like a ground loop to me. This can be cured with good copper foil grounding interconnected to each and every piece of metal equipment you have on your desk. This includes that big computer, too. **ANSWER A.**

G4C12 Why must all metal enclosures of station equipment be grounded?

A. It prevents a blown fuse in the event of an internal short circuit
B. It prevents signal overload
C. It ensures that the neutral wire is grounded
D. It ensures that hazardous voltages cannot appear on the chassis

Good station grounding ensures that ***no hazardous or dangerous voltages appear on the metal chassis of your equipment***. Without good grounding you could be shocked when you touch a piece of equipment. **ANSWER D.**

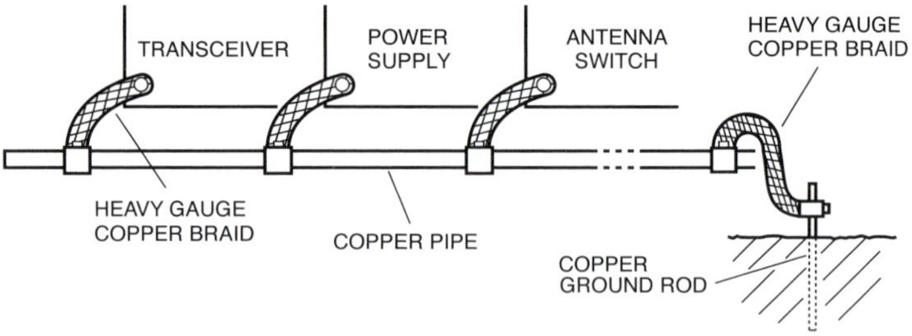

Grounding Equipment

G4C06 What is a possible effect of a resonant ground connection?

A. Overheating of ground straps
B. Corrosion of the ground rod
C. High RF voltages on the enclosures of station equipment
D. A ground loop

If you notice a tingle when you touch anything metal on your equipment during transmit, it is a sign that a ***resonant ground connection*** is ***causing high voltages*** to back up ***onto the case of the radio***. Time to switch over to some 3-inch wide copper foil. That's what Gordo and Eric use at their stations. **ANSWER C.**

G4C01 Which of the following might be useful in reducing RF interference to audio frequency circuits?

A. Bypass inductor
B. Bypass capacitor
C. Forward-biased diode
D. Reverse-biased diode

When you begin operating on General Class frequencies, your powerful, high-frequency SSB transceiver fed into a roof-top antenna system will probably create audio-frequency interference to your own home electronics and those of your neighbors. Bypass capacitors – usually 0.01 μF – will sometimes help minimize this problem when strategically placed across and onto speaker wires and wiring harnesses inside the affected home electronic systems. It's not a cure-all, but ***bypass capacitors*** are your first step in resolving interference complaints on a case-by-case basis. **ANSWER B.**

G4C08 Which of the following would reduce RF interference caused by common-mode current on an audio cable?

A. Place a ferrite choke on the cable
B. Connect the center conductor to the shield of all cables to short circuit the RFI signal
C. Ground the center conductor of the audio cable causing the interference
D. Add an additional insulating jacket to the cable

You can get some terrific audio DSP speakers to add on to older equipment that does not have audio DSP capability. If the speakers are amplified, sometimes RF transmit sounds come out over the speaker itself. You can minimize this common-mode current on the audio cable by ***placing ferrite chokes around the cable***. Use ferrite beads around all the computer and data cables, too. **ANSWER A.** Visit **Palomar-Engineers.com** for more information on ferrite beads.

Snap-on ferrite choke.

G4C03 What sound is heard from an audio device experiencing RF interference from a single sideband phone transmitter?

A. A steady hum whenever the transmitter is on the air
B. On-and-off humming or clicking
C. Distorted speech
D. Clearly audible speech

Single-sideband sounds like distorted speech coming over a public address system or certain home electronics. However, double sideband AM CB radio transmissions usually come through loud and clear, so these are easily distinguished from SSB ham transmissions. If someone says you are causing interference, ask the big question: "Does it sound clear, or does it sound garbled?" **ANSWER C.**

G4C04 What sound is heard from an audio device experiencing RF interference from a CW transmitter?

A. On-and-off humming or clicking
B. A CW signal at a nearly pure audio frequency
C. A chirpy CW signal
D. Severely distorted audio

CW transmissions come over an audio device or home electronics system as ***on-and-off humming or clicking sounds***. There is no mistaking the sound of CW. **ANSWER A.**

G4C02 Which of the following could be a cause of interference covering a wide range of frequencies?

A. Not using a balun or line isolator to feed balanced antennas
B. Lack of rectification of the transmitter's signal in power conductors
C. Arcing at a poor electrical connection
D. Using a balun to feed an unbalanced antenna

About once every 6 months, go around and tighten up all connections on your ham equipment. Most important is the tightening-up of the copper ground foil connections to the back of your rig. An ***intermittent RF ground*** will sometimes create ***broadband radio frequency noise*** that will magically go away as soon as you give that nut a little clockwise crank. **ANSWER C.**

G4E07 Which of the following may cause receive interference to an HF transceiver installed in a vehicle?

A. The battery charging system
B. The fuel delivery system
C. The control computers
D. All these choices are correct

The noise blankers on most HF mobile transceivers do a nice job of getting rid of sparkplug pops. But right where you want to operate on the "Gordo net"frequency at 7250 kHz you hear a steady, raspy carrier that only goes away when you shut off the ignition. Guess what? This steady carrier may be from your vehicle's computer system. The whistle sound that changes pitch when you rev up the engine could be from your alternator. And ticking sounds all over the band could be from your vehicle's electric fuel pump. ***All of these choices*** are possible sources of vehicle noise that may creep in to your mobile HF radio setup. Some can be cured with in-line DC filters, but suspect all of these as noise sources that disappear when you turn off the ignition on newer vehicles. **ANSWER D.**

HF Antennas

G9B10 What is the approximate length for a 1/2 wave dipole antenna cut for 14.250 MHz?

A. 8 feet
B. 16 feet
C. 24 feet
D. 33 feet

To calculate the length, in feet, of a half-wavelength dipole antenna, divide 468 by the antenna's operating frequency in MHz. Just remember: "2-4-6-8, who do we appreciate?" if you want your results in feet. This calculation is easy with the calculator you brought to the exam session. Divide 468 by the frequency in MHz, 14.250 to get 32.842 feet, rounded to ***33 feet.*** **ANSWER D.**

G9B11 What is the approximate length for a 1/2 wave dipole antenna cut for 3.550 MHz?

A. 42 feet
B. 84 feet
C. 132 feet
D. 263 feet

Let's do the math: 468 ÷ 3.55 = 131.8 feet! Rounded to ***132 feet***. Easy, huh? **ANSWER C.**

G9B09 Which of the following is an advantage of using a horizontally polarized as compared to a vertically polarized HF antenna?

A. Lower ground losses
B. Lower feed point impedance
C. Shorter radials
D. Lower radiation resistance

The well-constructed and properly-elevated 1/2 wave dipole that is horizontally polarized will generally outperform a ground mounted vertical antenna. This is because the ground mounted vertical antenna usually encounters ***ground losses*** from everything close to its base. **ANSWER A.**

G3C10 What is near vertical incidence skywave (NVIS) propagation?

A. Propagation near the MUF
B. Short distance MF or HF propagation at high elevation angles
C. Long path HF propagation at sunrise and sunset
D. Double hop propagation near the LUF.

Let's imagine you go out on a camping trip into a valley 200 miles away from your buddy's house. With a normal dipole up about 1/2 wave length, your 40 meter signal literally skips over his location. A neat way to "pull in" your first skywave hop is to lower your dipole so it is just high enough that no one can touch it. You

Elmer Point:

In case you're wondering where this 468 comes from, let's look at the speed of light in feet per second. The speed of light in free space is 186,292 miles per second. If we multiply that by 5280 feet per statute mile, we get 984,000,000 feet per second (rounded to three significant digits). If we divide that by 1 million, we get feet per *microsecond,* or 984. Okay, now what frequency radio wave has a *period* of 1 microsecond. Period is the reciprocal of frequency. The answer is 1 MHz. 984 is the wavelength in space, in feet, of a 1 MHz signal. But we know that a dipole is only ½ wavelength. So a dipole for 1 MHz is going to be 984/2 feet, or 492 feet. Well, 492 is *sort of* 468, but not quite. There's about a 5% error. What gives? As it turns out, radio waves don't quite travel in a wire at the speed of light in free space. There are a number of contributing effects, but they're all lumped into this mysterious entity called "end effect," which is really just a mathematical construct that gives you a bonus of 5% increase in effective length for a wire. The end effect is greater for fat conductors, such as tubing used for Yagi antennas and the like.

Now for those of you who have been "metricated" we can apply the same calculations, except using the speed of light in meters per second, which comes out to be almost exactly 300,000,000. Or 300 meters per *microsecond.* Again, this gives you the free space full wavelength of a 1 MHz signal. To find the actual length of a dipole, you want to divide this by a little over 2.

The half-wavelength dipole antenna offers no compromise when transmitting and receiving long-range signals. A half-wave dipole usually will outperform multi-band medium length verticals and excel above a fancy $800 mobile, big-coil whip. Dipoles are simple to construct and you can pull up the center section with a rope to configure it as an inverted vee. The only thing that beats a dipole is a big 3-element beam or a quad.

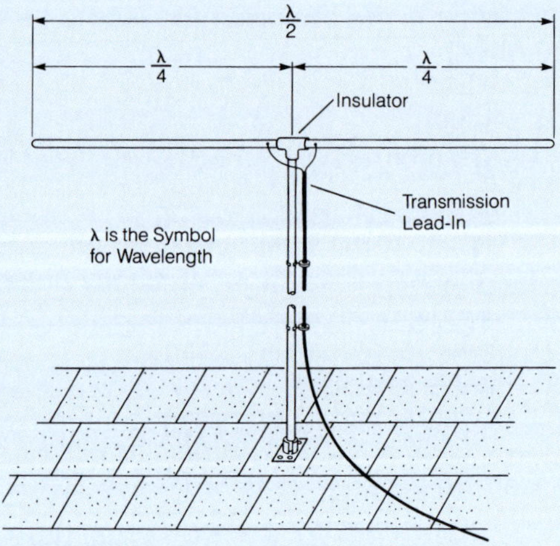

will find that your first skywave hop now arrives at your friend's house loud and clear. Dramatically lowering an antenna will develop a ***higher elevation angle of radiation***, causing your skip distance to "pull in," which establishes ***shorter-than- normal skywave communications***. **ANSWER B.**

G9D01 Which of the following antenna types will be most effective as a near vertical incidence skywave (NVIS) antenna for short-skip communications on 40 meters during the day?

A. A horizontal dipole placed between 1/10 and 1/4 wavelength above the ground
B. A vertical antenna placed between 1/4 and 1/2 wavelength above the ground
C. horizontal dipole placed at approximately 1/2 wavelength above the ground
D. A vertical dipole placed at approximately 1/2 wavelength above the ground

A simple ***dipole antenna, placed between 1/10 and 1/4 wavelength*** above the ground, will give you powerful daytime skywave communications on the 40 meter band. To reach out further, elevate it. To "pull in" your first hop, lower it slightly! **ANSWER A.**

G9B07 How does the feed point impedance of a horizontal 1/2 wave dipole antenna change as the antenna height is reduced to 1/10 wavelength above ground?

A. It steadily increases
B. It steadily decreases
C. It peaks at about 1/8 wavelength above ground
D. It is unaffected by the height above ground

The 1/2 wave dipole is an outstanding antenna system that will cost you little to build. This antenna elevated to roof level will generally outperform expensive, high-frequency mobile whips, expensive trap vertical antennas, and pricey automatic-tuner-fed long wires. But get the 1/2 wave dipole up high. If it is less than 1/4 wavelength above ground, the ***feed point impedance will dramatically decrease***, and your radiation pattern goes whacko, not to mention that you now have a source-to-load impedance mismatch that will affect your output power. **ANSWER B.**

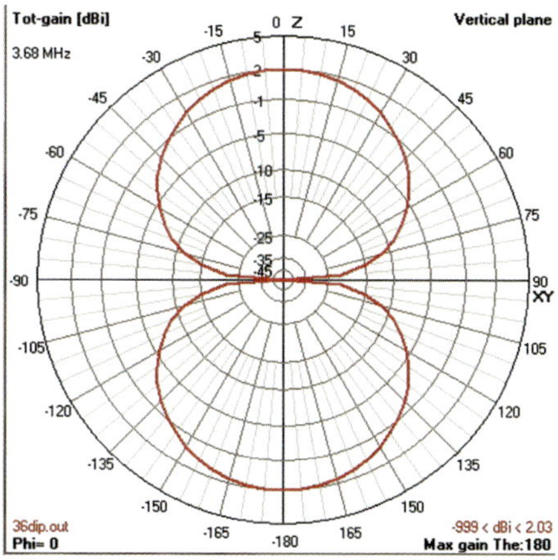

Have antenna will travel! Here is a portable half-wave dipole system that gives good results on shorter wavelengths. The plot to the right shows a typical dipole radiation pattern.

G9B08 How does the feed point impedance of a 1/2 wave dipole change as the feed point is moved from the center toward the ends?

A. It steadily increases
B. It steadily decreases
C. It peaks at about 1/8 wavelength from the end
D. It is unaffected by the location of the feed point

If you try to offset the feed point of a 1/2 wave dipole from the center toward the ends, ***feed point impedance will rise*** well above 50 ohms and your rig's automatic antenna tuner may have a hard time correcting to an SWR of 1:1. **ANSWER A.**

G9D12 What is the common name of a dipole with a single central support?

A. Inverted V
B. Inverted L
C. Sloper
D. Lazy H

The ***inverted V*** antenna is perhaps the easiest effective HF antenna to deploy because it needs only one support, and it has essentially the same characteristics as a dipole erected at the same height. It is a favorite of Field Day operations, as well as military HF operations. Two inverted Vs at right angles with a common central support pole can double nicely as the guy wires for that support pole. **ANSWER A.**

G9D02 What is the feed point impedance of an end-fed half-wave antenna?

A. Very low
B. Approximately 50 ohms
C. Approximately 300 ohms
D. Very high

A resonant dipole in free space has an impedance at the center of about 72 ohms, and many thousands of ohms at the ends. In fact, if the wire were infinitely thin, the impedance at the end of a dipole would be infinite. Fortunately we don't have to try to match to an infinite impedance with real-world, end-fed dipoles, but merely a ***very high impedance***, typically something on the order of 2500 ohms. **ANSWER D.**

G9B04 What is the radiation pattern of a dipole antenna in free space in a plane containing the conductor?

A. It is a figure-eight at right angles to the antenna
B. It is a figure-eight off both ends of the antenna
C. It is a circle (equal radiation in all directions)
D. It has a pair of lobes on one side of the antenna and a single lobe on the other side.

The dipole gives you a ***figure eight pattern at right angles to the antenna*** wire. Reception and transmission are minimal off the ends of the wire. **ANSWER A.**

G9D03 In which direction is the maximum radiation from a VHF/UHF "halo" antenna?

A. Broadside to the plane of the halo
B. Opposite the feed point
C. Omnidirectional in the plane of the halo
D. On the same side as the feed point

Halo antennas used to be very popular for VHF mobile operation in the late 1950s, back when most VHF was AM. Horizontal polarization was less subject to ignition noise, which became somewhat of a moot point with the advent of FM. However, now that hams are rediscovering weak signal VHF modes, the halo is becoming popular once more. The halo is ***omnidirectional in the plane of the halo***. **ANSWER C.**

G9B05 How does antenna height affect the azimuthal radiation pattern of a horizontal dipole HF antenna at elevation angles higher than about 45 degrees?

A. If the antenna is too high, the pattern becomes unpredictable
B. Antenna height has no effect on the pattern
C. If the antenna is less than 1/2 wavelength high, the azimuthal pattern is almost omnidirectional
D. If the antenna is less than 1/2 wavelength high, radiation off the ends of the wire is eliminated

Never mount a dipole antenna less than 1/2 wavelength above the ground for long-range DX. Any lower and you may have signal distortion, an ***omnidirectional radiation pattern***, and most of your signal going straight up. **ANSWER C.**

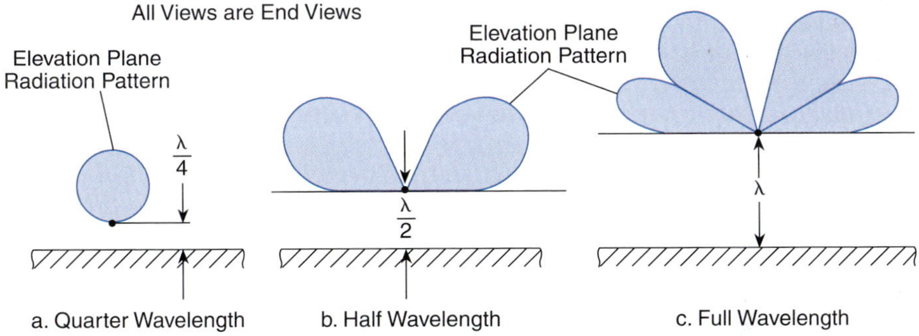

The radiation pattern of an antenna changes as height above ground is varied.
Source: *Antennas*, A.J. Evans, K.E. Britain, © 1998, Master Publishing, Niles, IL

G9B03 Which of the following best describes the radiation pattern of a quarter-wave ground-plane vertical antenna?

A. Bi-directional in azimuth
B. Isotropic
C. Hemispherical
D. Omnidirectional in azimuth

A single wire of any orientation radiates in an omnidirectional pattern broadside to the wire. If the wire is vertical, it will radiate a pattern that is ***omnidirectional in azimuth***. While the configuration of the ground plane may affect the pattern somewhat in elevation, a ground plane antenna of any length will be truly omnidirectional in the azimuth at zero degrees elevation. **ANSWER D.**

G9B12 What is the approximate length for a 1/4 wave monopole antenna cut for 28.5 MHz?

A. 8 feet
B. 11 feet
C. 16 feet
D. 21 feet

Let's say you want to operate 10 meters mobile. When you operate mobile, the metal frame of the vehicle makes up 1/4 wavelength of your antenna system, and the other 1/4 wavelength is the vertical radiating antenna. Think of your vertical whip as one side of a dipole and the vehicle chassis as the other. To calculate the length, in **feet**, of a 1/4 -wavelength vertical antenna, first find the length of a 1/2 wavelength in feet then take half of that. To find 1/2 wavelength, divide 468 by the antenna's operating frequency in MHz. Just remember: "2-**4-6-8**, who do we appreciate?" if you want your results in **feet**. This calculation is easy with the calculator you brought to the exam session. Divide 468 by the frequency in MHz, 28.5 to get 16.42 feet. Then 16.42 ÷ 2 = 8.2 ***rounded to 8 feet***. **ANSWER A.**

G9B06 Where should the radial wires of a ground-mounted vertical antenna system be placed?

A. As high as possible above the ground
B. Parallel to the antenna element
C. On the surface or buried a few inches below the ground
D. At the center of the antenna

Ground radial wires are important for the ground-mounted vertical antenna to establish its own counterpoise. To hear any real difference when you already have a few radials laid out per band, you must double the number of radials. If you have 2 per band, try 4. If you have 4, try 8. If you need more ground plane than 8 radials per band, try mounting your antenna on the aluminum shed in the backyard and use the roof of the shed as a substitute for the radials! The more ground radials you have on a ground plane antenna, the lower the takeoff angle of radiation, which means more DX. Get out the shovel, and ***start digging to install more ground radials***! **ANSWER C.**

G9C03 How do the lengths of a three-element Yagi reflector and director compare to that of the driven element?

A. The reflector is longer, and the director is shorter
B. The reflector is shorter, and the director is longer
C. They are all the same length
D. Relative length depends on the frequency of operation

It's pretty easy to identify which direction a three element Yagi is radiating; ***the reflector is longer, and the director is shorter***. In a typical 3-element Yagi, the reflector is about 5% longer than the driven element, and the director is about 5% shorter than the driven element. There's an interesting special case of the Yagi antenna, when just two elements exist. If the parasitic element is the same length as the driven element, it can either be a reflector or a director depending on the spacing! Also, some very closely-spaced, multi-element Yagis can appear to "fire backwards." But these are the exceptions. **ANSWER A.**

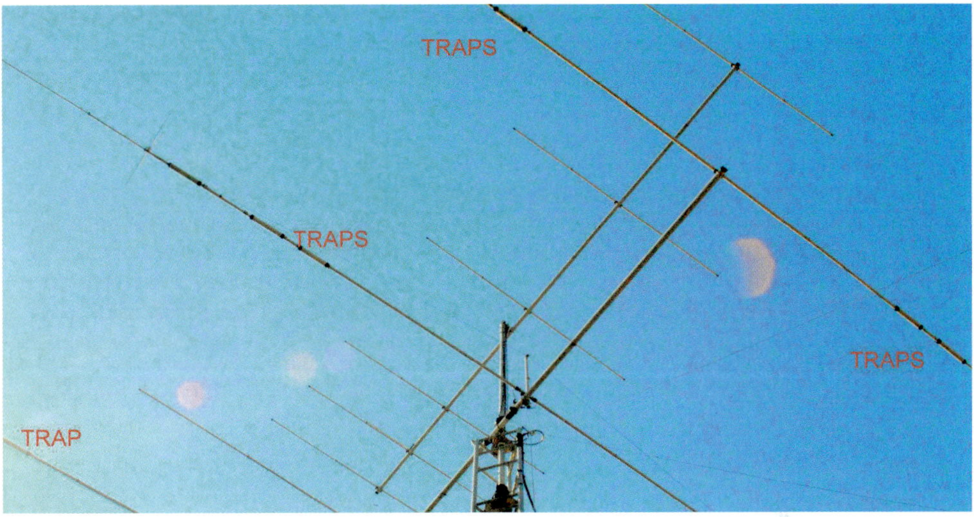

A 3 element beam antenna – the Yagi antenna
Source: *Antennas - Selection and Installation*,©1986 Master Publishing, Inc., Niles, IL

G9C02 What is the approximate length of the driven element of a Yagi antenna?

A. 1/4 wavelength
B. 1/2 wavelength
C. 3/4 wavelength
D. 1 wavelength

Since the Yagi antenna is a series of dipoles affixed to a boom in the same plane, the ***driven element is about 1/2 wavelength long***. The reflector is a little longer. The directors a little bit shorter. **ANSWER B.**

G9C05 What is the primary effect of increasing boom length and adding directors to a Yagi antenna?

A. Gain increases
B. Beamwidth increases
C. Front-to-back ratio decreases
D. Resonant frequency is lower

On a Yagi antenna, ***boom length*** determines the amount of ***gain***. The number of elements and the diameter of the elements influence the directivity and bandwidth of the antenna. **ANSWER A.**

G9C08 What is meant by the "main lobe" of a directive antenna?

A. The magnitude of the maximum vertical angle of radiation
B. The point of maximum current in a radiating antenna element
C. The maximum voltage standing wave point on a radiating element
D. The direction of maximum radiated field strength from the antenna

The ***main lobe*** is the ***main radiating direction*** of the signal. Use a field strength meter to determine the main lobe of most directional antennas. Incidentally, many beam antennas such as broadside arrays, curtain arrays, unterminated rhombics, Vee beams, and even quad loops are bidirectional, with two equal-gain lobes 180 degrees apart. **ANSWER D.**

G9C07 What does "front-to-back ratio" mean in reference to a Yagi antenna?

A. The number of directors versus the number of reflectors
B. The relative position of the driven element with respect to the reflectors and directors
C. The power radiated in the major lobe compared to that in the opposite direction
D. The ratio of forward gain to dipole gain

The Yagi antenna gives you an excellent front-to-back ratio. This means that the ***majority of the power is radiated out of the front lobe*** of the antenna with ***little signal wasted to the back*** or sides. **ANSWER C.**

It's hard to beat the beach for great antenna performance – even more so if you have a respectable antenna to start with, such as this three element Yagi at a reasonable height. Famed DXer Chip, K7JA, regularly works the world on 10 meters using his homebrew 3 element beam down at the beach!

G9C10 Which of the following can be adjusted to optimize forward gain, front-to-back ratio, or SWR bandwidth of a Yagi antenna?

A. The physical length of the boom
B. The number of elements on the boom
C. The spacing of each element along the boom
D. All these choices are correct

Any time you begin lengthening the boom, adding or subtracting elements along the boom, or spacing the elements differently on a Yagi antenna, you will affect gain, front to back ratios, and SWR bandwidth. So, ***all of the choices are correct.*** **ANSWER D.**

The larger your antennas and the higher they are mounted on your tower, the better your range to distant DX stations!

G9C01 Which of the following would increase the bandwidth of a Yagi antenna?

A. Larger-diameter elements
B. Closer element spacing
C. Loading coils in series with the element
D. Tapered-diameter elements

The ***greater the diameter of the elements***, the ***greater the bandwidth***. This is why a wire beam antenna does not offer as much bandwidth as one constructed of large aluminum tubes. **ANSWER A.**

G9C12 Which of the following is a characteristic of using a gamma match with a Yagi antenna?

A. It does not require the driven element to be insulated from the boom
B. It does not require any inductors or capacitors
C. It is useful for matching multiband antennas
D. All these choices are correct

High frequency Yagi antennas may achieve a more predictable radiation pattern by insulating all elements from the boom. Big improvements in those element insulators keep them from cracking when a giant crow lands on one of them. Some high frequency antennas ***couple the elements directly to the boom through stainless steel hardware and alignment brackets***. This simplifies the matching network to the popular gamma match. With the gamma match in place, you can hook up the Yagi antenna directly to a 50-ohm coax feed. While the pattern may not be quite as predictable, the gamma match metal-to-boom high frequency antenna is a solid performer. **ANSWER A.**

Eric's unusual homebrew VHF "Q-Pole" antenna uses the principle of the gamma match for precise impedance matching.

G9C11 What is a beta or hairpin match?

A. A shorted transmission line stub placed at the feed point of a Yagi antenna to provide impedance matching
B. A 1/4 wavelength section of 75-ohm coax in series with the feed point of a Yagi to provide impedance matching
C. A series capacitor selected to cancel the inductive reactance of a folded dipole antenna
D. A section of 300-ohm twin-lead transmission line used to match a folded dipole antenna

We know that a single dipole at average height above ground has a feed point impedance of about 50 ohms. When additional elements (either parasitic or driven) are constructed near the dipole, the impedance can fall dramatically. A typical 3-element Yagi has a driven element feed point impedance of between 20 and 30 ohms. Some form of impedance matching network is usually desirable, and the hairpin match is a very popular method. ***It is a shorted transmission line stub placed at the feed point of a Yagi antenna to provide impedance matching***. **ANSWER A.**

G9D05 What is an advantage of vertically stacking horizontally polarized Yagi antennas?

A. It allows quick selection of vertical or horizontal polarization
B. It allows simultaneous vertical and horizontal polarization
C. It narrows the main lobe in azimuth
D. It narrows the main lobe in elevation

Vertically stacking horizontal Yagis helps ***concentrate the main lobe in elevation*** for added signal strength to the desired station. **ANSWER D.**

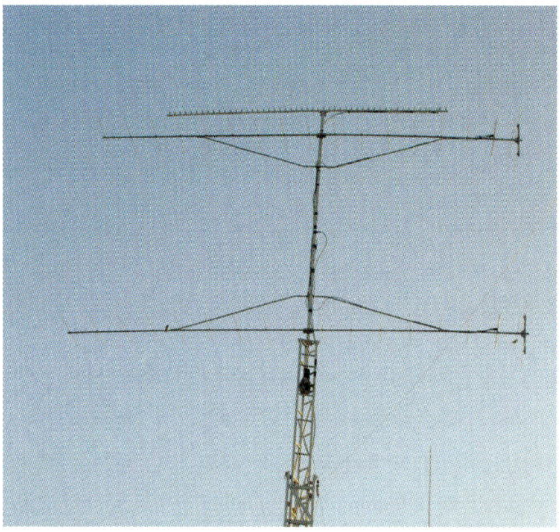

A pair of long-boom beam antennas on Gordo's tower add 3dB over a single antenna of the same type.

G9C09 In free space, how does the gain of two three-element, horizontally polarized Yagi antennas spaced vertically 1/2 wavelength apart typically compare to the gain of a single three-element Yagi?

A. Approximately 1.5 dB higher
B. Approximately 3 dB higher
C. Approximately 6 dB higher
D. Approximately 9 dB higher

You don't need a linear amplifier to boost your effective radiated power output or increase reception. You could stack a pair of Yagis about 1/2 wavelength apart and double your transmit and receive gain. Remember, 2 times the gain is ***3 dB***. **ANSWER B.**

G9D04 What is the primary function of antenna traps?

A. To enable multiband operation
B. To notch spurious frequencies
C. To provide balanced feed point impedance
D. To prevent out-of-band operation

A great way to get started on 40, 20, 15, and 10 meters is with a trap dipole, a trap beam antenna, or a trap vertical antenna. The traps allow the antenna to naturally tune to specific ham bands. Gordo operates a 4-element, 4-band beam antenna. The ***traps*** work great to give him high frequency operation on ***multiple ham bands with only one antenna***. **ANSWER A.**

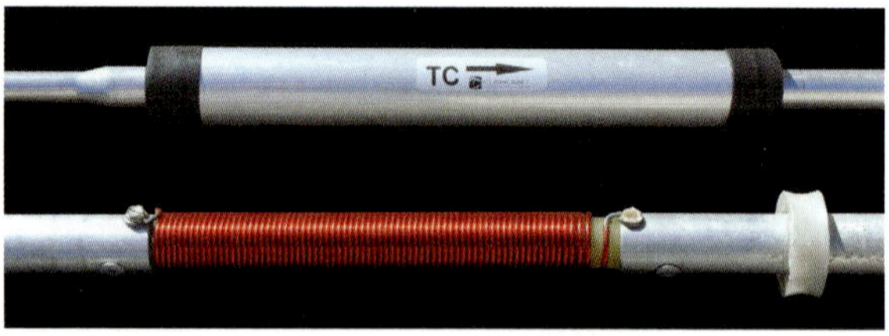

The inner workings of a typical multiband Yagi trap consist of a parallel coil and capacitor. In this case, the capacitor is formed by concentric aluminum tubing.

G9D11 Which of the following is a disadvantage of multiband antennas?

A. They present low impedance on all design frequencies
B. They must be used with an antenna tuner
C. They must be fed with open wire line
D. They have poor harmonic rejection

Newer high frequency radios have internal band pass filters to minimize harmonics. A harmonic is a multiple of your fundamental frequency that causes problems when you realize you are transmitting on two frequencies at once. If you are transmitting on 7 MHz, you want to minimize any harmonic on 14 MHz that would interfere with nearby hams on that frequency. Unfortunately, while ***multiband antennas*** have many advantages, they have the disadvantage of ***poor harmonic rejection***. **ANSWER D.**

G9B01 What is a characteristic of a random-wire HF antenna connected directly to the transmitter?

A. It must be longer than 1 wavelength
B. Station equipment may carry significant RF current
C. It produces only vertically polarized radiation
D. It is more effective on the lower HF bands than on the higher bands

Unless you use a remote-mounted automatic antenna tuner, the random-wire antenna can put a lot of ***RF feedback current*** in your station. **ANSWER B.**

G4A06 What is the purpose of an antenna tuner?

A. Reduce the SWR in the feed line to the antenna
B. Reduce the power dissipation in the feedline to the antenna
C. Increase power transfer from the transmitter to the feed line
D. All these choices are correct

An antenna tuner, alternately called a "matchbox," a "transmatch" or "antenna coupler" is a passive network designed to present a (usually) 50 ohm, non-reactive load to a transmitter, assuring maximum power transfer to the antenna system. There are countless varieties of these networks, but they all perform the same function. (In a vacuum tube transmitter or amplifier, the output tank circuit can perform the same function as an antenna tuner). Reflections, by Walter Maxwell, W2DU, should be required reading for every radio amateur. It clearly eliminates a lot of misinformation about antenna tuners and related topics. **ANSWER C.**

G9C04 How does antenna gain in dBi compare to gain stated in dBd for the same antenna?

A. Gain in dBi is 2.15 dB lower
B. Gain in dBi is 2.15 dB higher
C. Gain in dBd is 1.25 dBd lower
D. Gain in dBd is 1.25 dBd higher

In antenna work, there are actually two commonly used decibel references, one is the ***isotropic radiator (dBi)***, and the other is the ***dipole antenna (dBd)***. A ***dipole already has a gain of 2.15 dB over an isotropic radiator*** (about twice the power). So, let's say a manufacturer sells you an antenna with a gain of 4 dBd. To know what its gain is in dBi simply add the 2.15 dB gain that the dipole already has. An antenna with 4 dBd will have a gain of 6.15 dBi. **ANSWER B.**

Don't Dread the Decibel!

As hard as it may be to believe, a lot of the mathematical concepts we use in electronics and Amateur Radio were developed to make life EASIER, not to serve as some medieval torture device! One of these concepts is the decibel.

In radio we work with both extremely large and extremely small values. For example, a very weak UHF signal may be only a few femtowatts at the input of a receiver. A femtowatt is 0.000000000000001 watts. That's a whole lot of zeros to keep track of, especially if you're doing calculations that involve very large numbers, too. The decibel is a tool that shrinks the difference between those huge and minuscule numbers to a manageable size. When we work with decibels we're comparing two values. From a practical standpoint, we want to know if what we're doing is making something worse or better, and by how much.

If we want to know how much smaller a femtowatt is than a watt, without a truckload of zeros, we can use the decibel formula: dB = 10 log(P1/P2). P1 is 0.000000000000001 watts. P2 is 1 watt. So let's first divide P1 by P2, which gives us 0.000000000000001. Notice at this point there are no UNITS, since this is a ratio. Taking the logarithm of 0.000000000000001 gives us -15. Finally, we multiply that by 10, to give us -150 (decibels). -150dB is certainly a lot easier to manage than 0.000000000000001, isn't it? The minus sign simply tells us that the value is smaller. A femtowatt is 150 decibels smaller than a watt.

One final thing remains to tie things up. -150 dB needs to be associated with a unit to give it relevance. In this example, Watt is the unit. We put W with the dB figure to tell the whole story. So, a femtowatt is -150 dbW. Similarly, dbm, which uses the milliwatt as the basic unit, is a common unit in radio work.

Another way the decibel (dB) simplifies life is when we have a complex system with several GAINS and LOSSES. A good example of this is a radio circuit with a 10 dB antenna at each end and a 60 dB path loss in between. If each of these values is expressed in decibels, the calculations become a simple matter of addition and subtraction. We add the gains and subtract the losses to find the total SYSTEM gain (or loss). In this example, +10 +10 −60 = -40db, a total system loss since the result is negative. From the chart below you see that the signal power at the end of the system is 1/10,000 of the power it started out with. Looks like it's time to work on the system or get a really big amplifier! Nothing to it!

DB	P1/P2	DB	P1/P2
1	1.3	-1	0.794
2	1.6	-2	0.631
3	2	-3	0.5
6	4	-6	0.390
10	10	-10	0.1
20	100	-20	0.01
30	1,000	-30	0.001
40	10,000	-40	0.0001
50	100,000	-50	0.00001
60	1,000,000	-60	0.000001

ham apps

The decibel was invented to make life easier. This calculator makes it doubly easy to work with decibels, whether you're working with power or voltage.
https://itunes.apple.com/us/app/dbcalculator/id489100786?mt=8

G9D10 In which direction or directions does an electrically small loop (less than 1/10 wavelength in circumference) have nulls in its radiation pattern?

A. In the plane of the loop
B. Broadside to the loop
C. Broadside and in the plane of the loop
D. Electrically small loops are omnidirectional

The electrically small loop is the "king" of HF direction-finding antennas. It has near perfect ***nulls broadside to the loop***, which is just what you need to pinpoint a distant station. **ANSWER B.**

This small loop works well even low to the ground, and is easy to hide if you live in an antenna restricted neighborhood.

G9D07 Which of the following describes a log-periodic antenna?

A. Element length and spacing vary logarithmically along the boom
B. Impedance varies periodically as a function of frequency
C. Gain varies logarithmically as a function of frequency
D. SWR varies periodically as a function of boom length

They call this monster antenna a "logarithmic" periodic antenna because the ***length and spacing of the elements increase logarithmically from one end of the boom to the other***. These are very big antennas with limited applications for specific ham radio bands. Best to go with a multiband dipole or a multiband beam long before you ever consider the monster "log!" **ANSWER A.**

G9D06 Which of the following is an advantage of a log-periodic antenna?

A. Wide bandwidth
B. Higher gain per element than a Yagi antenna
C. Harmonic suppression
D. Polarization diversity

Some military stations may use an antenna system called a "log periodic." The elements get progressively shorter on a very long boom, allowing for a ***wide bandwidth*** over many MHz of radio bands. SWR remains flat on a high frequency log periodic antenna from 10 MHz all the way up to 50 MHz! The only problem with a log antenna is the low forward gain achieved with such a monster in the air. **ANSWER A.**

Log periodic antenna.

G9D09 What is the primary use of a Beverage antenna?

A. Directional receiving for MF and low HF bands
B. Directional transmitting for low HF bands
C. Portable direction finding at higher HF frequencies
D. Portable direction finding at lower HF frequencies

Some larger HF base station rigs have a separate antenna port to connect an optional directional low frequency band long wire ***receiving*** (only) ***antenna***. This would be perfect for a Beverage antenna that you can build yourself out of wire. **ANSWER A.**

G4E05 Which of the following most limits an HF mobile installation?

A. "Picket fencing"
B. The wire gauge of the DC power line to the transceiver
C. Efficiency of the electrically short antenna
D. FCC rules limiting mobile output power on the 75-meter band

75 meters is a great night-time band for talking more than 1,000 miles away. However, to get on 75 meters with a mobile unit ***you need an efficient electrically shortened antenna***. Problem is, on 40 meters and lower frequency bands, no mobile antenna is "efficient" – any electrically shortened antenna will operate at a loss. Go with the largest low-loss antenna coil loading system you can find. **ANSWER C.**

Effective HF Mobile

Operating HF mobile is one of the most fun activities in all of Amateur Radio. Having an effective mobile HF station is not only invaluable in emergencies, but can be an effective DX station as well. Many hams in antenna restricted or noisy home environments can evade those issues by taking their mobile station to quiet, secluded areas where they can operate to their heart's content! More than one ham has earned the coveted DXCC award entirely from a mobile station!

There are challenges to building an effective mobile HF station. Unlike 2-meter mobile, where you can simply plop a mag mount antenna on the roof of your car and have a great station, an effective HF mobile installation takes some planning. Mobile HF antennas, especially on the low bands, are by nature quite inefficient. But you can still do some great hamming if that antenna is installed and tuned properly. The famous "Texas Bugcatcher" design, while big and ungainly, is the most effective configuration for operating low band mobile. 40 meters has always been a popular mobile band, as it gives good regional coverage day and night. There are many 40 meter regional mobile nets that cater to just this kind of operation. Give mobile HF a try!

G4E06 What is one disadvantage of using a shortened mobile antenna as opposed to a full-size antenna?

A. Short antennas are more likely to cause distortion of transmitted signals
B. Q of the antenna will be very low
C. Operating bandwidth may be very limited
D. Harmonic radiation may increase

Lightweight, fiberglass/stainless steel high frequency mobile whips provide some amazing performance. However, ***the resonant bandwidth of these antennas may be only 20 or 30 kHz wide***. On 40 meters, the mobile whip will need to be tuned to either the top of the voice band or the bottom of the CW band. On 75 meters, the mobile whip needs to be tuned to a specific frequency where you want to operate. Mount the whips as high as possible on the vehicle for a good impedance match and good radiation. **ANSWER C.**

G9D08 How does a "screwdriver" mobile antenna adjust its feed point impedance?

A. By varying its body capacitance
B. By varying the base loading inductance
C. By extending and retracting the whip
D. By deploying a capacitance hat

Inductive base loading of a short vertical whip is the most popular method of doing HF mobile. While center loaded mobile antennas like the Texas Bugcatcher are far more efficient, they are difficult to adjust and have significant wind loading. The screwdriver antenna, so named because it originally used an electric screwdriver to perform the mechanical action, achieves resonance ***by varying the base loading inductance***. **ANSWER B.**

G4E01 What is the purpose of a capacitance hat on a mobile antenna?

A. To increase the power handling capacity of a whip antenna
B. To reduce radiation resistance
C. To electrically lengthen a physically short antenna
D. To lower the radiation angle

What's that eggbeater do-dad on top of my 40 meter high frequency antenna? That's a ***capacitance hat***, which makes my ***antenna look electrically longer*** than it physically is. On 40, 75, and 160 meters, when operating mobile, you really need a good capacitance hat to gain a little bit more radiation capability. **ANSWER C.**

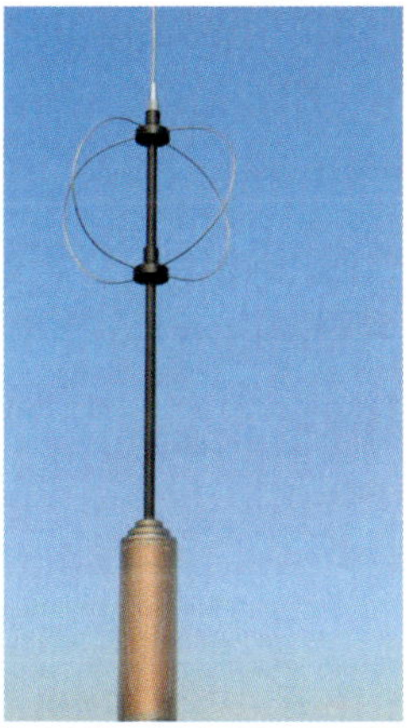

This home-brew capacity hat helps improve mobile HF antenna efficiency.

G4E02 What is the purpose of a corona ball on an HF mobile antenna?

A. To narrow the operating bandwidth of the antenna
B. To increase the "Q" of the antenna
C. To reduce the chance of damage if the antenna should strike an object
D. To reduce RF voltage discharge from the tip of the antenna while transmitting

When transmitting, the high frequency mobile antenna carries some very high voltage at the tip of the whip. A big ***corona ball*** at the tip of the mobile antenna will help ***minimize sparks coming off the tip*** when you transmit. Caution: never operate a mobile antenna in close proximity to trees. Even at 100 watts the signal could arc from the tip of a mobile antenna, with or without a coronal ball, to a nearby tree branch. **ANSWER D.**

Corona is the formation of a plasma (electric arc) due to a high voltage gradient caused by sharp conductors. This corona ball helps prevent sparks flying off the tip of the whip antenna on high power transmit.

G4B10 Which of the following can be determined with a directional wattmeter?

A. Standing wave ratio
B. Antenna front-to-back ratio
C. RF interference
D. Radio wave propagation

A directional watt meter makes a dandy ***standing wave ratio*** checker. Maximum forward power with minimum reflected power will indicate an acceptably low SWR. **ANSWER A.**

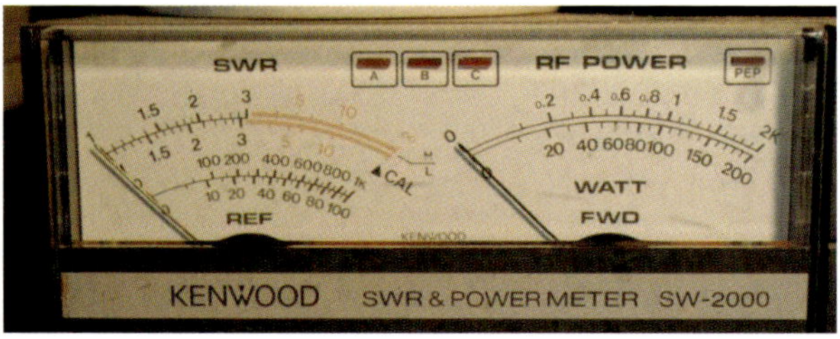

Directional Watt Meter

G4B11 Which of the following must be connected to an antenna analyzer when it is being used for SWR measurements?

A. Receiver
B. Transmitter
C. Antenna and feed line
D. All these choices are correct

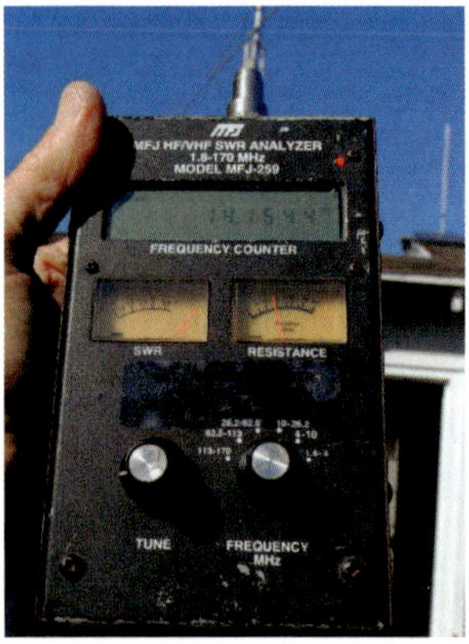

Invention of the portable antenna analyzer was a real improvement for anyone working with antennas. It allows you to test the SWR of the antenna without risking your expensive HF gear. The analyzer is hooked up only to the ***antenna and feed line*** to determine a standing wave ratio (SWR) measurement. **ANSWER C.**

The antenna analyzer is a must-have accessory when working with mobile and fixed antenna systems. It is battery powered and works from 160 meters through the VHF and UHF bands.

G4B13 Which of the following can be measured with an antenna analyzer?

A. Front-to-back ratio of an antenna
B. Power output from a transmitter
C. Impedance of coaxial cable
D. Gain of a directional antenna

There is plenty one can do with an antenna analyzer, such as "wringing out" coax cable for opens and shorts, determining the resonant frequency of an antenna, or ***determining the impedance of that unmarked coax cable*** you bought at a local swap meet. **ANSWER C.**

G4B12 What effect can strong signals from nearby transmitters have on an antenna analyzer?

A. Desensitization which can cause intermodulation products which interfere with impedance readings
B. Received power that interferes with SWR readings
C. Generation of harmonics which interfere with frequency readings
D. All these choices are correct

Modern antenna analyzers (including the amazing Vector Network Analyzers like the popular nanoVNA) are useful tools for any ham shack. All of these contain sensitive radio receivers that ***can be adversely affected by nearby radio transmitters, giving erroneous readings***. (Accidentally transmitting directly into the "front end" of any of these instruments can cause immediate destruction, so is to be avoided at all costs). In any case, be aware of any nearby transmitters when using your antenna analyzer. If there's a strong broadcast station in the vicinity, you may need to install a high pass or notch filter in the signal path. (Or kindly ask the broadcast station to go off the air when you're performing your measurements. This actually works better when you're the chief engineer of the broadcast station in question!). **ANSWER B.**

Website Resources

IF YOU'RE LOOKING FOR	THEN VISIT
Portable Satellite Beams	www.arrowantennas.com
HF Antennas	www.AORUSA.com
	www.directivesystems.com
	www.MFJEnterprises.com
	www.M2INC.com
	www.NEW-Tronics.com
	www.Radiowavz.com
	www.hiqantennas.com
	www.diamondantenna.net
	www.natcommgroup.com
	www.cushcraftamateur.com
	www.cubexquads.com
	www.alphadeltaradio.com
	www.arraysolutions.com
	www.buddypole.com
	www.elkantennas.com
	www.hy-gain.com
	www.ldgelectronics.com
	www.mosley-electronics.com
	www.sotabeams.co.uk
	www.steppir.com
Coax Cable	www.cablexperts.com
	www.coaxial.com
	www.coaxman.com
	www.abrind.com

The Halo antenna is popular for mobile 6 meter operation.

Effective Radiated Power (ERP)

One of the guiding principles in all that we do in radio is NFL – No Free Lunch – meaning that we never get something for nothing. Every improvement in radio performance comes at a cost. Nowhere is this more glaringly evident than when dealing with antennas.

An antenna can never put out more than you put into it; and in many cases, what we get out of an antenna is a great deal less than what we put into it. An antenna with gain gets the gain by subtracting radiation in some directions to concentrate it in other directions. This is where the concept of an isotropic radiator comes in. You will never see a true isotropic radiator (it is theoretical and cannot be built), but you can approach the behavior of one by shrinking a dipole antenna to near the vanishing point. A very very short (in terms of wavelength) antenna "radiates poorly in all directions," like an incandescent light bulb.

In order for an antenna to have gain, we need to take the radiation pattern of an isotropic radiator (which basically emits rays in all directions like the quills on a porcupine) and rearrange those rays so they all point in a useful direction. (Don't try rearranging the quills on a porcupine; they object strenuously to this!) Obviously, the more rays we have pointing in one direction, the fewer we have pointing in another.

Now, as useful in concept as an isotropic radiator is, since we can't build one we need to use the next best thing as a reference, the familiar dipole antenna. A dipole antenna squishes the spherical pattern of an isotropic radiator into sort of a doughnut shape. We sacrifice a lot of radiation off the ends and reorganize the rays to radiate at right angles from the center of the wire. The rearrangement of rays that the dipole provides gives us a gain of 2.15 dB over the theoretical isotropic radiator, or a power gain of a little over 1.6:1. This means that if we feed one watt of power into a dipole, the field strength broadside to the dipole is the same as putting a little over 1.6 watts into an isotropic radiator.

Is there something magic or "special" about a dipole? Not at all; it's just a very convenient reference. It's something we can actually make as opposed to the theoretically precise isotropic radiator.

To tie this all together, we have Effective Radiated Power, or ERP, a useful figure for calculating transmitted power based on the RF power put into an antenna, less any losses incurred in the process, plus the antenna gain. By convention, when calculating ERP, we use the antenna gain relative to the dipole or dBd. ERP is a reliable indicator of transmitted power in the direction of maximum radiation.

So, if we have a transmitter with 1500 watts output power, and an antenna gain of 7dBd (a reasonable figure for a moderately large Yagi), we have an ERP of about 7500 watts. Using the formula dB=10 log P1/P2, let's work backwards and determine the power ratios:

First, take our dB number, 7, and divide by 10, since the last thing we did to get this was multiplying by 10. This gives us 0.7. Now, let's take the antilog of this. If you're using a typical scientific calculator, this is the 10x key. Plug in 0.7, press that key, and we come up with 5.011 and some loose change. Rounding off to 5, we have a 5:1 power ratio (increase). Multiplying 1500 by 5 we get 7500 W.

Is this legal? Absolutely! Unlike commercial radio regulations, amateur radio rules place no restrictions whatsoever on effective radiated power. The only restrictions we have are found in what we can physically build! (Other than the 1500 watt transmitter output power limit, of course).

What have we sacrificed to get those 7500 watts ERP? Well, an antenna with that kind of gain has far less gain than a dipole in most directions other than that of the main lobe, and probably some nulls where the power level goes to almost nothing. So the cost we incur is the necessity of rotating the antenna to point it where we want to concentrate our signal, thus restricting our transmissions to one direction!

Coax Cable

G9A05 How does the attenuation of coaxial cable change with increasing frequency?

A. Attenuation is independent of frequency
B. Attenuation increases
C. Attenuation decreases
D. Attenuation follows Marconi's Law of Attenuation

The ***higher*** you go in ***frequency***, the ***greater the attenuation*** of the transmission line. This is why it's very important to always use the largest size coax cable available for VHF and UHF frequencies. **ANSWER B.**

G9A06 In what units is RF feed line loss usually expressed?

A. Ohms per 1,000 feet
B. Decibels per 1,000 feet
C. Ohms per 100 feet
D. Decibels per 100 feet

RF feed line losses are usually expressed in ***decibels (dB) per 100 feet***. See the decibels explanation and chart on page 178. **ANSWER D.**

	Attenuation
Frequency (MHz)	(dB/100 ft.)
2	0.21
10	0.5
20	0.71
100	1.7
200	2.4
1000	5.7

Attenuation of RG-8 coax with foam dielectric

G5B10 What percentage of power loss is equivalent to a loss of 1 dB?

A. 10.9 percent
B. 12.2 percent
C. 20.6 percent
D. 25.9 percent

For your examination, it is expected that certain things are committed to memory. In the real world of ham radio there are charts available for this information. This question, asks the percentage loss from a transmission line of 1 dB. ***One dB of loss*** results in 0.794 (79.4%) of the energy making it through the coax, leading to 20.6% getting lost in the transmission line (100% – 79.4% = ***20.6% loss***). **ANSWER C.**

G9A01 Which of the following factors determine the characteristic impedance of a parallel conductor feed line?

A. The distance between the centers of the conductors and the radius of the conductors
B. The distance between the centers of the conductors and the length of the line
C. The radius of the conductors and the frequency of the signal
D. The frequency of the signal and the length of the line

The characteristic impedance of parallel conductor antenna feed line is most influenced by the ***distance between the center of the conductors***, and slightly influenced by actual ***radius of the conductors***. **ANSWER A.**

G9A03 What is the nominal characteristic impedance of "window line" transmission line?

A. 50 ohms
B. 75 ohms
C. 100 ohms
D. 450 ohms

Hams are rediscovering the versatility and efficiency of balanced, open wire and "almost open wire" feed lines like window line. These were the original transmission lines and can handle extremely high SWR values with very little loss. While 600 ohm homebrew "ladder line" is the best of the best in this regard, commercial ***450 ohm window line*** runs a close second. If you are running parallel conductor feed line, keep it absolutely unkinked, keep it away from metal masts and, if that parallel conductor antenna feed line is part of the vertical radiator, make sure it hangs straight down and never coiled up on itself. **ANSWER D.**

Parallel conductor feedline.

G9A07 What must be done to prevent standing waves on a feed line connected to an antenna?

A. The antenna feed point must be at DC ground potential
B. The feed line must be an odd number of electrical quarter wavelengths long
C. The feed line must be an even number of physical half wavelengths long
D. The antenna feed point impedance must be matched to the characteristic impedance of the feed line

Always try to ***match feed point impedance*** of the antenna to the characteristic impedance of the feed line for maximum power transfer and minimum SWR. **ANSWER D.**

G6B07 Which of the following describes a type N connector?

A. A moisture-resistant RF connector useful to 10 GHz
B. A small bayonet connector used for data circuits
C. A low noise figure VHF connector
D. A nickel plated version of the PL-259

As a licensed Technician Class operator, chances are you encountered the type N connector when working with UHF and microwave equipment. The ***type N connector*** is great at VHF and UHF antenna feed points because it is ***moisture resistant*** and it works well all the way up to 10 GHz. When working with your high frequency transceiver, it is doubtful you will need a type N connector. **ANSWER A.**

Shown left to right are the BNC, PL-259, "N", SMA, and TV connectors.

G9A04 What causes reflected power at an antenna's feed point?

A. Operating an antenna at its resonant frequency
B. Using more transmitter power than the antenna can handle
C. A difference between feed line impedance and antenna feed point impedance
D. Feeding the antenna with unbalanced feed line

Keep the impedances of your feed line and antenna the same for minimum standing wave ratio. Standing waves are set-up on the feed line because power is being reflected back due to an ***impedance mismatch***. **ANSWER C.**

G6B10 How does a ferrite bead or core reduce common-mode RF current on the shield of a coaxial cable?

A. By creating an impedance in the current's path
B. It converts common-mode current to differential mode current
C. By creating an out-of-phase current to cancel the common-mode current
D. Ferrites expel magnetic fields

Radio frequency currents can travel on the outside surface of a coaxial cable shield, causing the cable to radiate. It is generally beneficial to insure that your transmission lines don't behave as antennas for a number of reasons. The "brute force" method of reducing such transmission line or common mode currents is to create a very-high impedance to these currents, primarily by means of inductance. A ferrite core, in conjunction with the transmission line itself chokes off this current ***by creating an impedance in the current's path***. **ANSWER A.**

Elmer Point: The characteristic impedance of a transmission line is impossible to measure directly. The best definition of characteristic impedance is given in the March 1956 ***QST*** article, "My Feedline Tunes My Antenna," by Byron Goodman, W1DX. "The characteristic impedance of a transmission line is the value of resistance that, when used as a termination for the line, makes the impedance of the line independent of the electrical length of the line." Practically speaking, the thinner and farther apart the conductors are, the higher the characteristic impedance. This applies to coaxial cable or parallel transmission lines.

When most radio amateurs think of transmission lines, they think of coaxial cable. The reality is that coaxial cable is a "Johnny Come Lately" development, almost unheard of until after World War II. Before then, open wire feed line or "ladder line" was the nearly universal transmission line. Closely related to ladder line is 450 ohm "window" line and 300 ohm twin lead, which still have advantages over coax in many instances. Coaxial cable is fairly limited with regard to SWR tolerance, while open wire feed line doesn't care. In fact in many systems, a high SWR is necessary for the system to work. A good example is the classic end-fed Zepp antenna which uses a ¼ wave length of open wire feed line, operating with nearly infinite SWR. This transmission line acts as a matching transformer by the very virtue of it having a large standing wave ratio.

In most modern implementations of parallel transmission lines, an open wire antenna coupler is used as a go-between for a 50 ohm transmitter and a random impedance load on the other side. This results in a very versatile and robust system.

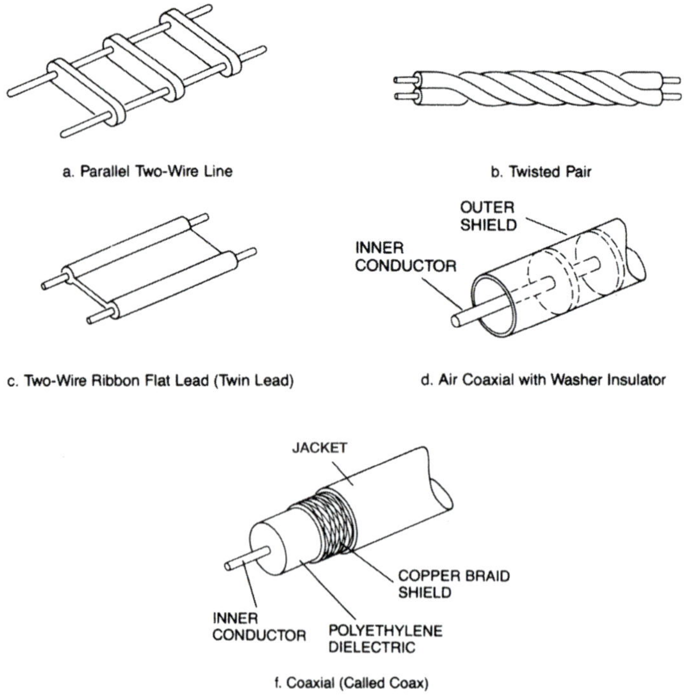

Different transmission lines

Source: *Antennas – Selection and Installation*, © 1986 Master Publishing, Inc., Niles, IL

G9A02 What is the relationship between high standing wave ratio (SWR) and transmission line loss?

A. There is no relationship between transmission line loss and SWR
B. High SWR increases loss in a lossy transmission line
C. High SWR makes it difficult to measure transmission line loss
D. High SWR reduces the relative effect of transmission line loss

In a transmission line that has measurable loss, ***the loss will increase as the SWR increases***. Therefore, in most cases, it's beneficial to reduce the SWR as much as possible by careful impedance matching at the load end. However, very low loss transmission lines such as open wire feed line are capable of operating efficiently with very high SWR values. They are useful when great flexibility takes precedence over a small amount of loss, such as when operating a random length doublet antenna on multiple bands. **ANSWER B.**

G9A11 What is the effect of transmission line loss on SWR measured at the input to the line?

A. Higher loss reduces SWR measured at the input to the line
B. Higher loss increases SWR measured at the input to the line
C. Higher loss increases the accuracy of SWR measured at the input to the line
D. Transmission line loss does not affect the SWR measurement

This is one of many cases in Amateur Radio where a little information can be a dangerous thing. A very low SWR can mean you have a very good antenna, or a very effective dummy load! If at all possible, SWR should be measured at the antenna. The reason for this is that if the transmission line is lossy, the reflected power will be attenuated, just like the forward power. Since SWR is calculated (indirectly) by looking at the ratio of reflected power to forward power, the ***SWR will always be lower at the input end of a lossy transmission line***. At UHF frequencies, the losses can be so great in low-grade coax that even with no antenna connected the SWR will read 1:1 or nearly so. All this is telling you is that the transmission line is absorbing all the power! So we need to understand what we're really measuring. An SWR meter is a handy tool, but it doesn't tell the whole story! Use it with discrimination. **ANSWER A.**

Here's a homebrew, brute force choke balun made out of good quality coax. It is an effective means of preventing your transmission line from radiating and causing other unpredictable behavior. It's sometimes called an "ugly balun," but if assembled neatly like this one it doesn't have to be ugly at all.

G9B02 Which of the following is a common way to adjust the feed point impedance of an elevated quarter-wave ground-plane vertical antenna to be approximately 50 ohms?

A. Slope the radials upward
B. Slope the radials downward
C. Lengthen the radials beyond one wavelength
D. Coil the radials

A "perfect" ¼ wave ground plane antenna (one with a quarter wave vertical section and an infinite number of ¼ wave horizontal radials) will have an impedance of 36 ohms, exactly half that of a dipole in free space (72 ohms). While this antenna will work quite well with no modification, you can achieve ***a better match to 50 ohms by slanting the radials downward***. (Your ground plane antenna will probably not have an infinite number of radials, usually four, so this job is pretty easy!) **ANSWER B.**

G9A09 What standing wave ratio results from connecting a 50-ohm feed line to a 200-ohm resistive load?

A. 4:1 C. 2:1
B. 1:4 D. 1:2

50 goes into 200 4 times, so the impedance of the mismatch is ***4:1***. 1:4 is not the correct answer, even though it looks correct. Whichever value is larger is the numerator, which means that SWR by definition will always be equal to or greater than 1:1. **ANSWER A.**

G9A10 What standing wave ratio results from connecting a 50-ohm feed line to a 10-ohm resistive load?

A. 2:1 C. 1:5
B. 1:2 D. 5:1

By definition, a perfect match is an SWR of 1:1, which is the lowest value possible. To calculate SWR, always divide the larger impedance by the smaller one. 10 goes into 50 5 times, so the mismatch is ***5:1***. 1:5 is not correct. **ANSWER D.**

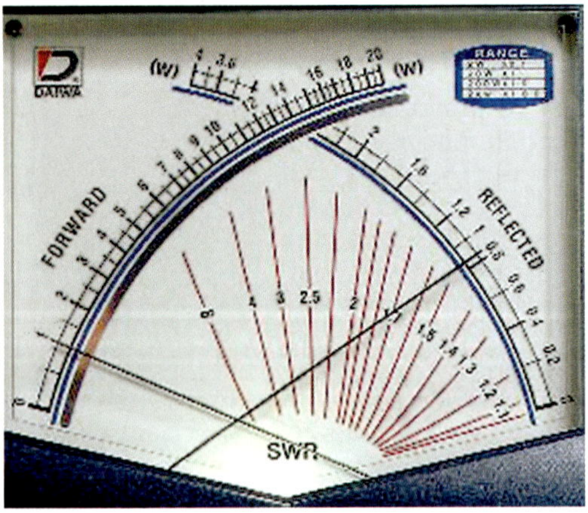

A common cross-needle SWR meter. The SWR is indicated by the red arcs where the forward and reflected meter needles cross. In this case the SWR is nearly infinite – normally, not a good condition!

G9A08 If the SWR on an antenna feed line is 5:1, and a matching network at the transmitter end of the feed line is adjusted to present a 1:1 SWR to the transmitter, what is the resulting SWR on the feed line?

A. 1:1
B. 5:1
C. Between 1:1 and 5:1 depending on the characteristic impedance of the line
D. Between 1:1 and 5:1 depending on the reflected power at the transmitter

SWR is determined only by the load impedance. The SWR will still be 5:1. An antenna tuner or coupler will only change the input impedance (the impedance your transmitter sees). Let's show how the system as a whole still delivers full power to the load, assuming the transmission line is not too lossy itself, and the antenna tuner is of high quality. Using some standard charts, we see that a 6:1 SWR results in 5:1 power being reflected from the load. (For simplicity, we'll round this down to 50%). This means that with no further action taken, with a 100 watt transmitter, 50 watts will be delivered to the load. (We'll assume the transmitter has no protective circuitry to back off the power). Now, let's put a GOOD antenna tuner in line, near the transmitter, and adjust the tuner until the transmitter "sees" 50 ohms. The transmitter is once again delivering 100 watts into the antenna tuner. Now, if we were to take a good directional wattmeter and put it on the OUTPUT side of the tuner, we would see 100 watts reflected from the load. This may seem a bit odd, since we know we're only reflecting 50% of the power from the mismatched load. Now remember, SWR is determined only by the load. So, where is that missing 100 watts going? Is it somehow lost in the tuner? No way! Let's switch our trusty Bird wattmeter to the forward direction. What do we see? 200 WATTS forward power! Well, now the numbers add up, but what's happening? What we're seeing is a DOUBLE reflection. When we adjust the tuner to create a 50 ohm load on the INPUT, we create a CONJUGATE match on the OUTPUT, which causes the reflected power to be re-reflected and ADDED to the power passing THROUGH the tuner. Subtracting 100 Watts reflected from 200 Watts forward, still gives us 100 Watts to the antenna. Pretty neat! Now, in all fairness, we need to mention that coax cable generally should not be operated with a 6:1 SWR, as any loss that coax has will be increased with high SWR. But as a general rule, most decent antenna tuners have very small losses, and can greatly increase your operating flexibility. **ANSWER B.**

Close up of an automatic antenna tuner control switches. Besides the "Auto" mode, you can make small changes in inductance (L) and capacitance (C) to fine-tune your antenna system.

G6B11 What is an SMA connector?

A. A type-S to type-M adaptor
B. A small threaded connector suitable for signals up to several GHz
C. A connector designed for serial multiple access signals
D. A type of push-on connector intended for high-voltage applications

The modern handheld has switched from an antenna connector called BNC to the *threaded antenna connector called SMA*. Even the microwave operators up at 10,000 MHz use SMA connectors. They are good for several GHz! **ANSWER B.**

SMA connector

G6B04 What is a typical upper frequency limit for low SWR operation of 50-ohm BNC connectors?

A. 50 MHz
B. 500 MHz
C. 4 GHz
D. 40 GHz

RF connectors such as the BNC and N-type connectors are constant impedance connectors, which very closely match the impedance of the coaxial cables with which they are used. (Each of these connector types are available in a number of different impedances, with 50 ohms and 75 ohms being the most common). ***BNC connectors have an extremely good match up to about 4 GHz***, though they can be used with some decrease in performance well above that. **ANSWER C.**

Elmer Point: The common UHF jack on the back of your new HF transceiver will accept the coax cable PL-259 connector, which is the common coax connector for high frequency use. However, the PL-259 is NOT waterproof. If you use an antenna feed point that takes a PL-259, make absolutely sure to completely waterproof the connection with flexible sealant, as well as an added wrap of self-vulcanizing tape. The number one reason why ham radio antenna systems fail is water migrating into the PL-259 and killing the feed point connection. When I visit your QTH, I don't want to see any exposed PL-259 connectors on the coax at the antenna feed point!

Coaxing R.F. Without Coax

Although most radio amateurs rely on coaxial cable transmission lines to get their signals from their shacks to their antennas (and vice versa), this is not the only way to accomplish this crucial task.

Long before coaxial cable was even thought of, most radio amateurs used open wire feedlines. An open wire feedline is simply two parallel wires separated by appropriate spacers. Although open wire feedline is not as convenient to install as coaxial cable, it is capable of excellent performance and flexibility. It can operate with extremely high standing wave ratios with very low loss. And best of all, it's very cheap if you roll your own! Yes, generations of hams used to do this. There are "snap in" insulator/spacers available to make this easy! One source of the spacers can be found on-line at: **www.73cnc.com/product_p/ls100.htm**

Open wire feedline is becoming quite popular again, and a number of commercial antenna tuners have provisions for attaching these "old-fangled" transmission lines. Check out the amateur radio literature for hints on how to install and use open wire feedline systems.

RF & Electrical Safety

G0B08 What should be done before climbing a tower that supports electrically powered devices?

A. Notify the electric company that a person will be working on the tower
B. Make sure all circuits that supply power to the tower are locked out and tagged
C. Unground the base of the tower
D. All these choices are correct

To insure that no one starts rotating a beam antenna using the electric powered rotator, double check that the rotator control unit is ***unplugged and tagged "climber aloft."*** **ANSWER B.**

Climbing a tower is serious business! Always observe all OSHA requirements for your climbing gear.

G0B07 Which of these choices should be observed when climbing a tower using a safety harness?

A. Always hold on to the tower with one hand
B. Confirm that the harness is rated for the weight of the climber and that it is within its allowable service life
C. Ensure that all heavy tools are securely fastened to the harness
D. All these choices are correct

Preventing falls from a tower is best achieved with a professional safety harness. Always be sure that the ***harness is rated for the weight of the climber and is within its service life***. It's good practice to attach the belt's safety hook to the "D" ring with the hook opening always away from the tower. We also recommend that you regularly inspect the safety harness as an added measure to prevent an accident. **ANSWER B.**

We're sending up your required hard hat and safety glasses!

G0A08 Which of the following steps must an amateur operator take to ensure compliance with RF safety regulations?

A. Post a copy of FCC Part 97.13 in the station
B. Notify neighbors within a 100-foot radius of the antenna of the existence of the station and power levels
C. Perform a routine RF exposure evaluation and prevent access to any identified high exposure areas
D. All these choices are correct

Performing a ***routine RF exposure evaluation*** is a good idea for all amateurs to ensure compliance with RF safety regulations and that you and your neighbors are not being "overexposed" to RF radiation. Be sure you prevent access to any identified high exposure areas, too. [97.13(c)(2)] **ANSWER C.**

G0A11 What precaution should be taken if you install an indoor transmitting antenna?

A. Locate the antenna close to your operating position to minimize feed-line radiation
B. Position the antenna along the edge of a wall to reduce parasitic radiation
C. Make sure that MPE limits are not exceeded in occupied areas
D. Make sure the antenna is properly shielded

It is always a good idea to locate an antenna as far away as possible from living spaces that will be occupied when you are transmitting. If you're just receiving, no problem – but when you're transmitting, get your antenna away from everyone to minimize RF exposure! This will help ensure that Maximum Permissible Exposure ***(MPE) limits are not exceeded***. **ANSWER C.**

G0A01 What is one way that RF energy can affect human body tissue?

A. It heats body tissue
B. It causes radiation poisoning
C. It causes the blood count to reach a dangerously low level
D. It cools body tissue

If RF energy from your antenna system is concentrated on the human body, it ***heats the body tissue*** just like your microwave oven heats your leftovers. RF burns are a very real thing. They include those experienced from poor grounding of the equipment to those received from touching or standing too close to an antenna while someone is transmitting. **ANSWER A.**

Don't Fry Yourself!

Study the FCC Maximum Permissible Exposure (MPE) Limit charts in the Appendix. Always remember, RF exposure at microwave frequencies can be very dangerous!

Speeding motorists don't need to panic! Gordo's on the 10,000 MHz X band working stations 300 miles away using his dish antenna. Always stand behind or well to the sides of a dish or horn antenna to avoid RF exposure.

G0A12 What stations are subject to the FCC rules on RF exposure?

A. All commercial stations; amateur radio stations are exempt
B. Only stations with antennas lower than one wavelength above the ground
C. Only stations transmitting more than 500 watts PEP
D. All stations with a time-averaged transmission of more than one milliwatt

RF exposure rules apply to any radio transmissions with a time averaged transmission of more than one milliwatt. This provision allows a lot of low power wireless devices to fly "under the wire." Although compliance with the RF exposure limits is extremely easy for the vast vast majority of hams, ***each ham is required to determine that he is indeed operating within those parameters***. Actual measurements are not required except in extreme cases; in almost every case the readily available charts are sufficient. [1.1307(1)(b)(3)(i)(A)] **ANSWER D.**

G0A03 How can you determine that your station complies with FCC RF exposure regulations?

A. By calculation based on FCC OET Bulletin 65
B. By calculation based on computer modeling
C. By measurement of field strength using calibrated equipment
D. All these choices are correct

You can determine how your station complies with FCC RF exposure regulations by using The W5YI RF Safety Tables in the Appendix of this book. These tables can be used to estimate safe distances based on FCC OET Bulletin No. 65. These distances can also be determined using your own calculations based on computer modeling. Alternately, you can actually go out there and measure the power density levels with a field strength meter making sure to use calibrated equipment. ***All of these choices*** are good ways to determine whether or not you are going to unnecessarily expose yourself or your neighbors to RF energy. [97.13(c)(1)] **ANSWER D.**

G0A06 What must you do if your station fails to meet the FCC RF exposure exemption criteria?

A. Perform an RF Exposure Evaluation in accordance with FCC OET Bulletin 65
B. Contact the FCC for permission to transmit
C. Perform an RF exposure evaluation in accordance with World Meteorological Organization guidelines
D. Use an FCC-approved band-pass filter

It is the responsibility of every radio amateur to determine the RF exposure of his amateur radio station. In the vast majority of amateur situations, RF exposure will be far far below safe limits, even while operating full legal power. ***The complete procedure for determining your actual situation can be found in FCC OET Bulletin 65***, as well as in FCC part [97.13(c)(2), 1.1307(1)(b)(3)(i)]. **ANSWER A.**

G0A04 What does "time averaging" mean when evaluating RF radiation exposure?

A. The average amount of power developed by the transmitter over a specific 24-hour period
B. The average time it takes RF radiation to have any long-term effect on the body
C. The total time of the exposure
D. The total RF exposure averaged over a certain period

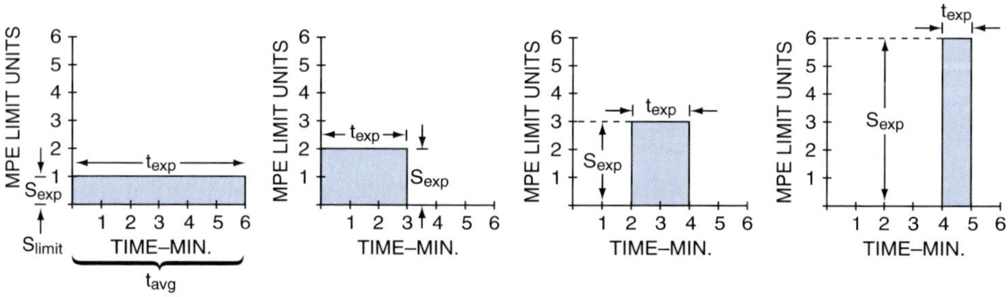

The general equation for time averaging exposure equivalence is: $S_{exp}\ t_{exp} = S_{limit}\ t_{avg}$

Time-averaging is a method of ***calculating*** an individual's ***total exposure to RF radiation over a certain period***. The premise of time-averaging is that the human body can tolerate larger amounts of RF radiation if the exposure is received in short "bursts" as compared to a constant exposure at the same high level of RF radiation. As depicted here, total exposure to various levels of radiation is averaged over a 6-minute period. On a time-averaged basis, the amount of thermal load on the body is equal in all cases. **ANSWER D.**

G0A07 What is the effect of modulation duty cycle on RF exposure?

A. A lower duty cycle permits greater power levels to be transmitted
B. A higher duty cycle permits greater power levels to be transmitted
C. Low duty cycle transmitters are exempt from RF exposure evaluation requirements
D. High duty cycle transmitters are exempt from RF exposure requirements

Duty cycle is the percentage of time the transmitter is actually sending out energy. If you hold down your telegraph key for continuous full-transmit-power output, the equipment would be operating at100% duty cycle. If the space in between each dit were equal to the duration of the transmitted signal, the equipment would be operating at 50% duty cycle. ***The lower duty cycle permits greater power levels to be transmitted***. **ANSWER A.**

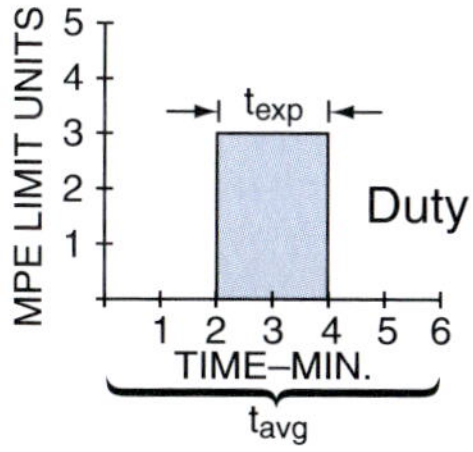

$$\text{Duty Cycle (in \%)} = \frac{t_{exp}}{t_{avg}} \times 100$$

Duty Cycle

G0A02 Which of the following is used to determine RF exposure from a transmitted signal?

A. Its duty cycle
B. Its frequency
C. Its power density
D. All these choices are correct

There is a lot to do before you can consider your station safe and be sure you are not exceeding the maximum permissible exposure (MPE) limits. ***Do all of these steps***. **ANSWER D.**

G0A05 What must you do if an evaluation of your station shows that the RF energy radiated by your station exceeds permissible limits for possible human absorption?

A. Take action to prevent human exposure to the excessive RF fields
B. File an Environmental Impact Statement (EIS-97) with the FCC
C. Secure written permission from your neighbors to operate above the controlled MPE limits
D. All these choices are correct

In Section 97.13, the FCC rules state that if your station's RF exceeds permissible limits, you "must ***take action to prevent human exposure*** to such RF electromagnetic fields." If your station exceeds permissible limits, you need to make changes to solve the problem. [97.13(c)(2), 1.1307(b)] **ANSWER A.**

G0A09 What type of instrument can be used to accurately measure an RF field strength?

A. A receiver with digital signal processing (DSP) noise reduction
B. A calibrated field strength meter with a calibrated antenna
C. An SWR meter with a peak-reading function
D. An oscilloscope with a high-stability crystal marker generator

Although a simple field-strength meter can show the presence of radio frequency emissions, it takes a precisely ***calibrated field-strength meter with a calibrated antenna*** to make accurate measurements of the RF field. **ANSWER B.**

G0A10 What should be done if evaluation shows that a neighbor might experience more than the allowable limit of RF exposure from the main lobe of a directional antenna?

A. Change to a non-polarized antenna with higher gain
B. Use an antenna with a higher front-to-back ratio
C. Take precautions to ensure that the antenna cannot be pointed in their direction when they are present
D. All these choices are correct

If your calculations indicate that you may be exposing your neighbors to too much RF, you need to relocate your entire antenna system, or take precautions to ***ensure it cannot be pointed in their direction*** when transmitting. **ANSWER C.**

G0B06 Which of the following is covered by the National Electrical Code?

A. Acceptable bandwidth limits
B. Acceptable modulation limits
C. Electrical safety of the station
D. RF exposure limits of the human body

The ***National Electrical Code*** covers ***electrical safety standards*** as they relate standards as they relate to the electrical safety of your station. RF exposure limits to the human body are covered by ANSI, not by the NEC. **ANSWER C.**

G0B05 Which of the following conditions will cause a ground fault circuit interrupter (GFCI) to disconnect AC power?

A. Current flowing from one or more of the hot wires to the neutral wire
B. Current flowing from one or more of the hot wires directly to ground
C. Overvoltage on the hot wires
D. All these choices are correct

Ground fault circuit interrupters are found in newer electrical plug outlets. They instantly open a circuit to halt current flow when they detect ***current flowing from one or more hot wires directly to ground***. **ANSWER B.**

Ground fault receptacle

G4C11 What technique helps to minimize RF "hot spots" in an amateur station?

A. Building all equipment in a metal enclosure
B. Using surge suppressor power outlets
C. Bonding all equipment enclosures together
D. Placing low-pass filters on all feed lines

While the terms bonding and grounding are often used interchangeably, they are actually two different but related disciplines. ***Bonding all equipment enclosures together*** with a low impedance RF connection, such as a wide copper strap or braid, will keep the RF potential uniform throughout the shack, generally reducing problems such as RF feedback. RF bonding can be very effective even if a true earth ground is not available. However, it is best to both bond and ground your radio equipment. **ANSWER C.**

G0B01 Which wire or wires in a four-conductor 240 VAC circuit should be attached to fuses or circuit breakers?

A. Only the hot wires
B. Only the neutral wire
C. Only the ground wire
D. All wires

Most ham transceivers run on 12 volts DC. Some base stations may have their own 110 VAC power supplies built-in. However, linear amplifiers may require 240 VAC. For single phase ***240 VAC, fuse only the hot wires***. Never fuse the neutral white wire or the neutral ground bare copper wire. Most amplifiers already have the fuse circuits built in. **ANSWER A.**

G0B03 Which size of fuse or circuit breaker would be appropriate to use with a circuit that uses AWG number 14 wiring?

A. 30 amperes
B. 25 amperes
C. 20 amperes
D. 15 amperes

Based on the American Wire Gauge (AWG) information shown, 14 gauge wire handles 15 amperes. The easy way to remember this is with the "F" for "Fourteen" (14 gauge) wiring will handle ***Fifteen (15) amps***. **ANSWER D.**

Wire Size A.W.G. (B&S)	Current-Amps (Continuous Duty)	
	Single Wire	Bundled Wire
8	73	46
10	55	33
12	41	23
14	32	17
16	22	13
18	16	10

American Wire Gauge (AWG) wire size vs. current capability.

G0B02 According to the National Electrical Code, what is the minimum wire size that may be used safely for wiring with a 20-ampere circuit breaker?

A. AWG number 20
B. AWG number 16
C. AWG number 12
D. AWG number 8

Based on the American Wire Gauge (AWG) information shown, ***20 amperes*** of continuous current requires a wire size of ***AWG #12***. The easy way to remember this is with the "T" for "Twenty" (20 amperes) current requires AWG number 12 ("T" for twelve). Don't confuse the "T" for twenty in the answers, current flow and wire size don't match like that. **ANSWER C.**

G0B12 What is the purpose of a power supply interlock?

A. To prevent unauthorized changes to the circuit that would void the manufacturer's warranty
B. To shut down the unit if it becomes too hot
C. To ensure that dangerous voltages are removed if the cabinet is opened
D. To shut off the power supply if too much voltage is produced

Linear amplifiers using vacuum tubes will likely have a power supply interlock switch. If the equipment is on and ***the power supply door is opened***, the equipment will either ***instantly power off***, or you will hear a loud "bang" when the high voltage gets shorted to ground tripping an internal fuse or breaker. This protects you and the equipment from a high voltage shock. **ANSWER C.**

G0B10 Which of the following is a danger from lead-tin solder?

A. Lead can contaminate food if hands are not washed carefully after handling the solder
B. High voltages can cause lead-tin solder to disintegrate suddenly
C. Tin in the solder can "cold flow," causing shorts in the circuit
D. RF energy can convert the lead into a poisonous gas

Any time you are working on radio equipment innards, ***wash your hands*** when you finish to remove any lead that might be contained in that roll of old solder before you grab a sandwich. **ANSWER A.**

G0B11 Which of the following is required for lightning protection ground rods?

A. They must be bonded to all buried water and gas lines
B. Bends in ground wires must be made as close as possible to a right angle
C. Lightning grounds must be connected to all ungrounded wiring
D. They must be bonded together with all other grounds

Good engineering practice for a lightning ground indicates that ***all grounds be bonded together*** with all other grounds. **ANSWER D.**

G0B04 Where should the station's lightning protection ground system be located?

A. As close to the station equipment as possible
B. Outside the building
C. Next to the closest power pole
D. Parallel to the water supply line

Whether you have a 100 foot tower, or a few yards of wire flung out a window for an antenna, you need to think about lightning protection. You've probably heard that lightning takes the path of least resistance. This is wrong. Lightning takes EACH and EVERY path it possibly can! Just be sure one of those paths isn't through your ham shack. ***Lightning protection should be located OUTSIDE whatever building your equipment is located*** in. **ANSWER B.**

G4C07 Why should soldered joints not be used in lightning protection ground connections?

A. A soldered joint will likely be destroyed by the heat of a lightning strike
B. Solder flux will prevent a low conductivity connection
C. Solder has too high a dielectric constant to provide adequate lightning protection
D. All these choices are correct

Carefully inspect tower grounding circuits and you will find that all the ground connections have been swaged rather than soldered. ***Solder might melt on a direct lightning strike*** destroying the route to ground. **ANSWER A.**

G0B13 Where should lightning arrestors be located?

A. Where the feed lines enter the building
B. On the antenna, opposite the feed point
C. In series with each ground lead
D. At the closest power pole ground electrode

Lightning protection takes several forms. Ideally, whatever lightning protection system you have actually prevents a lightning strike. Unfortunately, only the most extensive and elaborate lightning protection systems can do this, and even those can do nothing for nearby lightning strikes, which can be just as damaging as "direct hits" in many cases. Furthermore, lightning arrestors are actually misnamed; they don't actually do any arresting. The best that they can do is a certain amount of damage control, by redirecting electrical energy to somewhere where it will do the least amount of destruction. A lightning arrestor usually takes the form of some kind of arc gap, (even a spark plug in days of yore!) providing a low resistance path to ground outside the shack during a lightning strike, and being invisible to RF during normal conditions. ***They can be applied either to feedlines or control cables where they enter the building***. **ANSWER A.**

G0B09 Which of the following is true of an emergency generator installation?

A. The generator should be operated in a well-ventilated area
B. The generator must be insulated from ground
C. Fuel should be stored near the generator for rapid refueling in case of an emergency
D. All these choices are correct

Any time you use a generator for power, make sure the generator is ***operated in a well-ventilated area***; not where someone could inhale the toxic exhaust. The generator should be properly grounded, and always store the generator's fuel in a safe place away from any inhabited area. **ANSWER A.**

Portable generators must be placed well away from an operating position, have good ventilation, and never be operated with a container of gasoline nearby. In this picture, the generator is in storage, with no gas in the container.

4

Taking the General Class Examination

Get ready for worldwide skywave band privileges! As soon as you pass your General Class exam, you'll be licensed to transmit on frequency bands that regularly offer skywave excitement every hour of the day and all through the night. This chapter tells you how the examination will be given, who is qualified to administer the General Class exam, and what happens after you successfully complete the written exam.

PROOF OF LICENSE, FRN, & PHOTO ID

The VE team that administers your Element 3 General Class exam must be able to verify your existing, active Technician Class license and Federal Registration Number (FRN). You also will need a copy of a second form of identification, which must be a photo ID, such as your driver's license.

First, we need to tell you important information updating how amateur radio operators register with the FCC to obtain their FRN (Federal Registration Number) and pay fees for their Amateur Radio license grants.

FCC User Names and Passwords

Online access to FCC records and applications requires Amateur Radio licensees to interface with two websites:

- CORES (Commission Registration System), and
- ULS (Universal Licensing System)

Each has its own website and you need a Username and Password for each.

For CORES, your username is the email address you entered when you obtained your FRN number. You can retrieve your FRN from the CORES site by going to:

https://apps.fcc.gov/cores/userLogin.do

For ULS, your username is your FRN number, and may be the same password as your CORES account. Hopefully, you remember all of this, or have it written down.

You can print out a reference copy of your Tecchnician Class license from the ULS website by going to:

https://wireless2.fcc.gov/UlsEntry/licManager/login.jsp

BEFORE YOUR EXAM SESSION make sure to have a copy of your Technician Class license, which will show your FRN number. You will need these to complete the VEC Form 605, which is your application for the General Class license.

No FCC Fee for License Upgrades

In April, 2022, the FCC began charging a $35.00 application fee for new and renewal Amateur Radio licenses.

There is NO FEE for your upgrade from Technician Class to General Class or up to the Extra Class license.

There also is NO FEE to change your address on the FCC website.

Additional details about all of these changes and requirements can be found on the CORES homepage at:

https://apps.fcc.gov/cores/publicHome.do?faq6true&csfrToken

This FCC Registration Help Page provides guidance for how to:

- Register a New FCC User Name Account
- Register for a New FRN
- Reset your Username Password
- Update FRN Information

If you forgot the password you used when getting that first FCC license, or your e-mail address has changed, call the FCC on their toll free number 1-877-480-3201, Monday to Friday 8am - 6pm Eastern time. Tell them you want to associate your CURRENT user ID with a password, as you can't remember which e-mail you originally used, and forgot your password. Once the CORES Username Account Registration is complete and you have associated your FRN to the Username Account, the password to log into CORES and ULS will be the same. Use the UserName (email) to log into CORES and the FRN to log into ULS.

In addition, a thorough explanation of how to register on the FCC's CORES (Commission Registration System) and ULS (Universal Licensing System) websites, pay fees, and accomplish other tasks is included in the Appendix on page 226.

THE GENERAL CLASS EXAMINATION

Here is an overview of the General Class examination and what to expect when you go to the test session.

Examination Administration

The General Class exam is given by a team of 3 Volunteer Examiners (VEs) – hams who hold Advanced or Extra Class licenses and who are accredited to administer your exam by a Volunteer Examiner Coordinator (VEC).

Volunteer Examiner teams offer examinations on a regular basis at local sites to serve their communities. Generally, the VECs closely coordinate their activities with one another, so you should be able to find a nearby test site and exam date that is convenient for you. You can obtain information about VECs and exam sessions in your area by checking with your local radio club, or consult the list of VECs on page 216 and give one of them a call to identify an exam team in your area.

Once you have found your local VE team, contact them to select a test date and location and pre-register for your examination. They will hold a seat for you at the next available session. Don't be a no-show, and don't be a surprise-show. Call them ahead of time and pre-register!

The Volunteer Examiners are not compensated for their time and skills, but they are permitted to charge you a fee for certain reimbursable expenses incurred in preparing, administering, and processing the examination. The maximum fee is adjusted frequently and currently is about $14.00. When you call to make your exam reservation, ask the VE the current amount of the exam fee.

Want to find a test site fast?
Visit the W5YI-VEC website at:
https://www.w5yi.org/index.php/find-an-exam-session
or call them at 800-669-9594.

EXAM CONTENT

The questions, answers, and distracters for each question of the General Class written examination are public information. The question pool included in this book contains all 430 possible questions that can be used to make up your 35-question Element 3 written examination. The VEC is not permitted to change any of the wording, punctuation or numerical values included in any questions, answers, or distracters. The VEC can change the A-B-C-D order of the answers, if it wishes.

Also, the VEC is required to select one question from each syllabus topic under each subelement so you should expect an exam that contains one question from each syllabus topic within each subelement. Look again at the question pool syllabus on page 222 to see how the test will be constructed.

WHAT TO BRING TO THE EXAM SESSION

Here's what you'll need to bring with you for your General Class examination:

- The fee of approximately $14.00.
- A copy of your original license or a reference copy of your current Technician license. Make sure you bring a paper copy as proof of your existing license. If you recently passed your Technician exam and that license has not yet been granted, bring a copy of your Certificate of Successful Completion of Examination (CSCE) that proves the license elements passed.
- A photo identification card. Your driver's license is ideal for this purpose.
- Some sharp pencils and fine-tip pens. It's good to have a backup.
- Calculators may be used. However, the examiners may erase the memory before your exam begins.
- Any other items that the VE team asks you to bring.

COMPLETING NCVEC FORM 605

When you arrive at the examination site, one of the first things you will do is complete the NCVEC Form 605. This form is retained by the Volunteer Exam Coordinator which transfers your printed information to an electronic file and sends it to the FCC for your new or upgrade license. Your application may be delayed or kicked-back to you if the VEC can't read your writing. Make absolutely sure you print as legibly as you can, and carefully follow the instructions on the form.

NCVEC QUICK-FORM 605 APPLICATION
AMATEUR OPERATOR/PRIMARY STATION LICENSE

SECTION 1 - TO BE COMPLETED BY APPLICANT

PRINT LAST NAME	SUFFIX (Jr., Sr.)	FIRST NAME	M.I.	STATION CALL SIGN (IF ANY)
MAILING ADDRESS (Number and Street or P.O. Box)				FEDERAL REGISTRATION NUMBER (FRN) - IF NONE, THEN SOCIAL SECURITY NUMBER (SSN)
CITY	STATE CODE	ZIP CODE (5 or 9 Numbers)		DAYTIME TELEPHONE NUMBER (Include Area Code)
E-MAIL ADDRESS (MANDATORY)				

Basic Qualification Question:
Has the Applicant or any party to this application, or any party directly or indirectly controlling the Applicant, ever been convicted of a felony by any state or federal court? ☐ YES ☐ NO

If "YES", see "FCC BASIC QUALIFICATION QUESTION INSTRUCTIONS AND PROCEDURES" on the back of this form.

NCVEC Form 605 Dated September 2017

Name

If you are upgrading from a current license, it is very important to compare the information on your present license with what you are writing on NCVEC Form 605. Make sure that *everything* on NCVEC Form 605 *is identical* to how your present license reads. Fill in your last name, first name, middle initial, and suffix such as junior or senior. You must stay absolutely consistent with your name on any future Form 605s for upgrades or changes of address. If you start out as "Jack" and change your name to "John," you will need to file for a legal change of name on your next application. The 605 application form is a government application and you must use your legal name that is on your personal pictured IDs, such as your Driver's License, state ID card, or birth certificate. Your legal name and suffix, such as Jr, Sr, or II, III, should be used when filing out the 605 form. However, Mr, Ms, Dr, Phd, etc. are not acceptable in the FCC database.

FRN

You are required to fill in your Federal Registration Number (FRN)) in the designated box. Your current Technician Class license should show your FRN. If you do not have an FRN you should obtain an FRN ***before*** the exam session so that you can complete your Form 605 when you pass your test. To obtain an FCC Registration Number, go to the following website and follow the instructions there. Visit:

https://apps.fcc.gov/cores/userLogin.do

If you do preregister in CORES and obtain an FRN prior to going to the exam session for your first license, BE SURE TO USE THAT FRN ON YOUR 605 APPLICATION.

If you were previously licensed after 1998, you were issued an FRN, which is still shown on your active, expired, or cancelled license record in the FCC database until such time the FCC purges its data.

Address, Phone, and E-mail

Give your mailing address – one that you plan to keep as permanent as possible. If you move around a lot, you must file a change of address with the FCC to keep your address updated. The FCC uses this address to contact you by mail, if necessary, so you need to keep it current in the FCC database. Using a Post Office Box address is acceptable, or even the address of a relative or friend where you know they will receive mail for you and contact you should mail the FCC contact you by mail.

Your e-mail address is very important! This is how the FCC will notify you of your new license and call sign under the Universal Licensing System. When your license grant is issued, the FCC will send you an e-mail with a link to your new or upgrade license.

Basic Qualifying Question

As of September, 2017, the FCC requires license applicants to answer a Basic Qualifying Question. It asks if you have ever been convicted of a felony by any state or federal court. If you answer YES, then you will need to follow the instructions on the back of the NCVEC 605 form that requires you to submit a formal statement, within 14 days of your application being filled with the FCC by the VEC, explaining the circumstances as well as copies of your court documents. Your written statement to the FCC should contain the reasons why you believe that it would be in the public interest to award you an amateur radio license notwithstanding the actual or alleged misconduct. Instructions on how to file this statement appear on the back of the NCVEC Form 605.

Final Check

Once you're finished filling out your portion of the NCVEC Form 605, take a moment to double-check that your handwriting / printing is legible. If a single letter in your name can't be read clearly and is misinterpreted, subsequent electronic filings may be returned as "no action." Make sure your Form 605 is clear as a bell to your Volunteer Examiner team, who will then forward it to their VEC.

Your Examiners' Portion

Section 2 of the Form 605 is completed by your Volunteer Examiner team. The VEs will review your portion, making sure it is complete and legible, and when you pass your exam they will complete and sign their portion of the Form before sending it on to their Volunteer Examiner Coordinator.

Electronic Filing

After you pass your Element 3 General Class exam, your VE team will submit your amateur license application results to the VEC, either electronically or by snail mail. The VEC will certify your results and then electronically submit your application to the FCC. Within a day or two of having your application sent to the FCC, your call sign will be granted and it will show up on the FCC's ULS database. This is when you will receive that all-important e-mail announcing your new General Class upgrade, license!

TAKING THE EXAM

Don't speed read the examination! Read each question carefully. Take your time looking for the correct answer. Some answer choices start out looking correct, but end up wrong. When you finish, go back over every question and double-check your answers. When you are satisfied that you have passed the examination, turn in all of your test papers to the examination team. Make sure to thank your VEs and to let them know how much you appreciate their efforts to help promote our hobby.

AFTER THE EXAM

Wait patiently for your exam results. Chances are the VEs will greet you with a smile and your CSCE. When you are told you passed the exam, be sure you are given the appropriate paperwork:

- The CSCE, signed by all three examiners.
- Make sure the temporary identifier is filled in so you can use it to immediately go on the air with your new General Class frequency privileges.

If you didn't pass, they will tell you what to do next.

YOUR UPGRADE TO GENERAL CLASS

When the exam session is completed, the VE team sends your results to their VEC, which checks the paperwork. The VEC then submits the exam results electronically to the FCC. Your license grant will appear on the FCC database the next business day.

When the license is granted, the FCC sends you an email to the address you entered on the Form 605 Application. The applicant then logs into the FCC License Manager site using their FRN and FRN password. Go to:

https://wireless2.fcc.gov/UlsEntry/licManager/login.jsp

Print out a reference copy of your new upgrade license and begin enjoying your new skywave privileges!

However, if you are going from no license to General Class, you may not operate immediately based on just your CSCE because you have no call sign. You will receive an email from the FCC and then log in with your Username Account & Password within 10 days and pay the $35 Application fee. A guide on how to do this is in the Appendix on page 226.

GENERAL CLASS CALL SIGNS

The FCC has exhausted the availability of "Group C" Technician and General Class call signs that begin with the letter "N," a number, and three other letters, such as N9ABC.

If you did not check the "Change Call Sign" box on your NCVEC Form 605 application, you will simply keep your current call sign. However, if you do check the "Change Call Sign" box, you will receive an entry-level "Group D" call sign as if you were a newly-licensed amateur. We suggest you don't check the "Change Call Sign" box and stick with your present call sign.

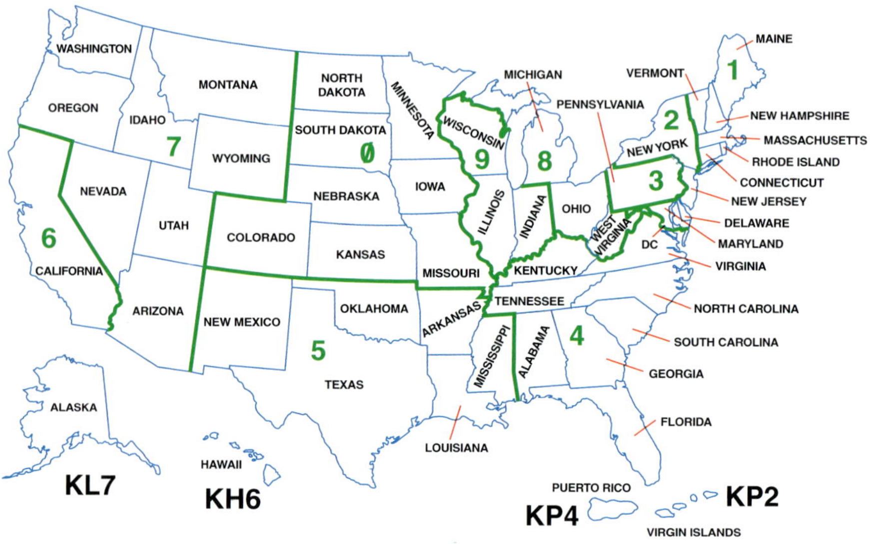

VANITY CALL SIGNS

You are eligible to replace your FCC systematically generated call sign with a vanity call sign of your choosing. This call sign could be made up of your initials, or represent your love of animals (K9DOG), or could be the call sign that your late mom or dad had when they got started in ham radio years ago. Or it could be a call sign of a close relative or former holder who is now deceased.

General Class amateur operators may request a vanity call sign from Group D or Group C. When you upgrade to Amateur Extra Class you can try for a 1x2, 2x1 or 2x2 call sign popular for CW and DX operations. You also may request a call sign that was previously assigned to you that may have expired years ago. Thousands of amateurs enjoy a call sign that has special meaning to them personally, or just sounds better phonetically. The FCC no longer charges a fee to file for a vanity call sign.

You can file for a vanity call directly with the FCC by mail using the required FCC 605 application form (not the NCVEC 605 Form), or electronically on the FCC web site, if you know your FRN and password to access your license record. Today, the best way to file a vanity application is electronically. In fact, since the applications are handled by the FCC as a lottery, the application must be filed electronically to make sure it gets processed timely with all other applications on the same day. Competition is fierce, especially for short call signs and those that have special meaning.

To make it easier for you and to assist you in getting the vanity call sign that you want, the W5YI Group at 800-669-9594 offers a vanity filing service. They do all the background work for you, researching when and if a specific call is available, and electronically file your application – all for a nominal service fee. Using their 99% success rate vanity filing service, you could end up with the exact call sign of your choice. You can enter your application and vanity call sign choices right on their web site at **www.w5yi.org**. Your application will be reviewed and confirmed to you by phone and or e-mail prior to processing. They have more than 25 years of experience making vanity call sign customers happy.

As for Gordo, he's staying with his original-issue WB6NOA call sign. If he changed it, he would be breaking a 50-year tradition!

CONGRATULATIONS! YOU PASSED!

After you pass the written exam, congratulations are in order and we offer you a big welcome to the worldwide privileges of General Class! Day or night, summer or fall, sunshine or rain, there is always a worldwide band open and ready for General Class voice, code, data modes, and television communications. Your new worldwide privileges are added to your existing VHF and UHF privileges. Before you go on the air, do a lot of listening. This will assure that you get started on the right foot with your new privileges. Remember, even the worldwide bands have band plans, so make sure you are operating within the plan for your worldwide communications.

Once again... *Welcome to General Class!* We hope to work you on one of the worldwide bands very soon. You can catch Gordo mobile in his communications van regularly on 14.240 MHz, and he's a "regular" on 10 meters from his Southern California home at 28.400 MHz.

Your next upgrade is Extra Class. For Extra Class, use our 3rd Ham Book, ***Extra Class***. Our explanations make the formula problem-solving easy and the learning fun! So start thinking about that upgrade now.

It's been fun teaching you the General Class. Good luck on that upcoming exam – We know you're going to pass!

Gordon West, WB6NOA

Eric P. Nichols, KL7AJ

An Invitation from Gordo

I also would like you to write me so I can send you an exclusive General Class passing certificate, plus some valuable manufacturers' catalogs and band charts. Send a self-addressed large envelope with 12 first class stamps loose on the inside to: Gordon West, WB6NOA, Radio School, Inc., 2414 College Drive, Costa Mesa, CA 92626.

PS: Keep reading! Chapter 5 will get you started on your journey to learn CW! Aw, come on – you can do it!!

5

Gordo's Guide to Learning Morse Code

On April 15, 2000, the FCC dropped the 20- and 13-word-per-minute Morse code requirements for worldwide frequency privileges for General and Extra Class operators down to 5 words per minute. On February 23, 2007, the FCC ***totally eliminated*** the Morse code test as a prerequisite for high frequency operation.

The elimination of the Morse code test for operation on worldwide frequencies conforms to international radio regulations. In 2003, the International Telecommunications Union (ITU) World Radiocommunication Conference voted to allow individual nations to determine whether or not to retain a Morse code test as a requirement to operate on frequencies below 30 MHz.

When the FCC eliminated the Morse code test for Technician Class operators in 1991 for VHF/UHF operating, the ruling was adopted with little opposition. However, the announcement that the FCC was considering total elimination of the Morse code test drew thousands of written comments to the FCC. Many comments supported code test elimination, while a minority urged the FCC to retain a code test because of the strong tradition of CW as a ham radio operating mode.

The Federal Communications Commission concluded that "…this change (eliminating the code test) eliminates an unnecessary burden that may discourage current amateur radio operators from advancing their skills and participating more fully in the benefits of amateur radio." The FCC Commissioners recognized the simple fact that learning Morse code was keeping many very technical, talented hams from obtaining their General and Extra Class licenses. Morse code is much like musical rhythms. Some people are tone deaf, and some people couldn't carry a rhythm in a hand basket.

So for years, the Morse code test was an insurmountable hurdle to many talented Technician Class hams who wanted to upgrade. If I could take these Techs and put them into one of my regular Morse code classes, we usually could get the majority of them through the CW test with outside home study, on the air practice (on 2 meters), and classroom study followed by the code test. But throughout the country, Morse code classes were few and far between and it is tough to learn new music and a new language without classroom instruction.

Technician Class operators could not practice on the worldwide airwaves to learn the code because these bands were reserved for only those operators who had already passed the code test. Running Morse code practice on a local 2 meter repeater was one option, but nothing beats the excitement of practicing code on the worldwide bands and hooking up with another station thousands of miles away.

As of February 23, 2007, we can now take new General Class operators and introduce them to Morse code on the exciting worldwide bands!

Morse code is the ham radio operator's most basic language of short and long sounds, dits and dahs, or dots and dashes. Sailors have pounded SOS when trapped beneath a sailboat hull. In submarines, the tapping of Morse code gets the message through when there is no other way to communicate. Prisoners of war have tapped out Morse code messages, or BLINKED the code when being publicly displayed on television.

Ham operators use the code to get through when noise would otherwise cover up data or voice signals. Years ago, before road rage, fellow hams driving might greet each other by sending on their car horns H-I, a friendly salute to another ham.

So I encourage you to learn code. It is best mastered by sound along with memorizing the Morse code patterns seen on the upcoming pages. The pages show the number of dots and dashes to learn for a specific character, and learning the sound (rhythm) of Morse code is always the best way to practice. Let's see what these short sounds and long sounds are all about.

LOOKING AT MORSE CODE

The International Morse code, originally developed as the American Morse code by Samuel Morse, is truly international — all countries use it, and most commercial worldwide services employ operators who can recognize it. It is made up of short and long duration sounds. Long sounds, called "dahs," are three times longer than short sounds, called "dits." *Figure 2-1* shows the time intervals for Morse code sounds and spaces. *Figure 2-3*, on the next page, indicates the sounds for all the CW characters and symbols.

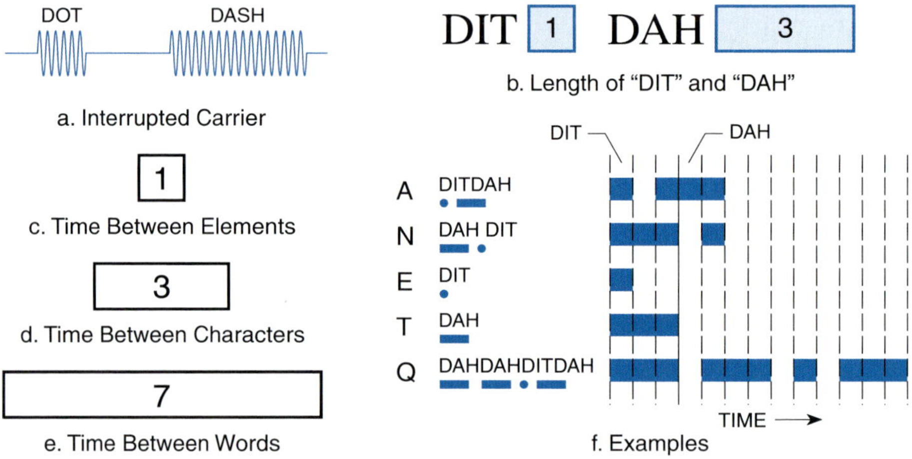

Figure 2-1. Time Intervals for Morse Code

a. Alphabet

LETTER	Composed of:	Sounds like:	LETTER	Composed of:	Sounds like:
A	▪ —	didah	N	— ▪	dahdit
B	— ▪ ▪ ▪	dahdididit	O	— — —	dahdahdah
C	— ▪ — ▪	dahdidahdit	P	▪ — — ▪	didahdahdit
D	— ▪ ▪	dahdidit	Q	— — ▪ —	dahdahdidah
E	▪	dit	R	▪ — ▪	didahdit
F	▪ ▪ — ▪	dididahdit	S	▪ ▪ ▪	dididit
G	— — ▪	dahdahdit	T	—	dah
H	▪ ▪ ▪ ▪	didididit	U	▪ ▪ —	dididah
I	▪ ▪	didit	V	▪ ▪ ▪ —	didididah
J	▪ — — —	didahdahdah	W	▪ — —	ditdahdah
K	— ▪ —	dahdidah	X	— ▪ ▪ —	dahdididah
L	▪ — ▪ ▪	didahdidit	Y	— ▪ — —	dahdidahdah
M	— —	dahdah	Z	— — ▪ ▪	dahdahdidit

b. Special Signals and Punctuation

CHARACTER	Meaning:	Composed of:	Sounds like:
$\overline{\text{AR}}$	(end of message)	▪ — ▪ — ▪	didahdidahdit
K	invitation to transmit (go ahead)	— ▪ —	dahdidah
$\overline{\text{SK}}$	End of work	▪ ▪ ▪ — ▪ —	didididahdidah
$\overline{\text{SOS}}$	International distress call	▪ ▪ ▪ — — — ▪ ▪ ▪	didididahdahdahdididit
V	Test letter (V)	▪ ▪ ▪ —	didididah
R	Received, OK	▪ — ▪	didahdit
$\overline{\text{BT}}$	Break or Pause	— ▪ ▪ ▪ —	dahdidididah
$\overline{\text{DN}}$	Slant Bar	— ▪ ▪ — ▪	dahdididahdit
$\overline{\text{KN}}$	Back to You Only	— ▪ — — ▪	dahdidahdahdit
Period		▪ — ▪ — ▪ —	didahdidahdidah
Comma		— — ▪ ▪ — —	dahdahdididahdah
Question mark		▪ ▪ — — ▪ ▪	dididahdahdidit
@	For Web Address	▪ — — ▪ — ▪	didahdahdidahdi

c. Numerals

NUMBER	Composed of:	Sounds like:
1	▪ — — — —	didahdahdahdah
2	▪ ▪ — — —	dididahdahdah
3	▪ ▪ ▪ — —	didididahdah
4	▪ ▪ ▪ ▪ —	dididididah
5	▪ ▪ ▪ ▪ ▪	dididididit
6	— ▪ ▪ ▪ ▪	dahdidididit
7	— — ▪ ▪ ▪	dahdahdididit
8	— — — ▪ ▪	dahdahdahdidit
9	— — — — ▪	dahdahdahdahdit
Ø	— — — — —	dahdahdahdahdah

Figure 2-3. Morse Code and Its Sound

CODE KEY

Morse code is usually sent by using a code key. A typical one is shown in *Figure 2-2a*. Normally it is mounted on a thin piece of wood or plexiglass. Make sure that what you mount it on is thin; if the key is raised too high, it will be uncomfortable to the wrist. The correct sending position for the hand is shown in *Figure 2-2b*.

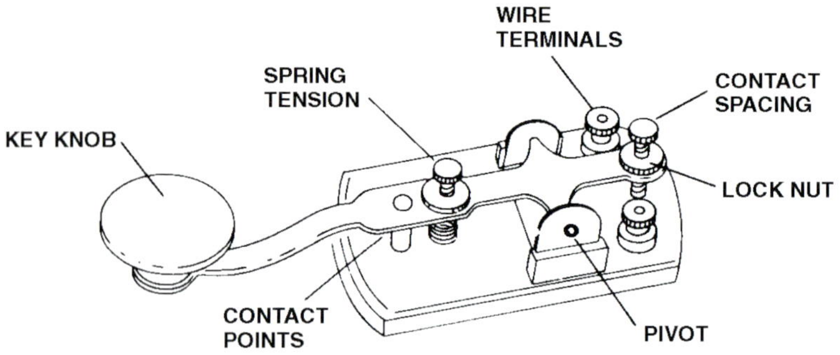

a. Code Key

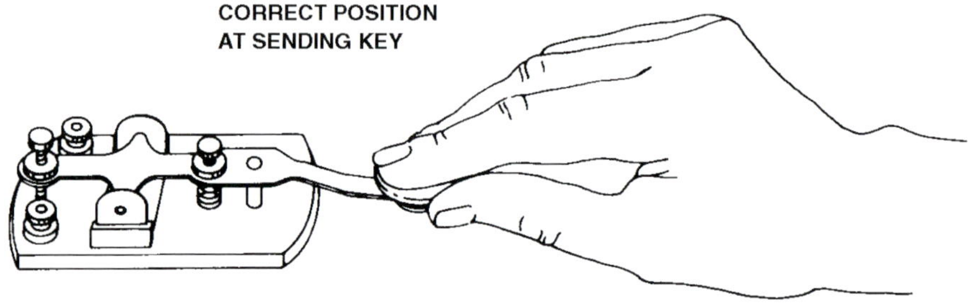

b. Sending Position

Figure 2-2. Code Key for Sending Code

LEARNING MORSE CODE

The reason you are learning the Morse code is to be able to operate all modes on the worldwide bands—including CW. Here are five suggestions (four serious ones) on how to learn the code:

1. Memorize the code from the code charts in this book.
2. Use my fun audio course available at all ham radio stores, and from the W5YI Group.
3. Go out and spend $450 and buy a worldwide radio, and listen to the code live and on the air. You don't need to spend that much, but you can listen to Morse code practice on the air, as shown in *Table 2-1.*
4. Use a code key and oscillator to practice sending the code. Believe it or not, someday you're actually going to do code over the live airwaves, using this same code key hooked up to your new megabuck transceiver.
5. Play with code programs on your computer, and *have fun!*

Table 2-1. Radio Frequencies and Times for Code Reception

Pacific	Mountain	Central	Eastern	Mon.	Tue.	Wed.	Thu.	Fri.
6 a.m.	7 a.m.	8 a.m.	9 a.m.		Fast Code	Slow Code	Fast Code	Slow Code
7 a.m. – 1 p.m.	8 a.m. – 2 p.m.	9 a.m. – 3 p.m.	10 a.m. – 4 p.m.	VISITING OPERATOR TIME				
1 p.m.	2 p.m.	3 p.m.	4 p.m.	Fast Code	Slow Code	Fast Code	Slow Code	Fast Code
2 p.m.	3 p.m.	4 p.m.	5 p.m.	Code Bulletin				
3 p.m.	4 p.m.	5 p.m.	6 p.m.	Digital Bulletin				
4 p.m.	5 p.m.	6 p.m.	7 p.m.	Slow Code	Fast Code	Slow Code	Fast Code	Slow Code
5 p.m.	6 p.m.	7 p.m.	8 p.m.	Code Bulletin				
6 p.m.	7 p.m.	8 p.m.	9 p.m.	Digital Bulletin				
6:45 p.m.	7:45 p.m.	8:45 p.m.	9:45 p.m.	Voice Bulletin				
7 p.m.	8 p.m.	9 p.m.	10 p.m.	Fast Code	Slow Code	Fast Code	Slow Code	Fast Code
8 p.m.	9 p.m.	10 p.m.	11 p.m.	Code Bulletin				

CW is broadcast on the following MHz frequencies: 1.8025, 3.5815, 7.0475, 14.0475, 18.0975, 21.0675, 28.0675, and 147.555. W1AW schedule courtesy of *QST* magazine.

DATA broadcasts: 3.5975, 7.095, 14.095, 18.1025, 21.095, 28.095 and 147.555 MHz

VOICE broadcasts: 1.855, 3.990, 7.290, 14.290, 18.160, 21.390, 28.590 and 147.555 MHz

CODE COURSES ON CDs

Five words per minute is so slow, and so easy, that many ham radio applicants learn it completely in a single week! You can do it, too, by using the code CDs mentioned above.

Code courses personally recorded by me make code learning *fun*. They will train you to send and receive the International Morse code in just a few short weeks. They are narrated and parallel the instructions in this book. The CDs have code characters generated at a 15-wpm character rate, spaced out to a 5-wpm word rate. This is known as Farnsworth spacing.

Getting Started

The hardest part of learning the code is taking the first CD out of the case, putting it in your player, and pushing the play button! Try it, and you will be over your biggest hurdle. After that, the CDs will talk you through the code in no time at all.

The CDs make code learning *fun*. You'll hear how humor has been added to the learning process to keep your interest high. Since ham radio is a hobby, there's no reason we can't poke ourselves in the ribs and have a little fun learning the code as part of this hobby experience. Okay, you're still not convinced — you probably have already made up your mind that trying to learn the code will be the hardest part of being a ham. It will not. Give yourself a fair chance. Don't get discouraged. Have patience and remember these important reminders when practicing to learn the Morse code:

- Learn the code by sound. Don't stare at the tiny dots and dashes that we have here in the book — the dit and dah sounds on the CDs and on the air and with your practice keyer will ultimately create an instant letter at your fingertips and into the pencil.
- *Never* scribble down dots or dashes if you forget a letter. Just put a small dash on your paper for a missed letter. You can go back and figure out what the word is by the letters you did copy!
- Practice only with fast code characters; 15-wpm character speed, spaced down to 5-wpm speed, is ideal.
- Practice the code by writing it down whenever possible. This further trains your brain and hand to work together in a subconscious response to the sounds you hear. (Remember Pavlov and his dog "Spot"?)
- Practice only for 15 minutes at a time. The CDs will tell you when to start and when to stop. Your brain and hand will lose that sharp edge once you go beyond 16 minutes of continuous code copy. You will learn much faster with five 15-minute practices per day than a one-hour marathon at night.
- Stay on course with the CD instructions. Learn the letters, numbers, punctuation marks, and operating signals in the order they are presented. My code teaching system parallels that of the American Radio Relay League, Boy Scouts of America, the Armed Forces, and has worked for thousands in actual classroom instruction.

It was no accident that Samuel Morse gave the single dit for the letter "E" which occurs most often in the English language. He determined the most used letters in the alphabet by counting letters in a printer's type case. He reasoned a printer would have more of the most commonly-used letters. It worked! With just the first lesson, you will be creating simple words and simple sentences with no previous background.

Table 2-2 shows the sequence of letters, punctuation marks, operating signals, and numbers covered in six lessons on the CDs recorded by me.

Table 2-2. Sequence of Lessons on Cassettes

▪ Lesson 1	E T M A N I S O $\overline{\text{SK}}$ Period
▪ Lesson 2	R U D C 5 Ø $\overline{\text{AR}}$ Question Mark
▪ Lesson 3	K P B G W F H $\overline{\text{BT}}$ Comma
▪ Lesson 4	Q L Y J X V Z $\overline{\text{DN}}$ 1 2 3 4 6 7 8 9
▪ Lesson 5	Random code with narrated answers
▪ Lesson 6	A typical 5-wpm code test

CODE KEY AND OSCILLATOR – HAM RECEIVER

All worldwide ham transceivers have provisions for a code key to be plugged in for both CW practice off the air as well as CW operating on the air. If you already own a worldwide set, chances are all you will need is a code key for some additional code-sending practice.

Read over your worldwide radio instruction manual where it talks about hooking up the code key. For code practice, read the notes about operating with a "side tone" but not actually going on the air. This "side tone" capability of most worldwide radios will eliminate your need for a separate code oscillator.

Code Key and Oscillator — Separate Unit

Many students may wish to simply buy a complete code key and oscillator set. They are available from local electronic outlets or through advertisements in the ham magazines.

Look again at the code key in *Figure 2-2a*. Note the terminals for the wires. Connect wires to these terminals and tighten the terminals so the wires won't come loose. The two wires will go either to a code oscillator set or to a plug that connects into your ham transceiver. Hook up the wires to the plug as described in your ham transceiver instruction book or the code oscillator set instruction book.

Mount the key firmly, as previously described, then adjust the gap between the contact points. With most new telegraph keys, you will need a pair of pliers to loosen the contact adjustment knob. It's located on the very end of your keyer. First loosen the lock nut, then screw down the adjustment until you get a gap no wider than the thickness of a business card. You want as little space as possible between the points. The contact points are located close to the sending plastic knob.

Now turn on your set or oscillator and listen. If your hear a constant tone, check that the right-hand movable shorting bar is not closed. If it is, swing it open. Adjust the spring tension adjustment screw so that you get a good "feel" each time you push down on the key knob. Adjust it tight enough to keep the contacts from closing while your fingers are resting on the key knob.

Pick up the key by the knob! This is the exact position your fingers should grasp the knob—one or two on top, and one or two on the side of it. Poking at the knob with one finger is unacceptable. Letting your fingers fly off the knob between dots and dashes (dits and dahs) also is not correct. As you are sending, you should be able to instantly pick up the whole key assembly to verify proper finger position.

Your arm and wrist should barely move as you send CW. All the action is in your hand — and it should be almost effortless. Give it a try, and look at *Figure 2-2b* again to double-check your hand position.

Letting someone else use the key to send CW to you will also help you learn the code.

Morse Code Computer Software

The newest way to learn Morse code is through computer-aided instruction. There are many good PC programs on the market that not only teach you the characters, but build speed and allow you to take actual telegraphy examinations, which the computer constructs. Personal computer programs also can be used to make audio tapes on your tape recorder so you can listen to them on the cassette player in your car.

A big advantage of computer-aided Morse code learning is that you can easily customize the program to fit your own needs! You can select the sending speed, Farnsworth character-spacing speed, duration of transmission, number of characters in a random group, tone frequency — and more!

Some have built-in "weighting." That means the software will determine your weaknesses and automatically adjust future sending to give you more study on your problem characters! All Morse code software programs transmit the tone by keying the PC's internal speaker. Some generate a clearer audio tone through the use of external oscillators or internal computer sound cards.

Here are three web addresses of sites that offer Morse code instruction for your computer:

- ☞ **http://lcwo.net**
- ☞ **http://numorse.com/**
- ☞ **http://www.dxzone.com/catalog/operatingmodes/morsecode/learningmorsecode/**

Morse Code Audio Courses

Learn Morse code, CW, with Gordo's narrated audio CD courses. Each course is an 8-CD set in a holder:

- Learn the code at 5 words per minute using his beginner course, GW05.
- Increase your code speed from 5 WPM to 16 WPM using his intermediate courses, GW13.
- Become a CW pro using Gordo's top course to increase your code speed to 28 WPM, GW20.
- Brush up on the CW you remember from your time in the Scouts or Service using Gordo's 2-CD refresher course, GWCT.

These audio CDs play in standard audio/music CD players, or on your computer's audio CD drive. Use your kid's audio CD player, too! Kids love the code!

I hope to hear your CW call on the worldwide bands soon!

APPENDIX

U.S. VOLUNTEER EXAMINER COORDINATORS IN THE AMATEUR SERVICE

W5YI-VEC
P.O. Box 200065
Arlington, TX 76006-0065
817-860-3800 / 800- 669-9594
e-mail: W5YI-VEC@w5yi.org
website: www.w5yi.org

Anchorage ARC VEC
P.O. Box 190192
Anchorage, AK 99519
907-632-3963
e-mail: vec@kl7aa.org
website: www.kl7aa.org/vec

American Radio Relay League (ARRL)
225 Main Street
Newington, CT 06111-1494
860-594-0300
860-594-0339 (fax)
email: vec@arrl.org
website: www.arrl.org

Central America CAVEC, Inc.
2751 Christian Ln NE
Huntsville, AL 35811
256-509-5271
e-mail: cavec.org@gmail.com
website: www.cavechamexam.com

Golden Empire Amateur Radio Society (GEARS)
P.O. Box 508
Chico, CA 95927-0508
530-893-9211
e-mail: myw6js@gmail.com
website: www.gearsw6rhc.org

Greater L.A. Amateur Radio Group(GLAARG)
23371 Mulholland Drive, Unit 186
Woodland Hills, CA 91364
(805) 410-4169
e-nail: vec@glaarg.org
website: www.glaarg.org

Jefferson Amateur Radio Club
P.O. Box 73665
Metairie, LA 70033
504-636-8809
e-mail: w5gad.vec@w5gad.org
website: www.w5gad.org

Laurel Amateur Radio Club, Inc.
5287 W Belmont Rd
Tucson, AZ 85743
520-664-5070 (1800-2100 hrs)
e-mail: aa3of@arrl.net
website: www.laurelvec.com

MRAC VEC, Inc.
c/o Tom Fuszard
2505 S. Calhoun Rd., #203
New Berlin, WI 53151
e-mail: mracvec@gmail.com
website: www.mracvec.org

MO-KAN VEC Coordinator
228 Tennessee Road
Richmond, KS 66080-9174
785-867-2011
e-mail: Bill.wo0e@gmail.com

Sandarc-VEC
5511 Maryland Ave.
La Mesa, CA 91942-1519
619-843-3747
e-mail: n6nyx@arrl.net
website: www.sandarc.org

Sunnyvale VEC Amateur Radio Club, Inc.
POB 70014
Sunnyvale, CA 94086-0014
408 255-9000 (24 hours)
e-mail: vec@amateur-radio.org
website: www.amateur-radio.org

W4VEC
Chairman - Billy Stewart WA4PVI
1150 ROCK GROVE CHURCH RD
SALISBURY, NC 28146-0325
901-691-8810
e-mail: BStewart@windstream.net
website: www.w4vec.org

Western Carolina Amateur Radio Society VEC, Inc.
7 Skylyn Court
Asheville, NC 28806-3922
828-253-1192
e-mail: wcarsvec@wcarsvec.net

THE W5YI RF SAFETY TABLES

(Developed by Fred Maia, W5YI, working in cooperation with the ARRL.)

There are two ways to determine whether your station's radio frequency signal radiation is within the MPE (Maximum Permissible Exposure) guidelines established by the FCC for ***"controlled"*** and ***"uncontrolled"*** environments. One way is direct ***"measurement"*** of the RF fields. The second way is through ***"prediction"*** using various antenna modeling, equations and calculation methods described in the FCC's *OET Bulletin 65* and *Supplement B.*

In general, most amateurs will not have access to the appropriate calibrated equipment to make precise field strength/power density measurements. The field-strength meters in common use by amateur operators are inexpensive, hand-held field strength meters that do not provide the accuracy necessary for reliable measurements, especially when different frequencies may be encountered at a given measurement location. It is more practical for amateurs to determine their PEP output power at the antenna and then look up the required distances to the controlled/uncontrolled environments using the following tables, which were developed using the prediction equations supplied by the FCC.

The FCC has determined that radio operators and their families are in the "controlled" environment and your neighbors and passers-by are in the "uncontrolled" environment. The estimated minimum compliance distances are in meters from the transmitting antenna to either the occupational/controlled exposure environment ("Con") or the general population/uncontrolled exposure environment ("Unc") using typical antenna gains for the amateur service and assuming 100% duty cycle and maximum surface reflection. Therefore, these charts represent the worst case scenario. They do not take into consideration compliance distance reductions that would be caused by:

(1) Feed line losses, which reduce power output at the antenna especially at the VHF and higher frequency levels.

(2) Duty cycle caused by the emission type. The emission type factor accounts for the fact that, for some modulated emission types that have a non-constant envelope, the PEP can be considerably larger than the average power. Multiply the distances by 0.4 if you are using CW Morse telegraphy, and by 0.2 for two-way SSB (single sideband) voice. There is no reduction for FM.

(3) Duty cycle caused by on/off time or "time-averaging." The RF safety guidelines permit RF exposures to be averaged over certain periods of time with the average not to exceed the limit for continuous exposure. The averaging time for occupational/controlled exposures is 6 minutes, while the averaging time for general population/uncontrolled exposures is 30 minutes. For example, if the relevant time interval for time-averaging is 6 minutes, an amateur could be exposed to two times the applicable power density limit for three minutes as long as he or she were not exposed at all for the preceding or following three minutes.

A routine evaluation is not required for vehicular mobile or hand-held transceiver stations. Amateur Radio operators should be aware, however, of the potential for exposure to RF electromagnetic fields from these stations, and take measures (such as reducing transmitting power to the minimum necessary, positioning the radiating antenna as far from humans as practical, and limiting continuous transmitting time) to protect themselves and the occupants of their vehicles.

Amateur Radio operators should also be aware that the FCC radio-frequency safety regulations address exposure to people — and not the strength of the signal. Amateurs may exceed the Maximum Permissible Exposure (MPE) limits as long as no one is exposed to the radiation.

How to read the chart: If you are radiating 500 watts from your 10 meter dipole (about a 3 dB gain), there must be at least 4.5 meters (about 15 feet) between you (and your family) and the antenna — and a distance of 10 meters (about 33 feet) between the antenna and your neighbors.

Medium and High Frequency Amateur Bands

All distances are in meters

Freq. (MF/HF) (MHz/Band)	Antenna Gain (dBi)	Peak Envelope Power (watts) 100 watts		500 watts		1000 watts		1500 watts	
		Con.	Unc.	Con.	Unc.	Con.	Unc.	Con.	Unc.
2.0 (160m)	0	0.1	0.2	0.3	0.5	0.5	0.7	0.6	0.8
2.0 (160m)	3	0.2	0.3	0.5	0.7	0.6	1.06	0.8	1.2
4.0 (75/80m)	0	0.2	0.4	0.4	1.0	0.6	1.3	0.7	1.6
4.0 (75/80m)	3	0.3	0.6	0.6	1.3	0.9	1.9	1.0	2.3
7.3 (40m)	0	0.3	0.8	0.8	1.7	1.1	2.5	1.3	3.0
7.3 (40m)	3	0.5	1.1	1.1	2.5	1.6	3.5	1.9	4.2
7.3 (40m)	6	0.7	1.5	1.5	3.5	2.2	4.9	2.7	6.0
10.15 (30m)	0	0.5	1.1	1.1	2.4	1.5	3.4	1.9	4.2
10.15 (30m)	3	0.7	1.5	1.5	3.4	2.2	4.8	2.6	5.9
10.15 (30m)	6	1.0	2.2	2.2	4.8	3.0	6.8	3.7	8.3
14.35 (20m)	0	0.7	1.5	1.5	3.4	2.2	4.8	2.6	5.9
14.35 (20m)	3	1.0	2.2	2.2	4.8	3.0	6.8	3.7	8.4
14.35 (20m)	6	1.4	3.0	3.0	6.8	4.3	9.6	5.3	11.8
14.35 (20m)	9	1.9	4.3	4.3	9.6	6.1	13.6	7.5	16.7
18.168 (17m)	0	0.9	1.9	1.9	4.3	2.7	6.1	3.3	7.5
18.168 (17m)	3	1.2	2.7	2.7	6.1	3.9	8.6	4.7	10.6
18.168 (17m)	6	1.7	3.9	3.9	8.6	5.5	12.2	6.7	14.9
18.168 (17m)	9	2.4	5.4	5.4	12.2	7.7	17.2	9.4	21.1
21.145 (15m)	0	1.0	2.3	2.3	5.1	3.2	7.2	4.0	8.8
21.145 (15m)	3	1.4	3.2	3.2	7.2	4.6	10.2	5.6	12.5
21.145 (15m)	6	2.0	4.6	4.6	10.2	6.4	14.4	7.9	17.6
21.145 (15m)	9	2.9	6.4	6.4	14.4	9.1	20.3	11.1	24.9
24.99 (12m)	0	1.2	2.7	2.7	5.9	3.8	8.4	4.6	10.3
24.99 (12m)	3	1.7	3.8	3.8	8.4	5.3	11.9	6.5	14.5
24.99 (12m)	6	2.4	5.3	5.3	11.9	7.5	16.8	9.2	20.5
24.99 (12m)	9	3.4	7.5	7.5	16.8	10.6	23.7	13.0	29.0
29.7 (10m)	0	1.4	3.2	3.2	7.1	4.5	10.0	5.5	12.2
29.7 (10m)	3	2.0	4.5	4.5	10.0	6.3	14.1	7.7	17.3
29.7 (10m)	6	2.8	6.3	6.3	14.1	8.9	19.9	10.9	24.4
29.7 (10m)	9	4.0	8.9	8.9	19.9	12.6	28.2	15.4	34.5

VHF/UHF Amateur Bands

All distances are in meters

Freq. (MF/HF) (MHz/Band)	Antenna Gain (dBi)	Peak Envelope Power (watts) 50 watts		100 watts		500 watts		1000 watts	
		Con.	Unc.	Con.	Unc.	Con.	Unc.	Con.	Unc.
50 (6m)	0	1.0	2.3	1.4	3.2	3.2	7.1	4.5	10.1
50 (6m)	3	1.4	3.2	2.0	4.5	4.5	10.1	6.4	14.3
50 (6m)	6	2.0	4.5	2.8	6.4	6.4	14.2	9.0	20.1
50 (6m)	9	2.8	6.4	4.0	9.0	9.0	20.1	12.7	28.4
50 (6m)	12	4.0	9.0	5.7	12.7	12.7	28.4	18.0	40.2
50 (6m)	15	5.7	12.7	8.0	18.0	18.0	40.2	25.4	56.8
144 (2m)	0	1.0	2.3	1.4	3.2	3.2	7.1	4.5	10.1
144 (2m)	3	1.4	3.2	2.0	4.5	4.5	10.1	6.4	14.3
144 (2m)	6	2.0	4.5	2.8	6.4	6.4	14.2	9.0	20.1
144 (2m)	9	2.8	6.4	4.0	9.0	9.0	20.1	12.7	28.4
144 (2m)	12	4.0	9.0	5.7	12.7	12.7	28.4	18.0	40.2
144 (2m)	15	5.7	12.7	8.0	18.0	18.0	40.2	25.4	56.8
144 (2m)	20	10.1	22.6	14.3	32.0	32.0	71.4	45.1	101.0
222 (1.25m)	0	1.0	2.3	1.4	3.2	3.2	7.1	4.5	10.1
222 (1.25m)	3	1.4	3.2	2.0	4.5	4.5	10.1	6.4	14.3
222 (1.25m)	6	2.0	4.5	2.8	6.4	6.4	14.2	9.0	20.1
222 (1.25m)	9	2.8	6.4	4.0	9.0	9.0	20.1	12.7	28.4
222 (1.25m)	12	4.0	9.0	5.7	12.7	12.7	28.4	18.0	40.2
222 (1.25m)	15	5.7	12.7	8.0	18.0	18.0	40.2	25.4	56.8
450 (70cm)	0	0.8	1.8	1.2	2.6	2.6	5.8	3.7	8.2
450 (70cm)	3	1.2	2.6	1.6	3.7	3.7	8.2	5.2	11.6
450 (70cm)	6	1.6	3.7	2.3	5.2	5.2	11.6	7.4	16.4
450 (70cm)	9	2.3	5.2	3.3	7.3	7.3	16.4	10.4	23.2
450 (70cm)	12	3.3	7.3	4.6	10.4	10.4	23.2	14.7	32.8
902 (33cm)	0	0.6	1.3	0.8	1.8	1.8	4.1	2.6	5.8
902 (33cm)	3	0.8	1.8	1.2	2.6	2.6	5.8	3.7	8.2
902 (33cm)	6	1.2	2.6	1.6	3.7	3.7	8.2	5.2	11.6
902 (33cm)	9	1.6	3.7	2.3	5.2	5.2	11.6	7.3	16.4
902 (33cm)	12	2.3	5.2	3.3	7.3	7.3	16.4	10.4	23.2
1240 (23cm)	0	0.5	1.1	0.7	1.6	1.6	3.5	2.2	5.0
1240 (23cm)	3	0.7	1.6	1.0	2.2	2.2	5.0	3.1	7.0
1240 (23cm)	6	1.0	2.2	1.4	3.1	3.1	7.0	4.4	9.9
1240 (23cm)	9	1.4	3.1	2.0	4.4	4.4	9.9	6.3	14.0
1240 (23cm)	12	2.0	4.4	2.8	6.2	6.2	14.0	8.8	19.8

All distances are in meters. To convert from meters to feet multiply meters by 3.28. Distance indicated is shortest line-of-sight distance to point where MPE limit for appropriate exposure tier is predicted to occur.

AUTHORIZED FREQUENCY BANDS – AMATEUR SERVICE (for U.S. Amateur Stations operating from ITU-Region 2–North and South America)

Current License Class[1]		Technician	General		Extra Class
Grandfathered[2] (METERS)	Novice	Technician	General	Advanced	Extra Class
2200			135.7-137.8 kHz/All	135.7-137.8 kHz/All	135.7-137.8 kHz/All
630			472-479 kHz/All	472-479 kHz/All	472-479 kHz/All
160			1800-2000 kHz/All	1800-2000 kHz/All	1800-2000 kHz/All
80 75	3525-3600 kHz/CW	3525-3600 kHz/CW	3525-3600 kHz/CW 3800-4000 kHz/Ph	3525-3600 kHz/CW 3700-4000 kHz/Ph	3500-4000 kHz/CW 3600-4000 kHz/Ph
60			5 channels	5 channels	5 channels
40	7025-7125 kHz/CW	7025-7125 kHz/CW	7025-7125 kHz/CW 7175-7300 kHz/Ph	7025-7125 kHz/CW 7125-7300 kHz/Ph	7000-7300 kHz/CW 7125-7300 kHz/Ph
30			10.1-10.15 MHz/CW	10.1-10.15 MHz/CW	10.1-10.15 MHz/CW
20			14.025-14.15 MHz/CW 14.225-14.35 MHz/Ph	14.025-14.15 MHz/CW 14.175-14.35 MHz/Ph	14.0-14.35 MHz/CW 14.15-14.35 MHz/Ph
17			18.068-18.11 MHz/CW 18.11-18.168 MHz/Ph	18.068-18.11 MHz/CW 18.11-18.168 MHz/Ph	18.068-18.11 MHz/CW 18.11-18.168 MHz/Ph
15	21.025-21.2 MHz/CW	21.025-21.2 MHz/CW	21.025-21.2 MHz/CW 21.275-21.45 MHz/Ph	21.025-21.2 MHz/CW 21.225-21.45 MHz/Ph	21.0-21.45 MHz/CW 21.2-21.45 MHz/Ph
12			24.89-24.99 MHz/CW 24.93-24.99 MHz/Ph	24.89-24.99 MHz/CW 24.93-24.99 MHz/Ph	24.89-24.99 MHz/CW 24.93-24.99 MHz/Ph
10	28.0-28.5 MHz/CW 28.3-28.5 MHz/Ph	28.0-28.5 MHz/CW 28.3-28.5 MHz/Ph	28.0-28.3 MHz/CW 28.3-29.7 MHz/Ph	28.0-28.3 MHz/CW 28.3-29.7 MHz/Ph	28.0-29.7 MHz/CW 28.3-29.7 MHz/Ph
6		50-54 MHz/CW 50.1-54 MHz/Ph	50-54 MHz/CW 50.1-54 MHz/Ph	50-54 MHz/CW 50.1-54 MHz/Ph	50-54 MHz/CW 50.1-54 MHz/Ph
2		144-148 MHz/CW 144.1-148 MHz/All	144-148 MHz/CW 144.1-148 MHz/Ph	144-148 MHz/CW 144.1-148 MHz/All	144-148 MHz/CW 144.1-148 MHz/All
1.25	222-225 MHz/All	222-225 MHz/All	222-225 MHz/All	222-225 MHz/All	222-225 MHz/All
0.70		420-450 MHz/All	420-450 MHz/All	420-450 MHz/All	420-450 MHz/All
0.33		902-928 MHz/All	902-928 MHz/All	902-928 MHz/All	902-928 MHz/All
0.23	1270-1295 MHz/All	1240-1300 MHz/All	1240-1300 MHz/All	1240-1300 MHz/All	1240-1300 MHz/All

[1] Effective 4-15-00 [2] Prior to 4-15-00

The following CEPT countries allow U.S. Amateurs to operate in their countries without a reciprocal license. Be sure to carry a copy of your FCC license and FCC Public Notice DA99-1098.

Austria
Belgium
Bosnia & Herzegovina
Bulgaria
Croatia
Cyprus
Czech Republic
Denmark
Estonia
Faroe Islands
Finland
France & its possessions
Germany
Greenland
Hungary
Iceland
Ireland
Italy
Latvia
Liechtenstein
Lithuania
Luxembourg
Monaco
Montenegro
Netherlands
Netherlands Antilles
Norway
Portugal
Romania
Slovak Republic
Slovenia
Spain
Sweden
Switzerland
Turkey
United Kingdom & its possessions

List of Countries Permitting Third-Party Traffic

Country	Call Sign Prefix	Country	Call Sign Prefix	Country	Call Sign Prefix
Antigua and Barbuda	V2	El Salvador	YS	Paraguay	ZP
Argentina	LU	The Gambia	C5	Peru	OA
Australia	VK	Ghana	9G	Philippines	DU
Austria, Vienna	4U1VIC	Grenada	J3	St. Christopher & Nevis	V4
Belize	V3	Guatemala	TG	St. Lucia	J6
Bolivia	CP	Guyana	8R	St. Vincent & Grenadines. .	J8
Bosnia-Herzegovina	T9	Haiti	HH	Sierra Leone	9L
Brazil	PY	Honduras	HR	South Africa	ZS
Canada	VE, VO, VY	Israel	4X	Swaziland	3D6
Chile	CE	Jamaica	6Y	Trinidad and Tobago	9Y
Colombia	HK	Jordan	JY	Turkey	TA
Comoros	D6	Liberia	EL	United Kingdom	GB*
Costa Rica	TI	Marshall Is	V6	Uruguay	CX
Cuba	CO	Mexico	XE	Venezuela	YV
Dominica	J7	Micronesia	V6	ITU-Geneva	4U1ITU
Dominican Republic	HI	Nicaragua	YN	VIC-Vienna	4U1VIC
Ecuador	HC	Panama	HP		

Countries Holding U.S. Reciprocal Agreements

Antigua, Barbuda
Argentina
Australia
Austria
Bahamas
Barbados
Belgium
Belize
Bolivia
Bosnia-Herzegovina
Botswana
Brazil
Canada[1]
Chile
Colombia
Costa Rica
Croatia
Cyprus
Denmark
Dominica
Dominican Rep.
Ecuador
El Salvador
Fiji
Finland
France[2]
Germany
Greece
Greenland
Grenada
Guatemala
Guyana
Haiti
Honduras
Iceland
India
Indonesia
Ireland
Israel
Italy
Jamaica
Japan
Jordan
Kiribati
Kuwait
Liberia
Luxembourg
Macedonia
Marshall Is.
Mexico
Micronesia
Monaco
Netherlands
Netherlands Ant.
New Zealand
Nicaragua
Norway
Panama
Paraguay
Papua New Guinea
Peru
Philippines
Portugal
Seychelles
Sierra Leone
Solomon Islands
South Africa
Spain
St. Lucia
St. Vincent and Grenadines
Surinam
Sweden
Switzerland
Thailand
Trinidad, Tobago
Turkey
Tuvalu
United Kingdom[3]
Uruguay
Venezuela

1. Do not need reciprocal permit
2. Includes all French Territories
3. Includes all British Territories

QUESTION POOL SYLLABUS

The syllabus used by the NCVEC Question Pool Committee to develop the question pool is included here as an aid in studying the subelements and topic groups. Reviewing the syllabus will give you an understanding of how the question pool is used to develop the Element 3 General Class written examination. Remember, one question will be taken from each topic group within each subelement to create your exam.

2023-2027 FCC Element 3 General Class Syllabus

G1 - Commission's Rules
[5 Exam Questions – 5 Groups] 57 Questions
G1A – General class control operator frequency privileges; primary and secondary allocations
G1B – Antenna structure limitations; good engineering and good amateur practice; beacon operation; prohibited transmissions; retransmitting radio signals
G1C – Transmitter power regulations; data emission standards; 60-meter operation requirements
G1D – Volunteer Examiners and Volunteer Examiner Coordinators; temporary identification; element credit; remote operation
G1E – Control categories; repeater regulations; third-party rules; ITU regions; automatically controlled digital station

G2 - Operating Procedures
[5 Exam Questions – 5 Groups] 60 Questions
G2A – Phone operating procedures: USB/LSB conventions, breaking into a contact, transmitter setup for voice operation; answering DX stations
G2B – Operating effectively; band plans; drills and emergencies; RACES operation
G2C – CW operating procedures and procedural signals; Q signals; full break-in
G2D – Volunteer Monitor Program; HF operations
G2E – Digital mode operating procedures

G3 - Radio Wave Propagation
[3 Exam Questions – 3 Groups] 37 Questions
G3A – Sunspots and solar radiation; geomagnetic field and stability indices
G3B – Maximum Usable Frequency; Lowest Usable Frequency; short path and long path propagation; determining propagation conditions; ionospheric refraction
G3C – Ionospheric regions; critical angle and frequency; HF scatter; near vertical incidence skywave (NVIS)

G4 - Amateur Radio Practices
[5 Exam Questions – 5 groups] 60 Questions
G4A – Station configuration and operation
G4B – Tests and test equipment
G4C – Interference to consumer electronics; grounding and bonding
G4D – Speech processors; S meters; sideband operation near band edges
G4E – Mobile and portable HF stations; alternative energy source operation

G5 - Electrical Principles
[3 Exam Questions – 3 Groups] 40 Questions
G5A – Reactance; inductance; capacitance; impedance; impedance transformation; resonance
G5B – The decibel; current and voltage dividers; electrical power calculations; sine wave root-mean-square (RMS) values; PEP calculations
G5C – Resistors, capacitors, and inductors in series and parallel; transformers

G6 - Circuit Components
[2 Exam Questions – 2 Groups] 24 Questions
G6A – Resistors; capacitors; inductors; rectifiers; solid-state diodes and transistors; vacuum tubes; batteries
G6B – Analog and digital integrated circuits (ICs); microwave ICs (MMICs); display devices; RF connectors; ferrite cores

G7 - Practical Circuits
[3 Exam Questions – 3 Groups] 38 Questions
G7A – Power supplies; schematic symbols
G7B – Digital circuits; amplifiers and oscillators
G7C – Transceiver design; filters; oscillators; digital signal processing (DSP)

G8 - Signals and Emissions
[3 Exam Questions – 3 Groups] 43 Questions
G8A – Carriers and modulation: AM, FM, and single sideband; modulation envelope; digital modulation; overmodulation; link budgets and link margins
G8B – Frequency changing; bandwidths of various modes; deviation; intermodulation
G8C – Digital emission modes

G9 - Antennas and Feed Lines
[4 Exam Questions – 4 Groups] 46 Questions
G9A – Feed lines: characteristic impedance and attenuation; standing wave ratio (SWR) calculation, measurement, and effects; antenna feed point matching
G9B – Basic dipole and monopole antennas
G9C – Directional antennas
G9D – Specialized antenna types and applications

G0 - Electrical and R F Safety
[2 Exam Questions – 2 Groups] 25 Questions
G0A – RF safety principles, rules, and guidelines; routine station evaluation
G0B – Station safety: electrical shock, grounding, fusing, interlocks, and wiring; antenna and tower safety

2023-2027 ELEMENT 3 Q&A CROSS REFERENCE

The following cross reference presents all 430 question numbers included in the 2023-27 Element 3 question pool in numerical order, followed by the page number on which the question begins in the book. This will allow you to locate specific questions by question number.

COMMON CW ABBREVIATIONS

AA	**All** after
AB	**All** before
ABT	**About**
ADR	**Address**
AGN	**Again**
ANT	**Antenna**
AR	**End** of message
BCI	**Broadcast** interference
BK	**Break;** break me; break in
BN	**All** between; been
B4	**Before**
C	**Yes**
CFM	**Confirm;** I confirm
CK	**Check**
CL	**I** am closing my station; call
CLD-CLG	**Called;** calling
CUD	**Could**
CUL	**See** you later
CUM	**Come**
CW	**Continuous** Wave
DLD-DLVD	**Delivered**
DX	**Distance**
FB	**Fine** business; excellent
GA	**Go** ahead (or resume sending)
GB	**Good-by**
GBA	**Give** better address
GE	**Good** evening
GG	**Going**
GM	**Good** morning
GN	**Good** night
GND	**Ground**
GUD	**Good**
HI	**The** telegraphic laugh; high
HR	**Here;** hear
HV	**Have**
HW	**How**
KN	**Listening** for specific station(s)
LID	**A** poor operator
MILS	**Milliamperes**
MSG	**Message;** prefix to radiogram
N	**No**
ND	**Nothing** doing
NIL	**Nothing;** I have nothing for you
NR	**Number**
NW	**Now;** I resume transmission
OB	**Old** boy
OM	**Old** man
OP-OPR	**Operator**
OT	**Old** timer; old top
PBL	**Preable**
PSE-PLS	**Please**
PWR	**Power**
PX	**Press**
R	**Received** as transmitted; are
RCD	**Received**
REF	**Refer** to; referring to; reference
RPT	**Repeat;** I repeat
SED	**Said**
SEZ	**Says**
SIG	**Signature;** signal
SKED	**Schedule**
SRI	**Sorry**
SVC	**Service;** prefix to service message
TFC	**Traffic**
TMW	**Tomorrow**
TNX	**Thanks**
TU	**Thank** you
TVI	**Television** interference
TXT	**Text**
UR-URS	**Your;** you're; yours
VFO-	**Variable-frequency** oscillator
VY	**Very**
WA	**Word** after
WB	**Word** before
WD-WDS	**Word;** words
WKD-WKG	**Worked;** working
WL	**Well;** will
WUD	**Would**
WX	**Weather**
XMTR	**Transmitter**
XTAL	**Crystal**
XYL	**Wife**
YL	**Young** lady
73	**Best** regards
88	**Love** and kisses

FCC Fee for New and Renewal Licensees

In April, 2022, the FCC began charging a $35.00 fee for new and renewal of Amateur Radio licenses. Previously, licenses were granted free of charge. This FCC fee is in addition to the examination fee paid to the VE Team.

There is no FCC fee charged when you upgrade from Tech, to General, or to Extra Class when you have a current, active Amateur Radio license. There also is no fee when you make an address change on the FCC ULS database.

When the FCC receives your examination information from the VEC and approves the application, you will receive an email with a link to the FCC Fee Payment Portal that includes payment instructions. You pay the fee using your credit or debit card.

You have 10 days from the date of the email to pay the fee. The fee must be paid from a computer or laptop and NOT from a cell phone or tablet. Make sure to monitor your e-mail inbox and spam folder so you can pay your application fee promptly.

Alternatively, if you are unable to monitor your email inbox and spam folder, you can go to the FCC website:

https://wireless2.fcc.gov/UlsApp/ApplicationSearch/searchAppl.jsp

and search for your pending application using your FRN number. When you see your pending application, you can follow the instructions and go to the FCC Payment Portal **https://apps.fcc.gov/cores/userLogin.do** to pay the $35.00 fee.

Once you select "Make Payment" you'll be taken to the Payment Summary Screen where you'll be given 4 options to make your payment:

- ACH (electronic debit) from a checking or savings account.
- Pay by Credit Card or Debit Card
- Wire Transfer
- Pay by Check/Money Order (This form of payment is discouraged. Applicants are strongly encouraged to submit payment electronically.

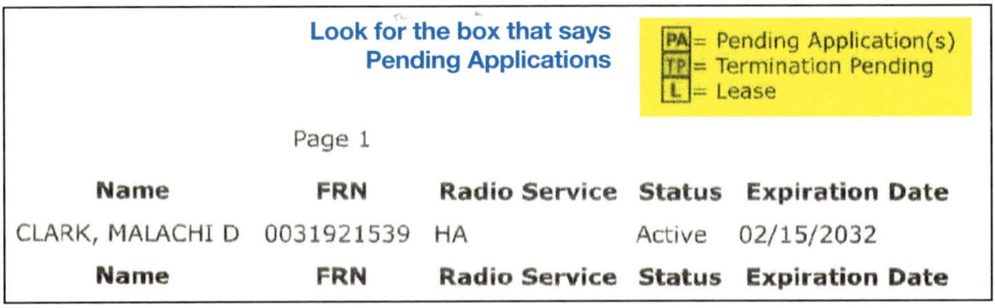

Your ULS FRN search on the FCC website will look like this.

Either way, once your fee is paid, the FCC will issue your license grant the following business day. You will receive a second email from the FCC with a link directly to your official license record. This link is good for 30 days. You will be able to view, print, and download an official copy of your license by logging into your FCC ULS account.

The FCC discontinued mailing or providing printed licenses in February, 2015. Licensees can log into ULS with their FRN and password at any time to view and manage their license record, including updating their email or mailing address.

Glossary

Amateur communication: Noncommercial radio communication by or among amateur stations solely with a personal aim and without personal or business interest.

Amateur operator/primary station license: An instrument of authorization issued by the FCC comprised of a station license, and also incorporating an operator license indicating the class of privileges.

Amateur operator: A person holding a valid license to operate an amateur station issued by the FCC. Amateur operators are frequently referred to as ham operators.

Amateur Radio services: The amateur service, the amateur-satellite service, and the radio amateur civil emergency service.

Amateur-satellite service: A radiocommunication service using stations on Earth satellites for the same purpose as those of the amateur service.

Amateur service: A radiocommunication service for the purpose of self-training, intercommunication and technical investigations carried out by amateurs; that is, duly authorized persons interested in radio technique solely with a personal aim and without pecuniary interest.

Amateur station: A station licensed in the amateur service embracing necessary apparatus at a particular location used for amateur communication.

AMSAT: Radio Amateur Satellite Corporation, a nonprofit scientific organization. (P.O. Box #27, Washington, DC 20044)

ANSI: American National Standards Institute. A non-government organization that develops recommended standards for a variety of applications.

APRS: Automatic Position Radio System, which takes GPS (Global Positioning System) information and translates it into an automatic packet of digital information.

ARES: Amateur Radio Emergency Service — the emergency division of the American Radio Relay League. Also see RACES

ARRL: American Radio Relay League, national organization of U.S. Amateur Radio operators. (225 Main Street, Newington, CT 06111)

Audio Frequency (AF): The range of frequencies that can be heard by the human ear, generally 20 hertz to 20 kilohertz.

Automatic control: The use of devices and procedures for station control without the control operator being present at the control point when the station is transmitting.

Automatic Volume Control (AVC): A circuit that continually maintains a constant audio output volume in spite of deviations in input signal strength.

Beam or Yagi antenna: An antenna array that receives or transmits RF energy in a particular direction. Usually rotatable.

Block diagram: A simplified outline of an electronic system where circuits or components are shown as boxes.

Broadcasting: Information or programming transmitted by radio means intended for the general public.

Bulletin No. 65: The Office of Engineering & Technology bulletin that provides specified safety guidelines for human exposure to radiofrequency (RF) radiation.

Business communications: Any transmission or communication the purpose of which is to facilitate the regular business or commercial affairs of any party. Business communications are prohibited in the amateur service.

Call Book: A published list of all licensed amateur operators available in North American and Foreign editions.

Call sign: The FCC systematically assigns each amateur station its primary call sign.

Certificate of Successful Completion of Examination (CSCE): A certificate providing examination credit for 365 days. Both written and code credit can be authorized.

Coaxial cable, Coax: A concentric, two-conductor cable in which one conductor surrounds the other, separated by an insulator.

Controlled Environment: Involves people who are aware of and who can exercise control over radiofrequency exposure. Controlled exposure limits apply to both occupational workers and Amateur Radio operators and their immediate households.

Control operator: An amateur operator designated by the licensee of an amateur station to be responsible for the station transmissions.

Coordinated repeater station: An amateur repeater station for which the transmitting and receiving frequencies have been recommended by the recognized repeater coordinator.

Coordinated Universal Time (UTC): (Also Greenwich Mean Time, UCT or Zulu time.) The time at the zero-degree (0°) Meridian which passes through Greenwich, England. A universal time among all amateur operators.

Crystal: A quartz or similar material which has been ground to produce natural vibrations of a specific frequency. Quartz crystals produce a high degree of frequency stability in radio transmitters.

CW: See Morse code.

Dipole antenna: The most common wire antenna. Length is equal to one-half of the wavelength. Fed by coaxial cable.

Dummy antenna: A device or resistor which serves as a transmitter's antenna without radiating radio waves. Generally used to tune up a radio transmitter.

Duplexer: A device that allows a single antenna to be simultaneously used for both reception and transmission.

Duty cycle: As applies to RF safety, the percentage of time that a transmitter is "on" versus "off" in a 6- or 30-minute time period.

Effective Radiated Power (ERP): The product of the transmitter (peak envelope) power, expressed in watts, delivered to the antenna, and the relative gain of an antenna over that of a half-wave dipole antenna.

Electromagnetic radiation: The propagation of radiant energy, including infrared, visible light, ultraviolet, radiofrequency, gamma and X-rays, through space and matter.

Emergency communication: Any amateur communication directly relating to the immediate safety of life of individuals or the immediate protection of property.

Examination Element: The written theory exam or CW test required for various classes of FCC Amateur Radio licenses. Technician must pass Element 2 written theory; General must pass Element 3 written theory plus Element 1 CW; Extra must pass Element 4 written theory.

Far Field: The electromagnetic field located at a great distance from a transmitting antenna. The far field begins at a distance that depends on many factors, including the wavelength and the size of the antenna. Radio signals are normally received in the far field.

FCC Form 605: The FCC application form used to apply for a new amateur operator/primary station license or to renew or modify an existing license.

Federal Communications Commission (FCC): A board of five Commissioners, appointed by the President, having the power to regulate wire and radio telecommunications in the U.S.

Feedline: A system of conductors that connects an antenna to a receiver or transmitter.

Field Day: Annual activity sponsored by the ARRL to demonstrate emergency preparedness of amateur operators.

Field strength: A measure of the intensity of an electric or magnetic field. Electric fields are measured in volts per meter; magnetic fields in amperes per meter.

Filter: A device used to block or reduce alternating currents or signals at certain frequencies while allowing others to pass unimpeded.

Frequency: The number of cycles of alternating current in one second.

Frequency coordinator: An individual or organization which recommends frequencies and other operating and/or technical parameters for amateur repeater operation in order to avoid or minimize potential interferences.

Frequency Modulation (FM): A method of varying a radio carrier wave by causing its frequency to vary in accordance with the information to be conveyed.

Frequency privileges: The transmitting frequency bands available to the various classes of amateur operators. The various Class privileges are listed in Part 97.301 of the FCC rules.

FT-8: Sophisticated software from Nobel Prize honoree Dr. Joe Taylor, K1JT, for weak signal reception and transmission, utilizing time synchronization and numerical analysis, with forward error correction, to allow signals below the audible threshold to be decoded reliably.

Ground: A connection, accidental or intentional, between a device or circuit and the earth or some common body and the earth or some common body serving as the earth.

Ground wave: A radio wave that is propagated near or at the earth's surface.

Handi-Ham system: Amateur organization dedicated to assisting handicapped amateur operators. (3915 Golden Valley Road, Golden Valley, MN 55422)

Harmful interference: Interference which seriously degrades, obstructs or repeatedly interrupts the operation of a radio communication service.

Harmonic: A radio wave that is a multiple of the fundamental frequency. The second harmonic is twice the fundamental frequency, the third harmonic, three times, etc.

Hertz: One complete alternating cycle per second. Named after Heinrich R. Hertz, a German physicist. The number of hertz is the frequency of the audio or radio wave.

High Frequency (HF): The band of frequencies that lie between 3 and 30 Megahertz. It is from these frequencies that radio waves are returned to earth from the ionosphere.

High-Pass filter: A device that allows passage of high frequency signals but attenuates the lower frequencies. When installed on a television set, a high-pass filter allows TV frequencies to pass while blocking lower-frequency amateur signals.

Inverse Square Law: The physical principle by which power density decreases as you get further away from a transmitting antenna. RF power density decreases by the inverse square of the distance.

Ionization: The process of adding or stripping away electrons from atoms or molecules. Ionization occurs when substances are heated at high temperatures or exposed to high voltages. It can lead to significant genetic damage in biological tissue.

Ionosphere: Outer limits of atmosphere from which HF amateur communications signals are returned to earth.

IRC: International Reply Coupon, a method of prepaying postage for a foreign amateur's QSL card.

Jamming: The intentional, malicious interference with another radio signal.

Key clicks, Chirps: Defective keying of a telegraphy signal sounding like tapping or high varying pitches.

Linear amplifier: A device that accurately reproduces a radio wave in magnified form.

Long wire: A horizontal wire antenna that is one wavelength or longer in length.

Low-Pass filter: Device connected to worldwide transmitters that inhibits passage of higher frequencies that cause television interference but does not affect amateur transmissions.

Machine: A ham slang word for an automatic repeater station.

Malicious interference: See jamming.

MARS: The Military Affiliate Radio System. An organization that coordinates the activities of amateur communications with military radio communications.

Maximum authorized transmitting power: Amateur stations must use no more than the maximum transmitter power necessary to carry out the desired communications.

The maximum P.E.P. output power levels authorized Novices are 200 watts in the 80-, 40-, 15- and 10-meter bands, 25 watts in the 222-MHz band, and 5 watts in the 1270-MHz bands.

Maximum Permissible Exposure (MPE): The maximum amount of electric and magnetic RF energy to which a person may safely be exposed.

Maximum usable frequency (MFU): The highest frequency that will be returned to earth from the ionosphere.

Medium frequency (MF): The band of frequencies that lies between 300 and 3,000 kHz (3 MHz).

Microwave: Electromagnetic waves with a frequency of 300 MHz to 300 GHz. Microwaves can cause heating of biological tissue.

Mobile operation: Radio communications conducted while in motion or during halts at unspecified locations.

Mode: Type of transmission such as voice, teletype, code, television, facsimile.

Modulate: To vary the amplitude, frequency, or phase of a radiofrequency wave in accordance with the information to be conveyed.

Morse code: The International Morse code, A1A emission. Interrupted continuous wave communications conducted using a dot-dash code for letters, numbers and operating procedure signs.

Near Field: The electromagnetic field located in the immediate vicinity of the antenna. Energy in the near field depends on the size of the antenna, its wavelength and transmission power.

Nonionizing radiation: Electromagnetic waves, or fields, which do not have the capability to alter the molecular structure of substances. RF energy is nonionizing radiation.

Novice operator: An FCC licensed, entry-level amateur operator in the amateur service.

Occupational exposure: See controlled environment.

OET: Office of Engineering & Technology, a branch of the FCC that has developed the guidelines for radiofrequency (RF) safety.

Ohm's law: The basic electrical law explaining the relationship between voltage, current and resistance. The current (I) in a circuit is equal to the voltage (E) divided by the resistance (R), or I = E/R.

OSCAR: "Orbiting Satellite Carrying Amateur Radio." A series of satellites designed and built by amateur operators of several nations.

Oscillator: A device for generating oscillations or vibrations of an audio or radiofrequency signal.

Packet radio: A digital method of communicating computer-to-computer. A terminal-node controller makes up the packet of data and directs it to another packet station.

Peak Envelope Power (PEP): 1. The power during one radiofrequency cycle at the crest of the modulation envelope, taken under normal operating conditions. 2. The maximum power that can be obtained from a transmitter.

Phone patch: Interconnection of amateur radio to the public switched telephone network, and operated by the control operator of the station.

Power density: A measure of the strength of an electromagnetic field at a distance from its source. Usually expressed in milliwatts per square centimeter (mW/cm2). Far-field power density decreases according to the Law of Inverse Squares.

Power supply: A device or circuit that provides the appropriate voltage and current to another device or circuit.

Propagation: The travel of electromagnetic waves or sound waves through a medium.

Public exposure: See "uncontrolled" environment.

Q-signals: International three-letter abbreviations beginning with the letter Q used primarily to convey information using the Morse code.

QSL Bureau: An office that bulk processes QSL (radio confirmation) cards for (or from) foreign amateur operators as a postage-saving mechanism.

RACES (Radio Amateur Civil Emergency Service): A radio service using amateur stations for civil defense communications during periods of local, regional, or national emergencies.

Radiation: Electromagnetic energy, such as radio waves, traveling forth into space from a transmitter.

Radiofrequency (RF): The range of frequencies over 20 kilohertz that can be propagated through space.

Radiofrequency (RF) radiation: Electromagnetic fields or waves having a frequency between 3 kHz and 300 GHz.

Radiofrequency spectrum: The eight electromagnetic bands ranked according to their frequency and wavelength. Specifically, the very-low, low, medium, high, very-high, ultra-high, super-high, and extremely-high frequency bands.

Radio wave: A combination of electric and magnetic fields varying at a radiofrequency and traveling through space at the speed of light.

Repeater operation: Automatic amateur stations that retransmit the signals of other amateur stations.

Routine RF radiation evaluation: The process of determining if the RF energy from a transmitter exceeds the Maximum Permissible Exposure (MPE) limits in a controlled or uncontrolled environment.

RST Report: A telegraphy signal report system of Readability, Strength and Tone.

S-meter: A voltmeter calibrated from 0 to 9 that indicates the relative signal strength of an incoming signal at a radio receiver.

Selectivity: The ability of a circuit (or radio receiver) to separate the desired signal from those not wanted.

Sensitivity: The ability of a circuit (or radio receiver) to detect a specified input signal.

Short circuit: An unintended, low-resistance connection across a voltage source resulting in high current and possible damage.

Shortwave: The high frequencies that lie between 3 and 30 Megahertz that are propagated long distances.

Single-Sideband (SSB): A method of radio transmission

in which the RF carrier and one of the sidebands is suppressed and all of the information is carried in the one remaining sideband.

Skip wave, Skip zone: A radio wave reflected back to earth. The distance between the radio transmitter and the site of a radio wave's return to earth.

Sky-wave: A radio wave that is refracted back to earth. Sometimes called an ionospheric wave.

Specific Absorption Rate (SAR): The time rate at which radiofrequency energy is absorbed into the human body.

Spectrum: A series of radiated energies arranged in order of wavelength. The radio spectrum extends from 20 kilohertz upward.

Spurious Emissions: Unwanted radiofrequency signals emitted from a transmitter that sometimes cause interference.

Station license, location: No transmitting station shall be operated in the amateur service without being licensed by the FCC. Each amateur station shall have one land location, the address of which appears in the station license.

Sunspot Cycle: An 11-year cycle of solar disturbances which greatly affects radio wave propagation.

Technician operator: An Amateur Radio operator who has successfully passed Element 2.

Technician-Plus: An amateur operator who has passed a 5-wpm code test in addition to Technician Class requirements.

Telegraphy: Communications transmission and reception using CW, International Morse code.

Telephony: Communications transmission and reception in the voice mode.

Telecommunications: The electrical conversion, switching, transmission and control of audio video and data signals by wire or radio.

Temporary operating authority: Authority to operate your amateur station while awaiting arrival of an upgraded license.

Terrestrial station location: Any location of a radio station on the surface of the earth including the sea.

Thermal effects: As applies to RF radiation, biological tissue damage resulting because of the body's inability to cope with or dissipate excessive heat.

Third-party traffic: Amateur communication by or under the supervision of the control operator at an amateur station to another amateur station on behalf of others.

Time-averaging: As applies to RF safety, the amount of electromagnetic radiation over a given time. The premise of time-averaging is that the human body can tolerate the thermal load caused by high, localized RF exposures for short periods of time.

Transceiver: A combination radio transmitter and receiver.

Transition region: Area where power density decreases inversely with distance from the antenna.

Transmatch: An antenna tuner used to match the impedance of the transmitter output to the transmission line of an antenna.

Transmitter: Equipment used to generate radio waves. Most commonly, this radio carrier signal is amplitude varied or frequency varied (modulated) with information and radiated into space.

Transmitter power: The average peak envelope power (output) present at the antenna terminals of the transmitter. The term "transmitted" includes any external radio-frequency power amplifier which may be used.

Ultra High Frequency (UHF): Ultra high frequency radio waves that are in the range of 300 to 3,000 MHz.

Uncontrolled environment: Applies to those persons who have no control over their exposure to RF energy in the environment. Residences adjacent to ham radio installations are considered to be in an "uncontrolled" environment.

Upper Sideband (USB): The proper operating mode for sideband transmissions made in the new Novice 10-meter voice band. Amateurs generally operate USB at 20 meters and higher frequencies; lower sideband (LSB) at 40 meters and lower frequencies.

Very High Frequency (VHF): Very high frequency radio waves that are in the range of 30 to 300 MHz.

Volunteer Examiner: An amateur operator of at least a General Class level who prepares and administers amateur operator license examinations.

Volunteer Examiner Coordinator (VEC): A member of an organization which has entered into an agreement with the FCC to coordinate the efforts of volunteer examiners in preparing and administering examinations for amateur operator licenses.

Index

Let Forrest M. Mims, III Teach You Electronics

Getting Started in Electronics

This is a complete electronics course in 128 pages! This famous electron-ics inventor teaches you the basics, takes you on a tour of analog and digital components, explains how they work, and shows how they are combined for various applications. Includes circuit assembly tips and 100 electronic circuits you can build and test. Forrest has written dozens of books, hundreds of articles, invented scientific devices and travelled to the Amazon for NASA, and loves to share his knowledge with eager students!

GSTD $19.95

Engineer's Mini Notebooks by Mims

These 4 Mini Notebooks include wonderful project ideas for students and hobbyists. Forrest's little books have stimulated many science fair projects and are popular with hobbyists of all ages. Even professional scientists recommend them as a fun way to learn about electronics!

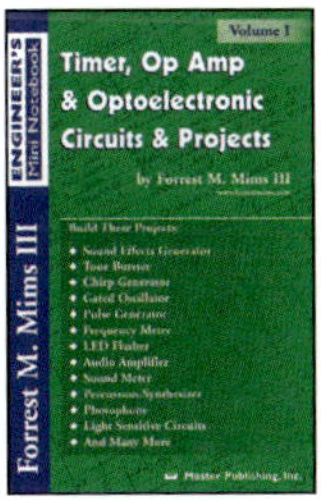

Timer, Op Amp, and Optoelectronic Circuits & Projects

This Mini Notebook features more than two dozen 555 timer circuits that you can build, 50 operational amplifier (Op Amp) circuits, and a wide range of optoelectronic circuits and projects including many LED and lightwave circuits. **MINI-1 $12.95**

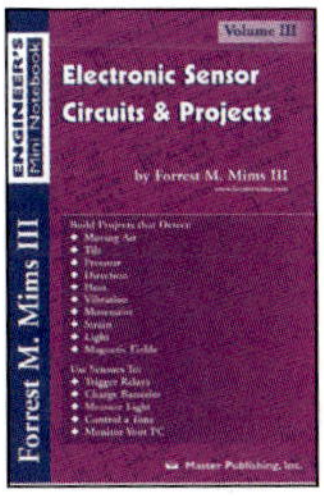

Electronic Sensor Circuits & Projects

Electronic sensors convert light, temperature, sound, and other signals into a form that can be processed by electronic circuits. Learn about solar cells, photoresistors, thermistors, and magnet switches. Then build circuits that respond to heat, pressure, light, and more. **MINI-3 $12.95**

Science and Communication Circuits & Projects

Use these plans to make a simple seismometer; build a sun photo-meter to make accurate measurements of the atmosphere; study rain, lightning, and sunlight; and build a wide variety of lightwave and radio communication circuits. **MINI-2 $12.95**

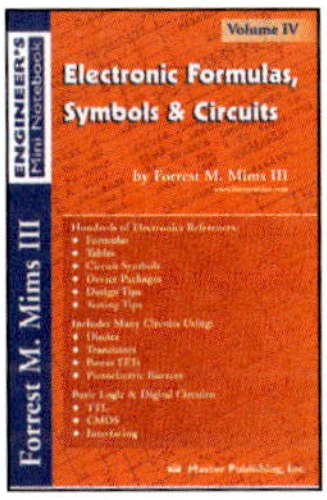

Electronic Formulas, Symbols & Circuits

This Mini Notebook provides a complete, basic electronics reference guide for the workshop or your ham shack. Includes many frequently-used formulas, tables, circuit symbols, and device packages. Design and testing tips are provided to help you plan and troubleshoot your circuits. **MINI-4 $12.95**

FCC Commercial Radio License Study Materials

General Radiotelephone Operator's License

GROL+RADAR

Get your FCC commercial radio licenses and add valuable credentials to your resume! *GROL+RADAR* includes the new FCC Element 1 question pool for the Marine Radio Operator Permit (MROP), the Element 3 pool for the General Radiotelephone Operator License (GROL), and the Element 8 pool for the RADAR Endorsement. Many employers require these licenses for jobs in marine, aero, safety, and municipal positions. Gordo and his team have written clear explanations for all the Q&A to make studying for these exams educational and fun. If you're an Extra Class ham, many of the technical/math questions will look familiar to you. Fully-illustrated to aid your learning. **GROL $49.95**

GROL+RADAR Book & Software Package Enhance your learning experience using our practice exam software along with the *GROL+RADAR* book. Software includes answer explanations from the book – when you select a wrong answer, the explanation from the book appears to reinforce your learning. **GRSP $79.95**

Learn More With Our 'Basic' Series

Basic Electronics

by Gene McWhorter & Alvis Evans is for anyone who wants to understand the fundamentals of electronics. Explains electronic devices and circuits – how they work and are used. Contains detailed illustrations that support easy-to-read text. Practical, worked-out examples demonstrate circuit applications.

BELC $19.95

Basic Communications Electronics

by Jack Hudson, W9MU, & Jerry Luecke, KB5TZY. Explains analog electronic devices and circuits – how they work and how they are used to build communications systems. Emphasis on semiconductor devices and integrated circuits (ICs). For anyone who wants to understand analog electronics and wireless communications. **BCOM $19.95**

Basic Digital Electronics

by Alvis Evans. Explains digital system functions and how circuits are used to build them. Discusses the functions required to design digital systems, the circuits used to make decisions, code conversions, data selections, interfacing and storage, and the circuits that keep all operations in time and under control.

BDIG $19.95

The Worldwide Listening Guide

By John Figliozzi. Modeled on his popular *Worldwide Shortwave Listening Guide*, this new book explains radio listening in all today's formats – "live," on-demand, WiFi, podcast, terrestrial, satellite, internet, digital and, of course, analog, AM, FM and SW. Book includes a comprehensive programming guide to what can be heard how, when and where. Spiral-bound to open in a flat, easy-to-use format. **WWLG $29.95**

Radio Science for the Radio Amateur

By Eric P. Nichols, KL7AJ. You can contribute to big science as a radio amateur! As a ham radio operator, you have what it takes to make a meaningful contribution to science and technology. Eric's book explores and explains the often profound differences between science and technology, and dispels the notion that we know all there is to know about radio. Eric guides you through some of the most fascinating "nooks and crannies" of the radio universe. Along the way, you'll find out how solving long-standing mysteries of radio, of which there are still many, doesn't require expensive hardware, but merely a scientific mindset and attention to detail. **RSCI $29.95**

Mail Ordering Information

If you would like to order any of our products by mail, send your check or money order to:

W5YI Group
POB 200065
Arlington, TX 76011-0065

SHIPPING: Please add $7.00 for the first item, and $1.00 for each additional item. Items are shipped via USPS Priority Mail.